ADVANCES IN PRIMATOLOGY
Volume 1

THE PRIMATE BRAIN

ADVANCES IN PRIMATOLOGY
Volume 1

THE PRIMATE BRAIN

EDITORS

CHARLES R. NOBACK

Department of Anatomy
Columbia University
College of Physicians and Surgeons
New York, New York

WILLIAM MONTAGNA

Oregon Regional Primate Research Center
Beaverton, Oregon

APPLETON-CENTURY-CROFTS
EDUCATIONAL DIVISION/MEREDITH CORPORATION
New York

QL
933
.P7

PRINTED IN THE UNITED STATES OF AMERICA
390-67250-5

CONTRIBUTORS

ORLANDO J. ANDY
Department of Neurosurgery,
University of Mississippi Medical Center,
Jackson, Mississippi 39216

ROLAND BAUCHOT
Laboratoire d'Anatomie,
Faculté des Sciences de Paris,
Paris, France

ROLAND A. GIOLLI
Department of Human Morphology,
University of California, Irvine,
College of Medicine
Irvine, California 92664

RALPH L. HOLLOWAY, JR.
Department of Anthropolgy,
Columbia University,
New York, New York 10027

HARRY J. JERISON
Antioch College,
Yellow Springs, Ohio;
Present address:
The Neuropsychiatric Institute,
UCLA Center for the Health Sciences,
Los Angeles, California 90024

LOIS K. LAEMLE
Department of Anatomy,
Albert Einstein College of Medicine of Yeshiva
  University,
Bronx, New York 10461

LEO C. MASSOPUST, JR.
Laboratory of Neurophysiology,
Research Division,
Cleveland Psychiatric Institute,
Cleveland, Ohio 41109

CHARLES R. NOBACK
Department of Anatomy,
Columbia University
College of Physicians and Surgeons,
New York, New York 10032

LEONARD B. RADINSKY
Department of Anatomy,
University of Chicago,
Chicago, Illinois 60637

GEORGE A. SACHER
Division of Biological and Medical Research,
Argonne National Laboratory,
Argonne, Illinois 60439

FRIEDRICH SANIDES
Department of Anatomy,
University of Ottawa, Canada,
Present address:
Abteilung Anatomie,
Rhein. Westf. Techn. Hochschule,
51 Aachen, Germany

HEINZ STEPHAN
Max-Planck-Institut für Hirnforschung,
Neuroanatomische Abteilung,
Frankfurt (Main)-Niederrad, Germany

JOHANNES TIGGES
Yerkes Regional Primate Research Center, and
  the Department of Anatomy,
Emory University,
Atlanta, Georgia 30322

W. J. C. VERHAART
Laboratorium voor Neuro-anatomie,
Wassenaarseweg 62,
Leiden, The Netherlands

LEE R. WOLIN
Laboratory of Neurophysiology,
Research Division,
Cleveland Psychiatric Institute,
Cleveland, Ohio 44109

PREFACE

This is the first of a series of publications, each volume of which will contain the latest studies and critical appraisals on a specific topic in primatology and allied fields. The editors will make efforts to produce volumes that will be understandable and interesting to investigators in the field, graduate students, and others who may not share a professional interest in primatology. The articles will stress fundamental principles and, wherever possible, approach the subject from a phylogenetic or comparative point of view. The chapters will be more than exhaustive annotated bibliographies. Contributors have aimed at presenting factual material supplemented by discussions of the significant and provocative aspects of each topic. Other objectives of the series are to evaluate the concepts and to crystallize the guidelines in the field. In summary, the editors and the publisher hope that this series will provide an effective vehicle for communication among primatologists and those with allied interests.

In this initial volume several aspects of the nervous system of primates are presented. The authors of these chapters have established guidelines and standards for the future publications of the series. We thank them for their efforts and cooperation.

We wish to thank the publisher, especially Mr. Richard van Frank and Mr. William Belfer for their support, guidance, and professional assistance.

CHARLES R. NOBACK
WILLIAM MONTAGNA

Plate I. Photographs of the fundus of a representative sample of primates.

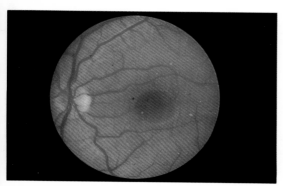

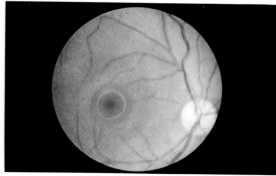

a. *Homo sapiens.* Lightly pigmented (blond) subject. Note light pigmentation of retina, large, round nerve head, large, slightly oval macula, smooth appearance of retinal surface, and termination of vessels outside fovea centralis.

b. *Colobus polykomos.* Characteristic higher primate retina. Note relatively lighter pigmentation which in part permitted photography of extremely well-defined macular ring reflex. Macular area is quite regular, and nerve head is round as in human.

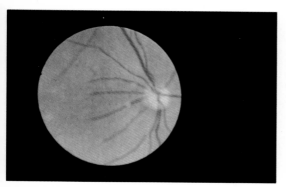

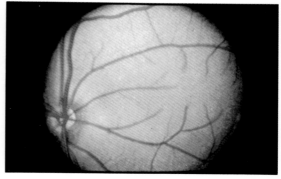

c. *Aotes trivirgatus.* This is the first nocturnal species represented, but it is more closely related to *Cebus* and *Saimiri* than to other nocturnal species. No macula or fovea can be visualized on a funduscopic examination, though a "foveal" area has been described in histological sections. Note spotted appearance of retina, which is found in most nocturnal species.

d. *Tarsius syrichta.* Highest of the prosimians represented here. This eye is unique among nocturnal species in revealing a macular ring reflex and foveal spot (the photograph barely does justice to these features, which are most distinctly seen with an ophthalmoscope). Note the relatively small nerve head and complex intertwining of vessels as they emerge. The beginning of dense peripheral deposits of pigment can be seen in the temporal and inferior portions of the photograph.

Plate I. (con't). Photographs of the fundus of a representative sample of primates.

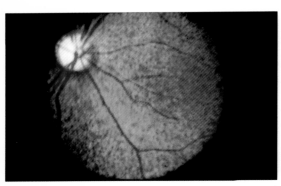

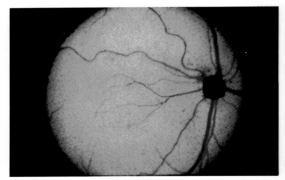

e. *Lemur fulvis.* One of the more darkly pigmented retinas among the nocturnal species, this retina has an extremely mottled appearance. Dense accumulation of pigment may be noted just below the nerve head. The periphery of this retina (not shown in Plate) is almost black due to the density of the pigment.

f. *Nycticebus coucang.* This is the most highly reflective of the primate retinas shown. Use of neutral density filters in order to photograph the major portion of the retina produced blacking out of the optic nerve head. Note small size of nerve head and relatively large distance between nerve head and central retinal area (as defined by terminal pattern of blood vessels).

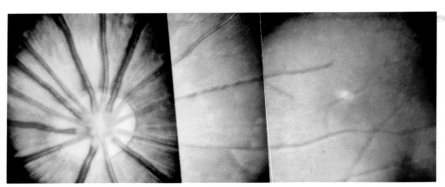

g. *Tupaia glis.* Composite photograph from the nasal to temporal portions of the fundus. Note the spoke-like radiation of the vessels from the optic nerve head. The central retinal area is located temporarily (upper right corner) in this species.

CONTENTS

ADVANCES IN PRIMATOLOGY
Volume 1

THE PRIMATE BRAIN

1

Morphology of the Primate Retina

Lee R. Wolin and Leo C. Massopust, Jr.

Laboratory of Neurophysiology, Research Division
Cleveland Psychiatric Institute
1708 Aiken Avenue, Cleveland, Ohio 44109

Introduction

The study of the central nervous system has tended more and more in recent years to focus on primates. The structure and function of the nervous system of humans are more similar to those of primates than to those of any other experimental animal. This same observation applies to the visual system in general and to its most peripheral representation, the retina. If we wish to generalize from experimental animals to humans, obviously we must use subjects for which such generalizations have some validity. In neuroanatomical, neurophysiological, neuropsychological, and biochemical investigations, primates are certainly the experimental subjects of choice.

The primates are predominantly visual animals. Although the other senses are well developed and quite acute, visual guidance of behavior is dominant under ordinary circumstances. Since the visual system and brain of higher primates closely resemble that of man, studies of vision in primates have increased tremendously in recent years. By far the majority of these studies have dealt with psychophysical and electrophysiological problems. Studies of the anatomy of the primate visual system, and the eye in particular, have been relatively sparse.

Among recent investigations of the primate eye, especially the retina, a large proportion have been electron microscopic studies, even though there is a dearth of light microscopic and gross morphological studies of the primate retina.

This review attempts to cover the comparative work done on the primate retina. We feel that it is reasonably comprehensive, particularly with respect to recent investigations, but is not exhaustive, since we have had to rely on secondary sources to some extent, particularly in relation to the very early investigations.

In researching studies of retinal structure, the names of a few investigators continually recur. These we believe represent the better, more detailed, and most comprehensive studies done. Where a given species has been studied by several investigators, we have attempted to present a consistent description of that retina. We have also tried to present some historical perspective in the investigation of various species and,

1

where possible, have included the major areas of agreement and disagreement with respect to the characteristics of retinal structure.

Unfortunately there are a number of problems which are not easily resolved. Species designations are not always clear, and the work of earlier investigators, using different species designations, is sometimes impossible to correlate with later investigations. Where it has been possible to identify a species with surety, we have designated it according to current taxonomy (Hill, 1953, 1955, 1957, 1960, 1962, 1966; Walker et al., 1964; Buettner-Janusch, 1966; Napier and Napier, 1967). Often the material on which some reports are based consisted of old or poorly fixed eyes, and the interpretation of findings involved a very large element of judgement on the part of the investigator. We have evaluated these findings and attempted to present as accurate a picture of the retina as possible.

In addition to reviewing the work on retinal histology, we have included funduscopic studies of the retinas of various primates. This provides another useful and informative approach to the study of the primate retina.

Finally, we will discuss individual features of the primate retina, summarizing what is known and what remains unknown and indicating special problems requiring further study.

Comparative Anatomical Studies of Primate Retinas

PROSIMII

Tupaiiformes. Most authors agree that the retina of *Tupaia* is a diurnal type predominantly cone retina (Castenholz, 1965; Rohen, 1962; Rohen and Castenholz, 1967; Samorajski et al., 1966; Woollard, 1926).

The most detailed description of the retina of *Tupaia glis* is provided by Castenholz and is supported in its various details by other investigators.

The pigment epithelium is a single layer of cells throughout the retina and is uniformly heavily pigmented. In conformity with the cone structure of this retina, no tapetum lucidum is to be found.

The receptors are short thick cones that appear quite uniform across the retinal expanse. There is an increased density of receptors per unit area in the temporal retina (20 to 22 per 100 μ as contrasted with the nasal side (16 per 100 μ). The inner segments of the cones are longer (by 1.5 to 2 times) than are the outer segments. Among the prosimians, only *Lemur fulvis* shows such a proportion between inner and outer segments. In the other species studied, either the two segments tend to be approximately equal, or the outer segment exceeds the inner segment in length.

The cone nuclei of the outer nuclear layer form only one row throughout the retina, but again some differentiation between the nasal and temporal halves is found, the nuclei being elongated and oval on the temporal side and more rounded on the nasal side of the retina.

The outer plexiform layer is quite thin and shows no great differentiation between retinal areas.

The inner nuclear and inner plexiform layers are both well developed. The inner nuclear layer shows a differential nasal-temporal development. Temporally the bipolars form as many as eight rows of cells, while on the nasal side only six rows are found (Fig. 1).

The ganglion cell layer consists mostly of one row of cells, but there is a gradual increase in thickness temporally, and a fairly large area of the temporal retina contains four to five rows of ganglion cells.

The layer of nerve fibers increases in thickness nasally, reaching its greatest thickness around the nerve head.

Overall, the temporal retina is much thicker than the nasal half. A prominent area of about 2.5 mm in diameter located 3 to 4 mm temporal from the center of the papilla shows the greatest thickening. Castenholz (1965) describes this as a central "area-like" development, noting that no fovea-like depression is to be found.

This area centralis corresponds well to that which Wolin and Massopust (1967) described as a central retinal area of the fundus (Plate I, g).

Rohen and Castenholz (1967), by sectioning through the skull of *Tupaia*, including the eyes, have shown that the area-like retinal thickening is located in the relatively limited portion of the temporal retina which represents a binocular visual field. This provides additional anatomical support for the statements of Wolin and Massopust (1967) regarding the use of binocular vision by *Tupaia*.

The retinal vasculature shows a pattern unlike that of any of the other primates. The arteries and veins radiate out from the nerve head like the spokes of a wheel. Temporally in the fundus, however, there is a vascular free area which ophthalmoscopically looks much like a central visual area.

Rohen and Castenholz (1967) have also studied the retina of *Urogale everetti*. This retina is generally quite similar to that of *Tupaia glis* with the significant exception that no temporal specialized area equivalent to that of *Tupaia* was found.

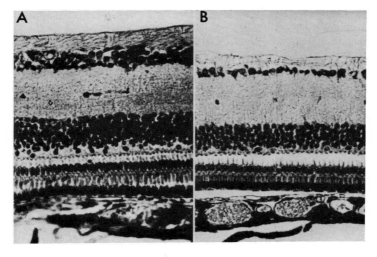

Figure 1. The retina of *Tupaia glis*. The temporal half (a) is thicker than the nasal half (b). From Castenholz, E. 1965. Z. Zellforsch., 65:646-661.

Lorisiformes. A variety of Lorisiformes are reported in the literature. These include *Loris tardigradus* (Rohen, 1962), *Nycticebus coucang* (Detwiler, 1943; Franz, 1911; Kolmer, 1930; Woollard, 1926), *Perodicticus potto* (Rohen, 1962), *Galago crassicaudatus* (Kolmer, 1930), *Galago "mala"* (Detwiler, 1939), *Galago demidovii* (Rohen, 1962), and *Galago senegalensis* (Castenholz, 1965; Rohen and Castenholz, 1967).

All of the Lorisiformes are basically nocturnal in habit, though some of them have been observed to be active in food seeking and other activities during the daytime (Hill, 1953; Walker et al., 1964).

The occurrence of a tapetum lucidum appears to be characteristic of the Lorisiformes. Both cellular and fibrous tapeta have been described. The distinction between the two types of tapeta, at least within the prosimians, may not, however, be as clear as is usually indicated. *Galago crassicaudatus* has a tapetum cellulosum (Kolmer, 1930; Rohen, 1962, also cites Luck, 1958, but gives no reference). *Perodicticus potto* is reported by Rohen (1962) to have a tapetum fibrosum. With respect to *Loris* and *Nycticebus*, however, the picture becomes less clear. Kolmer (1930) describes *Loris gracilis* (=*Loris tardigradus*) as having a small cellular tapetum, while Rohen (1962), in describing *Loris tardigradus,* reports a fibrous tapetum. Both Detwiler (1943) and Kolmer (1930) report studies of *Nycticebus coucang*, Detwiler designating the tapetum in this case as fibrous, while Kolmer classifies it as cellular.

Finally, with respect to *Galago senegalensis*, Rohen (1962) describes it as having a relatively thin tapetum cellulosum, as does Castenholz (1965). Rohen and Castenholz (1967, p. 113), however, list this same species as having a tapetum fibrosum.

We thus find agreement concerning the occurrence of a tapetum lucidum in all the Lorisiformes studied, but some lack of agreement regarding the structure of the tapetum in several species.

In the Lorisiformes the pigment epithelium is often differentially pigmented in the central fundus and in the periphery. The cells of the central portion of the pigment epithelium (where the tapetum is well developed) contain few if any pigment granules (Kolmer, 1930; Rohen, 1962; Detwiler, 1943), while in the periphery the cells are heavily pigmented.

Rarely does a definite report concerning the finding of cones in the retinas of any of these species appear. Kolmer (1930) reported apparently rudimentary, sparsely occurring small cones in the retina of *Nycticebus coucang* (Fig. 2). Rohen (1962) may also have seen some cone-like structures in the retina of *Loris tardigradus* but could not conclusively demonstrate them to be cones.

In all species reported, the outer nuclear layer is thicker than the inner layer. The differences between genera are not striking, the outer layer being reported as being 10 to 12 rows of cells and the inner nuclear layer 3 to 6 rows of cells in most species. Rohen (1962) reports 12 to 16 rows of cells in the outer nuclear layer of *Loris tardigradus.*

The inner reticular layer is characteristically thicker than the outer reticular layer in the genera reported. The differences between genera with respect to the thickness of these layers are more striking than is the case with reference to the nuclear layers. The extremes are *Galago crassicaudatus,* with an outer reticular layer 9 μ

Figure 2. Retinal section from *Nycticebus coucang*. Note the thick outer nuclear layer, moderate inner nuclear layer, and sparse ganglion cells. From Kolmer, W. 1930. Z. Anat. Entwicklungsgesch., 93:679-722.

thick and inner reticular layer 20 μ thick (Rohen, 1962), and *Loris tardigradus*, with an outer reticular layer measuring 15 μ and an inner reticular layer of 40 μ.

The receptors are generally long (42 to 64 μ) and thin (1 to 1.5 μ), with the outer segments measuring approximately twice the length of the inner segments.

The ganglion cell layer contains only one row of cells in *Nycticebus coucang* (Rohen, 1962; Woollard, 1926) and in *Loris tardigradus* (Rohen, 1962), whereas in *Galago senegalensis* Rohen and Castenholz (1967) report a single row of ganglion cells peripherally, but three rows in the central area.

Lemuriformes. The lemurs are an unusual, varied, and little understood group of primates. The few species which survive well in captivity have aroused considerable interest and have been extensively studied. The remaining members of this infraorder are little known, some species being designated on the basis of observation by a few individuals. Only recently have the eyes of some of the lesser known species been subject to study (Rohen and Castenholz, 1967).

The Lemuriformes represented in the literature on the retina include *Lemur catta* (Castenholz, 1965; Kolmer, 1930; Rohen, 1962; Rohen and Castenholz, 1967), *Lemur fulvis* (Castenholz, 1965; Rohen, 1962; Rohen and Castenholz, 1967), *Lemur macaco* (Rohen, 1962), *Lemur rufifrons* (Kolmer, 1930), *Lemur variegatus* (Rohen, 1962; Rohen and Castenholz, 1967), *Lemur "niger"* (Woollard, 1927), Cheirogaleinae (Kolmer, 1930; Rohen and Castenholz, 1967), *Microcebus murinus, Indri indri, Avahi laniger,* and *Propithecus verreauxi* (Rohen and Castenholz, 1967).

Lemur catta is diurnal in habit (Walker et al., 1964). Nevertheless it has in many respects a retina well adapted to nocturnal life. It has a tapetum cellulosum in the central fundus, and the pigment epithelium contains little pigment except in the periphery beyond the boundaries of the tapetum (Kolmer, 1930; Rohen and Castenholz, 1967).

The receptors include rods and cones (Kolmer, 1930) with a ratio of about five rods to one cone (Fig. 3). Castenholz (1965) describes some cone-like structures in *Lemur catta* but does not regard them as true cones. Kolmer (1930) bases his judgment on both the receptor structure and the synaptic endings in the outer plexiform layer. He notes that the differentiation between the two types of receptors is not as obvious in the area centralis as it is more peripherally.

In support of Kolmer's report of cone receptors in this species, it should be noted that Bierens de Haan and Frima (1930) found evidence for some color perception in both *Lemur catta* and *Lemur mongoz*. The area centralis is well defined in this species, forming a dome-shaped thickening of the retina (Rohen and Castenholz, 1967). The receptors are longer in this region (40 μ), and the outer nuclear layer increases to 12 rows of nuclei. The other retinal layers also show an increase in thickness, and the ganglion cell layer which contains only 1 row of nuclei through the rest of the retina develops to 4 rows in this area. The overall increase in retinal thickness from the vicinity of the ora to the central area is about 65 percent.

Lemur fulvis is described by Rohen and Castenholz (1967) as having the largest eye of all the prosimians they investigated. It has an equatorial diameter of 18 mm. There is a central thickening of the retina produced by some thickening of all the respective layers. The ganglion cell layer, which consists of a single row of nuclei throughout, shows an increase in density of nuclei from 2 per 100 μ peripherally to 11 per 100 μ centrally. There are apparently some cone-like receptors, but there is doubt that these are true cones (Rohen, 1962; Rohen and Castenholz, 1967).

Rohen (1962) says that the existence of a tapetum cannot be definitely established in this species but that there is a lamellar layer of the choroid which could presumably be a tapetum. The pigment layer of the retina is relatively lacking in pigment in parts of the central area. Castenholz (1965) reports a multilayered tapetum cellulosum and a considerable reduction of pigmentation of the pigment layer in the central area. Rohen and Castenholz (1967), however, do not report the presence of a

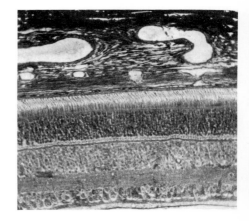

Figure 3. Retinal section from *Lemur catta*, taken near the central area. From Kolmer, W. 1930. Z. Anat. Entwicklungsgesch., 93: 679-722.

tapetum in *Lemur fulvis,* and they note that the periphery of the retina is lightly pigmented while the midfundus is unpigmented.

Kolmer (1930) describes the retina of *Lemur rufifrons* as a mixed rod and cone retina with numerous small cones interspersed between the rods, "resembling those seen in dogs and cats." The cones are more numerous in the central fundus and sparse in the peripheral retina. He finds no clear evidence of a specialized central area and no indication of a macula or fovea. Both deeply pigmented and weakly pigmented portions of the retina are described, but unfortunately he fails to specify their location. He also finds no evidence of tapetum in this species.

Kolmer (1930) describes the ganglion cell layer as being particularly poorly developed, with small sparsely located ganglion cells. He also notes the nerve fiber layer to be unusually thin and the Müllers cells to be well developed. In commenting on these findings, Rohen (1962) suggests that Kolmer may have been studying an eye(s) which showed the beginning of a retinal degeneration, such as he himself has occasionally found in other primates.

Woollard (1927) describes the retina of *Lemur niger,* which we are unable to place in current taxonomy. He describes it as "generally thin and without differentiation" and containing only rods in the receptor layer. The rods in the middle portion of the retina are much shorter than those of the periphery, but become elongated in the central portion. The outer nuclear layer consists of 10 rows centrally and 3 rows peripherally. The outer plexiform layer is so poorly developed that the inner and outer nuclear layers are almost in contact. The inner nuclear layer contains 5 or 6 rows of nuclei centrally but only 1 or 2 rows peripherally. The ganglion cell layer is 1 row throughout the retina, but the cells are closer together toward the center. Woollard finds no evidence of a macula or fovea and does not mention the occurrence of any tapetum, but he does comment on the moderate pigmentation of the pigment layer.

Kolmer (1930) describes the retina of *Lemur macaco* as a mixed rod and cone retina. Differences in size and staining of the receptor elements and well-differentiated synaptic endings in the outer plexiform layer provide the basis of this distinction. The pigment layer contains pigment throughout, and there is no evidence of a specialized central area or of any tapetum. Rohen (1962) gives essentially the same description of this retina.

Lemur variegatus is described by Rohen and Castenholz (1967). In general this retina is similar to that of *Lemur fulvis.* The presence of cones could not be determined with certainty although there is an area centralis which shows an increase in ganglion cells. The thickness of this part of the retina is only 7 percent greater than the surrounding area.

The retina has been described in two species of Cheirogaleinae. Kolmer (1930) describes the retina of *Cheirogaleus* (species undesignated) as being comprised predominantly of rods, small cones being seen only in the ratio of 1 to 1,000 rods. The outer nuclear layer is thicker than the inner, and the inner reticular layer is much better developed than the outer. From his illustration of this retina, the ganglion cells appear relatively sparse. The fundus is unpigmented, while a tapetum cellulosum composed of many layers of large flat cells is found, similar to that seen in the carnivores.

Rohen and Castenholz (1967) describe the retina of *Cheirogaleus medius* as an extreme example of a pure rod retina. There is a thickening of the retina in the central region, due primarily to an increase in thickness of the outer nuclear layer. Some less significant increase occurs in the outer layers as well. There is beyond this no specialized development of a central retinal area. The existence of a tapetum is not determined, but the midfundus is designated as unpigmented and the periphery of the retina is heavily pigmented. The retina of *Microcebus murinus* is so similar that these authors include the details of both eye specimens within the same descriptive paragraph. They do, however, indicate the presence of a tapetum cellulosum in *Microcebus murinus*.

Rohen and Castenholz (1967) also present, for the first time, descriptions of the retinas of three species of Indriidae. The retina of *Avahi laniger* is generally similar to that of *Microcebus* and *Cheirogaleus*. The retina shows a thickening toward the central region with an increase of over 300 percent in width of the outer nuclear layer and an increase of slightly less than 300 percent in the inner nuclear layer. The ganglion cell layer is composed of only one row of nuclei throughout, but there is about eight times the density of nuclei/unit area in the central region. *Avahi* is reported to have a tapetum fibrosum and a pigment layer with no pigmentation centrally and moderate pigmentation in the periphery.

Propithecus verreauxi and *Indri indri* are also described by Rohen and Castenholz (1967). The receptors are primarily rods, but thicker cone-like receptors are also found. The layering of the retina in these two species is similar to that of *Avahi*, *Microcebus*, and *Cheirogaleus*, but in addition there is a clear central area. In this central area the inner nuclear layer is well developed, and the difference between this layer and the outer nuclear layer is not so striking as in the other species. The ganglion cell layer increases to five rows of nuclei in the central region. The central area of *Propithecus* is flat and has a diameter of about 1.1 mm, while that of *Indri* is contained in a smaller area and has a more dome-shaped structure. *Propithecus* is reported to have a tapetum cellulosum, while *Indri* has a tapetum fibrosum. In both species the central fundus region is described as unpigmented, but the periphery in *Propithecus* is described as heavily pigmented and that of *Indri* is lightly pigmented.

Tarsiiformes. The retina of *Tarsius* has been described by several investigators. Woollard (1926) described the retina of *Tarsius spectrum*, as did Kolmer (1930). Castenholz (1965), Rohen (1966), and Rohen and Castenholz (1967) describe the retina of *Tarsius bancanus*. Needless to say, the retina of *Tarsius* has been of particular interest both because of its controversial taxonomic status and because of Woollard's report (1925) of a fovea-like development in this retina. The question of whether or not the retina of *Tarsius* represents a transitional form between the prosimian and simian retinas is still of interest and still being debated.

Woollard (1926) noted a gradual thickening of the layers of the retina from the periphery toward the more central region. He reported a "differentiated area which is nearly circular in outline" lying "immediately on the lateral side of the optic disk." This area measured about 2 mm horizontally and about 2.2 mm vertically. He stated that the receptor layer throughout the retina, including this specialized area, consists entirely of rods. The outer nuclear layer increases to 12 rows of nuclei centrally as opposed to 8 rows in the adjacent retina. The outer reticular layer is slightly thicker, as are the inner nuclear layer and the inner reticular layer. He reports "marked changes" in the ganglion cell layer which first called his attention to this area.

Woollard also gives a detailed description of the percipient layer which "is thrown into convolutions" and describes variations in the external limiting membrane and the accumulation of cells of the pigment layer between the convolutions. Woollard proposed that this differentiated area could "be regarded as a primordium macula lutea" and described changes in the lateral geniculate body of *Tarsius* which he felt confirmed this conclusion.

Kolmer (1930) believed that Woollard's description of the specialized area in *Tarsius* retina was based on fixation artifact and that in fact this retina was essentially like that of *Loris*. He found no evidence of a fovea, nor did he see the retinal convolution or accumulations of pigment cells reported by Woollard.

Castenholz (1965) studied the retina of *Tarsius bancanus*. He noted a gradual thickening of all layers from the periphery toward the central retina. The receptors, which are all rods, are uniform in appearance throughout the retina and have "remarkably long outer segments" which are as much as 3.5 times as long as the inner segments. The outer nuclear layer contains 15 rows of nuclei in the central area, while the inner nuclear layer has 10 to 12 rows. The outer plexiform layer is very thin, and the inner plexiform layer is three to four times as thick. The ganglion cell layer consists of only one row of cells throughout the retina. The pigment layer consists of one layer of cells with very little pigment appearing in the central area. Castenholz was unable to find any central area or fovea even by carefully searching serial sections of several eyes. He also failed to find the convolutions reported by Woollard, undoubtedly due to better fixation, in Castenholz specimen.

Rohen (1966) also studied the retina of *Tarsius bancanus*. He also finds the receptor layer to be composed entirely of rods showing essentially the same characteristics as described by Castenholz. The outer nuclear layer is thick (12 to 16 rows of nuclei) in the central area and thinner (3 to 4 rows) in the region of the ora. The outer plexiform layer is thin, and its inner portion is penetrated by capillary loops. The inner nuclear layer consists of 10 to 12 rows of nuclei. These nuclei are larger than those of the outer nuclear layer and not so closely packed. Capillary endings are frequently encountered in this layer. The inner reticular layer is thicker than the outer and is uniformly structured. The ganglion cell layer is only a single row of nuclei throughout most of the retina. About 3 to 3.2 mm from the center of the optic papilla there appears a small pit-shaped depression (Fig. 4). This is produced by a decrease in size of the inner retinal layers (i.e., ganglion cell, inner reticular, and inner nuclear layers). Around this depression there is a slight thickening of the retina due in large part to the accumulation of ganglion cells, here forming 2 to 3 rows of closely packed nuclei. In the fovea only a few bipolar cells are present, while the inner and outer reticular layers become very thin and poorly defined. The outer nuclear layer, however, becomes somewhat thicker in the foveal area. Some capillaries are found in fovea, passing through the bipolar layer and penetrating to the outer plexiform layer. Rohen, like previous investigators, finds no tapetum in *Tarsius*.

One particularly interesting point is his description of a dual capillary network

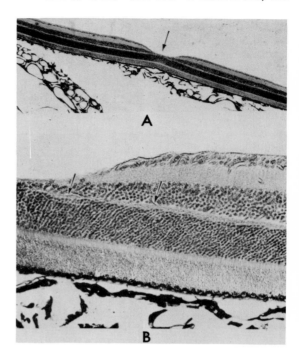

Figure 4. Retina of *Tarsius banca-nus*, showing structure of the fovea. Arrows in (b) point to capillaries. (a) x 25; (b) x 208. From Rohen, J. W. 1966. Graefe Arch. Klin. Exp. Ophthal., 169:299-317.

in *Tarsius* retina. One lies in the area of the inner plexiform layer, the other at the border of the outer plexiform layer. Such a dual system of capillaries has also been described for the human retina by Michaelson (1954).

With respect to the foveal region in *Tarsius*, Rohen (1966) makes several interesting points. The eye of *Tarsius* is in most respects a nocturnally adapted eye in conformity with the tarsier's predominantly nocturnal habits. The gross structural changes represented by the fovea are only slightly reflected in the relationship of the cellular layers of the retina. In other words, the absence of cones and the maintenance of a fairly high ratio of receptors to ganglion cells (about eight to one) are more similar to the other prosimians than to the foveal structure of simians. Rohen, therefore, does not believe that it is possible to conclude that *Tarsius* represents a transitional form between the prosimians and the higher primates.

Rohen and Castenholz (1967) provide an additional description of the retina of *Tarsius bancanus*. They find only very long rods (up to 52 μ), with extremely elongated outer segments (as much as five times the length of the inner segments). The density of receptors is much greater in the central area than in the periphery (73 per 100 μ vs 49 per 100 μ). The outer nuclear layer is more than 2.5 times as thick in the central retina as in the periphery, and the inner nuclear layer is almost three times as thick centrally as peripherally. The outer nuclear layer is throughout thicker than the inner nuclear layer. The inner plexiform layer is fairly well developed, and the ganglion cell layer consists of one row of nuclei. Near the nerve head there is a fovea centralis which "morphologically resembles that of the higher primates." "The foveal crater is flat and trough-shaped." Around the fovea there is a thickening of the ganglion cell layer, which here consists of three rows of nuclei. Even in the foveal pit some bipolar and ganglion cell nuclei are found. The receptor layer is slightly thicker in the foveal center. The ratio of ganglion cells to bipolar cells to receptor nuclei is 1:21:35 in the peripheral retina, 1:10.4:17.9 in the central retina, and 1:4.1:7.4 in the parafoveal region. Again, no evidence of any tapetum was found. The pigment epithelium, which is well developed, is lightly pigmented througout the central fundus, while in the periphery it is heavily pigmented. Despite the well-developed fovea which is found in this retina, Rohen and Castenholz feel that the basic plan of the tarsier retina is essentially like that of *Galago senegalensis*. They appear to feel that the retina of *Tarsius* shows some relationship to the evolutionary development between the prosimians and the simians but that this relationship has not yet been clarified.

ANTHROPOIDEA

Ceboidea. The Ceboidea are divided into two large families, the Callitrichidae and the Cebidae. The Callitrichidae which have been studied include *Callithrix jacchus (Hapale jacchus)* (Woollard, 1926; Kolmer, 1930; Castenholz, 1965; Rohen and Castenholz, 1967; Marback and Costa, 1962), *Leontocebus (Leontideus rosalia)* and *Oedipomidas (Sanguinus oedipus)* (Rohen, 1962). There appear to be few differences among the retinas of the various species which have been studied. Such differences as are reported, primarily regarding the shape of the fovea, are probably due to fixation artifact. Except where otherwise noted, the following description refers to the retina of *Callithrix jacchus*.

The receptor layer is quite rich in cones. Rohen (1962) in his description of *Oedipomidas* states that at least 50 percent of the receptors in the midfundus are cones. The foveal area consists entirely of cones. The cones are thicker in the periphery and thinner and more densely packed in the foveal region.

The outer nuclear layer is relatively thin, consisting of two rows of nuclei peripherally and five rows centrally. Through a small section of the fovea as many as eight rows of nuclei may be found (Fig. 5). The inner nuclear layer which consists of two rows of nuclei peripherally increases to eight rows in the parafoveal region. In the fovea only a few bipolar cells are found. The ganglion cell layer, which outside the central area contains only one row of nuclei, increases to six rows in the parafovea (Castenholz, 1965).

The fovea has steep sides and is relatively flat in the center. There is a sudden thinning of the inner retinal layers at the foveal border, but they do not completely disappear within the fovea (Castenholz, 1965; Kolmer, 1930). The fovea is small (Kolmer, 1930) and lies about 1.8 mm temporal to the optic nerve (Castenholz, 1965). In the foveal area, the pigment epithelium is lightly pigmented, and the choroid increases in thickness (Kolmer, 1930).

Woollard (1926) reported similar findings, except for some variation in his description of the macular area. According to his report, the fovea is shallower, and there is a much greater increase in the outer nuclear layer (up to 15 rows of cells). The foveal depression is about 0.12 mm in diameter. "Corresponding to the fovea

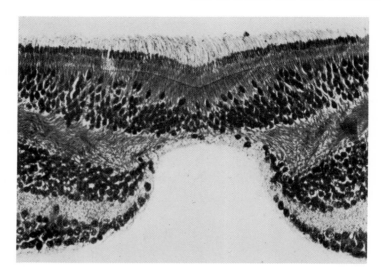

Figure 5. Retinal section showing fovea of *Callithrix jacchus.* Note the lengthening of the receptor outer segments in the center of the fovea. From Kolmer, W. 1930. Z. Anat. Entwicklungsgesch., 93:679-722.

interna there is, in the outer layer of the retina, a slight depression, a fovea externa." This may be fixation artifact involving retinal detachment.

The genus *Cebus* has also been extensively described. *Cebus capucinus* is reported by Kolmer (1930), Rohen (1962), and Rohen and Castenholz (1967). Rohen (1962) also describes the retina of *Cebus albifrons.* Woollard (1927) reported on the retina of *Cebus apella fatuellus.* The differences among the three species are not striking. All show the typical duplex retinal structure of the anthropoids with a well-developed macula and fovea. The ratio of rods to cones in the midfundus is about 4:1 or 5:1, while the periphery shows a somewhat higher proportion of rods. The fovea is of course composed entirely of cones (Kolmer, 1930; Rohen, 1962; Woollard, 1927). Rohen (1962) reports a somewhat higher incidence of cones in *Cebus albifrons* than in *Cebus capucinus.* In the middle fundus region of *Cebus apella,* the reticular layers are well developed, with the inner reticular layer being broader than the outer. The outer layer in *Cebus* is, however, better defined than in the *Lemur* (Woollard, 1927). The inner nuclear layer contains five to six rows of cells, while the outer nuclear layer consists of six to seven rows of closely packed cells.

The fovea is about 0.5 mm in diameter and is surrounded by a macula which extends for more than 1 mm around it (Woollard, 1927). As the fovea is approached, the ganglion cell layer reduces from six or seven rows of cells to only one row, which disappears completely at the margin of the fovea. The inner molecular and inner nuclear layers also terminate completely at the border of the fovea.

The cones, which are short and thick in the periphery, become much longer and thinner in the foveal area, particularly the outer segments.

Saimiri sciureus was investigated by Menner (1931) and Rohen (1962). This retina is described as a "typical daylight retina with well developed cones in the macula" (Rohen, 1962). The cone inner and outer segments are about equal in length. In the central retina the outer nuclear layer consists of five to six rows of nuclei, while the inner layer has four rows. The inner and outer reticular layers are well developed.

Rohen (1962) and Rohen and Castenholz (1967) provide descriptions of the retina of *Alouatta*. This is a duplex retina with rod to cone ratios of 7:1 in the periphery, reducing to 1:1 around the fovea. The fovea contains only thin cones, which are almost twice as long as those in the periphery. It is located about 4 mm temporal to the optic nerve. The retina shows a thickening of all layers from the periphery toward the parafoveal area. The outer nuclear layer increases from three nuclear rows at the periphery to six rows in the midfundus and then to ten rows in the fovea. The inner nuclear layer increases from two nuclear rows in the periphery to four rows in the midfundus and then to nine rows in the parafoveal region. The ganglion cell layer contains only one row of nuclei except in the parafoveal region where five rows are seen. The inner plexiform layer is thicker than the outer layer except in the fovea where only the outer plexiform layer is seen. The ratio of receptors to ganglion cells in the parafoveal region is 2:1, while in the peripheral retina it is almost 18:1.

Ateles ater was studied by Rohen and Castenholz (1967), and Kolmer (1930) reported on *Ateles hypoxanthus*. The retina contains both rods and cones, with only cones in the fovea. The retina is relatively thin with a flat "dish-shaped" fovea (Rohen and Castenholz, 1967). In general this retina is very similar to that of *Cebus* and *Alouatta*. The outer nuclear layer contains four rows of cells peripherally and six rows in the fovea. The inner nuclear layer has two to three rows of cells peripherally, ten rows in the parafoveal region, and one row of cells extending across the fovea. The ganglion cell layer has only one row of cells throughout most of the retina but increases to five rows in the parafoveal region and does not extend into the fovea. The inner plexiform layer is generally thicker than the outer plexiform except in the parafoveal region. Only the outer plexiform layer extends across the fovea. The receptors are longer in the fovea than throughout the remainder of the retina, and the inner segments are between 2.5 and 3 times the length of the outer segments (Rohen and Castenholz, 1967). This is itself a rather interesting finding, since only in *Tupaia* and *Urogale* is a similar relationship noted. The pigment layer is heavily pigmented in the foveal and peripheral areas and moderately pigmented in the parafoveal region. Kolmer (1930) describes the fovea in *Ateles hypoxanthus* as being deep. He describes the receptors in this species as being comparable with those of *Macaca*. The rods and cones are easily distinguished by their staining characteristics.

Aotes has aroused considerable interest, it being the only nocturnal member of the *Anthropoidea*. Consequently a number of investigators have studied the retina of *Aotes trivirgatus* (*Nyctipithecus*). Woollard (1927) states that this retina is composed entirely of rods. Among the basal portions of the rods he found "scattered nuclei belonging to the outer nuclear layer. In the periphery the return is thin," "the inner and outer nuclear layers are fused but are soon separated by the formation of the outer molecular layer." The inner nuclear layer contains two layers of cells, the outer three rows of cells which are more closely packed than those of the inner layer. The inner molecular layer is wide, and the ganglion cell layer contains widely separated cells. As the center of the retina is approached, the retina thickens. The outer nuclear layer enlarges to twelve rows of cells, the inner nuclear layer to three rows. The ganglion cell layer increases only slightly, and the cells are still widely spaced. The receptor layer is composed of tightly packed rods. In the central retina near the optic nerve, the rods are considerably elongated, the outer nuclear layer increases to thirteen rows of cells and accounts for almost one third the thickness of the retina. The inner nuclear layer increases to five rows of cells. The inner reticular layer is slightly wider than the outer reticular layer. The ganglion cell layer still contains one row of cells, but they are much closer together in this area. Woollard found no evidence of any macular or foveal development.

Kolmer (1930) found in *Aotes* retina evidence of "rudimentary cones." Both the staining qualities of the cells and the synaptic endings suggested this distinction. He found no evidence of any tapetum. Kolmer also failed to find any evidence of a fovea, but he did find a thickening of the retina with a "fovea externa." Kolmer makes one further interesting observation concerning this retina. He notes that while the ganglion cell layer contains few cells, the nerve fiber layer has many fibers. He concludes from this that there are ganglion elements in the inner nuclear layer which contribute fibers to the nerve fiber layer and that a complete separation of these layers appears not to have been accomplished.

Detwiler (1943) states that the receptors of *Aotes* "are very similar in shape, size and number to those of the nocturnal lemuroids." *Aotes*, however, has a pigment epithelium which is pigmented in the fundus as well as the periphery, unlike *Galago* and *Nycticebus*. Rohen (1962), however, states that in *Aotes* the pigmentation is weaker in the fundus than in the periphery. Rohen and Castenholz (1967) say that the central retina of *Aotes* is comparable in the quantitative relationships of the layers to that found in the *Lemurs* and *Indrii*. They report the proportion of ganglion cells to receptor cells as 1:60 in the periphery and 1:17.6 in the central retina. They also decribe the central portion of the pigment epithelium as being more heavily pigmented than the periphery. While most authors deny the existence of a tapetum in *Aotes* (Detwiler, 1943; Kolmer, 1930; Rohen and Castenholz, 1967), Rochon-Duvigneaud (1943) and Walls (1963) describe a tapetum fibrosum in this species.

Three recent papers have dealt with the question of the existence of cones in *Aotes* retina. Jones (1965) finds no evidence of any cones, nor of a fovea, in *Aotes*, but he does find evidence for an area centralis.

Hamasaki (1967) found two types of photoreceptors in *Aotes*. A small percentage of receptors are identified as cones because of short pyramidally shaped inner segments, shorter outer segments than in the rods, changes in size and shape throughout the retina, and different staining properties than the rods.

Both Hamasaki (1967) and Jones and Jacobs (1963) find electrophysiological evidence of photopic activity. Finally, Ferraz de Oliveira and Ripps (1968) report not only that the retina of *Aotes* is afoveate but that the central retina is not avascular, there being a "continuous capillary network derived from the retinal vessels." They did, however, find evidence of cones in both the central and peripheral retina of *Aotes* (Fig. 6).

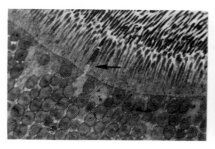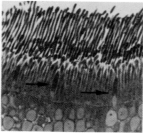

Figure 6. Sections through the central retina of *Aotes trivirgatus* showing cones (arrows) in the receptor layer. From Ferraz de Oliveira, L., and H. Ripps. 1968. Vision Res. 8:223-228.

CERCOPITHECIDAE

The family Cercopithecidae consists of two subfamilies, Cercopithecinae and Colobinae, of which only the first has been studied with respect to retinal structure. Four genera have been studied, two of these fairly extensively.

Several species of macaques have been studied, including *Macaca mulatta* (Kolmer, 1930; Polyak, 1936, 1941, 1957; Woollard, 1927), *Macaca nemistrina* (Kolmer, 1930), and *Macaca sinicus* (Kolmer, 1930). Woollard's description (1927) of *Macaca mulatta* is quite representative for this genus.

In the region of the ora the ganglion cells are widely separated and irregularly spaced. The inner nuclear layer consists of two rows of cells, some of which are displaced into the adjacent reticular layers. The outer nuclear layer consists of three rows of cells. The receptor layer contains both rods and cones.

In the midfundus the cells of the ganglion layer remain in one row but are more closely packed. The inner nuclear layer consists of five rows of loosely packed cells, while the outer nuclear layer is made up of six rows of compactly arranged nuclei. The inner reticular layer is broader than the outer reticular layer. The cones become proportionately more numerous and more elongated, with inner and outer segments of about equal length. The overall thickness of the central retina is about double that of the periphery.

In the macular region the ganglion cell layer increases to three to four rows. The inner nuclear layer has increased to nine rows of cells, while the outer nuclear layer still contains six rows. Cones now predominate in the receptor layer. They are longer than cones in the peripheral and the outer segments now exceed the inner segments in length.

The fovea is well developed, almost 1.9 mm in diameter and 5 mm from the optic disk. The ganglion cell layer and the inner reticular layer do not cross the fovea, but the inner nuclear layer continues as a few scattered cells.

Polyak (1957) estimates that the area of the "flat foveal floor" which measures about 300 μ across contains approximately 17,000 cones.

Kolmer (1930) notes that a well-developed vacuole is found, in well-fixed material, between the inner and outer segments of the cones. He felt that this served an optical function, such as concentrating the light transmitted to the outer segments.

In an earlier study of postnatal retinal development in this species (Ordy, Masso-pust, and Wolin, 1962) functional maturation of the retina as indicated by visual acuity and the electroretinogram was accomplished by 30 days of age, whereas the fundus picture did not approach mature characteristics until 60 days.

Keefe, Ordy, and Samorajski (1966) have studied the prenatal and postnatal development of photoreceptors in the retina of *Macaca mulatta*. They report that the fovea and the photoreceptors are well developed at birth in this species.

The retina of *Macaca nemistrina* is essentially like that of *Macaca mulatta* except that the fovea is a bit larger in *Macaca nemistrina* (Kolmer, 1930).

Cercocebus torquatus fuliginosus (the sooty mangabey) was studied by Woollard (1927) and Kolmer (1930). The description of this retina is very much like that of *Macaca,* with a few exceptions (Woollard, 1927). This retina is slightly thinner throughout, and the outer nuclear layer is much thinner, containing only two rows of cells in the macular region. The retina is composed almost entirely of cones, only a few rods occurring in the periphery. At the border of the fovea the outer nuclear layer increases to nine rows of cells.

Kolmer (1930) offers a somewhat different description. Particularly, he reports the retina as being much broader than did Woollard (1927). The difference appears to lie primarily in the receptor outer layer which Kolmer reports as being extremely long. These may have been broken off in Woollard's sections. In the area of the optic disk the cones are over 100 μ long, while in the fovea they measure 130 μ. The rod-free fovea (Fig. 7) measures 300 μ in diameter, and the densely packed cones within it are very thin, the inner segments measuring 1.5 μ while the outer segments measure only 0.5 μ in width. Kolmer also found rods in the periphery of the macula, but these too were very long and thin and may have been mistaken by Woollard for cones. Kolmer proposes on the basis of the retinal structure that the visual acuity of *Cerco-cebus* is better than that of other mammals and more comparable to that of birds.

Genus *Cercopithecus* has been described by several authors. Several species have also been described, including *Cercopithecus aethiops* (Castenholz, 1965; Rochon-Duvigneaud, 1943; Rohen and Castenholz, 1967; Woollard, 1927), *Cercopithecus*

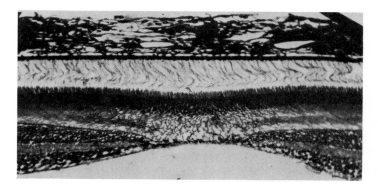

Figure 7. Paramedian section through the fovea of *Cercocebus torquatus fuliginosus.* From Kolmer, W. 1930. Z. Anat. Entwicklungsgesch., 93:679-722.

talapoin (Rohen and Castenholz, 1967), *Cercopithecus diana* and *Cercopithecus hamlyni* (Kolmer, 1930).

Kolmer (1930) describes a well-developed, regularly structured retina in *Cercopithecus diana*. The fovea and macula are large, and in addition a fovea externa is found. In the macular area the inner nuclear layer is eight layers, the ganglion cell layer five to six layers. At the edge of the fovea the ganglion cells build up to seven rows, and a single row of sparsely distributed ganglion cells continues across the fovea. The foveal cones are long and thin. Other retinal layers are not described. *Cercopithecus aethiops* has the greatest difference in thickness between the peripheral and central retina of any eye studied by Rohen and Castenholz (1967), an increase of 140 percent. The fovea has steep sides and a relatively flat floor and lies about 1.5 mm from the nerve head. In the central fovea the outer nuclear layer contains 12 rows of nuclei, the more central layers are extremely reduced. In the parafoveal region the inner nuclear layer builds up to 14 rows of nuclei, while the ganglion cell layer contains 12 to 14 rows. The cones in the fovea are exceptionally small and very densely packed. Rods appear sparsely in the parafoveal region, but in the extreme periphery they outnumber the cones about six to one (Castenholz, 1965).

The retina of *Cercopithecus talapoin* is thinner than that of either *Cercopithecus aethiops* or *Cercopithecus diana* (Rohen and Castenholz, 1967). The fovea is relatively flat and trough-shaped. The parafoveal region is not strikingly developed. The ratio of ganglion cells to bipolar cells to receptor nuclei (1:2.1:0.8) in the parafoveal region is not very different from the equivalent values (1:1.7:0.9) reported for *Cercopithecus aethiops* in spite of the apparent morphological differences. The retina of *Cynocephalus leukophaeus* (*Mandrillus leucophaeus*) is intermediate between the "long-tailed monkeys" (*Cercopithecus*) and the "anthropoids" (Pongidae) (Kolmer, 1930). It is rich in cones which are long and thin.

HOMINOIDEA

Pongidae. Kolmer (1930) examined the eye of the Gibbon (*Hylobates leuciscus*). He describes the retina as being generally similar to that of the human. Rohen (1962) estimates the ratio of rods to cones in *Hylobates* to be about 5:1 or 7:1. The macula and fovea are well developed and comparable to the human. In the midfundus the outer nuclear layer contains eight rows of cells, and the inner nuclear layer six rows, while the ganglion cell layer has only one row of nuclei.

Pan troglodytes has been investigated by Kolmer (1930), Woollard (1927), and Rohen and Castenholz (1967). The chimpanzee is the only primate other than man which has a true ora serrata (Woollard, 1927). Each retinal layer begins gradually from the ora but quickly achieves considerable size. In the periphery the ganglion cells are arranged in widely scattered groups of two or three cells. There are numerous unmyelinated fibers even in the periphery. The inner nuclear layer starts with a single row of nuclei, but soon a second row appears. This layer, which is not well defined at the periphery of the retina, develops well-defined margins as the center is approached. In the periphery the outer reticular layer has cells from the inner nuclear layer scattered throughout. The outer nuclear layer consists of three rows of densely packed nuclei. The receptor layer contains both rods and cones in a ratio of about 4:1.

More centrally the ganglion cell layer has become a continuous layer of cells and "is covered by a thin felt of nonmedullated fibers." The inner reticular layer is well defined and about twice as thick as the outer reticular layer. The inner nuclear layer contains five rows of cells, which include two distinguishable types of cells. The outer nuclear layer consists of seven rows of nuclei, while the proportion of cones in the receptor layer has increased, the ratio of rods to cones now being about 2:1. As the parafoveal region is approached, the ganglion cell layer increases to six rows of closely packed nuclei. The inner nuclear layer increases in size to nine rows of cells, and the two types of cells, noted earlier, become "segregated, so that the small densely-staining type forms three rows along the inner margin."

The outer molecular layer is narrow, and two parts may be distinguished. The outer portion "consists of a dense felt-work: the inner part appears looser and more transparent." The outer nuclear layer decreases in size, the inner part "corresponding to the rod nuclei has disappeared." There are only three rows of nuclei. The receptor layer consists entirely of cones which are more elongated than those further toward the periphery. The fovea is about 0.5 mm in diameter, with sharp walls. The inner nuclear layer continues across the fovea as a single row of cells, while the inner reticular layer and the ganglion cell layers are absent within the fovea (Woollard, 1927). Kolmer (1930) gives a similar but less detailed description of this retina. He described a small foveola within the fovea and gives the length of the foveal cones as 80 μ, of which 48 μ represents the outer segments. Rohen and Castenholz (1967) give the length of the foveal cones as 40 μ, of which only 16 μ represents the outer segments. The ratio of ganglion cells to receptors in the parafoveal region is given as 1:1.4.

Homo. The human retina has been extensively studied with respect to both normal and pathological anatomy. For comparative purposes, the descriptions provided by the same authors as above (Polyak, 1957; Rohen and Castenholz, 1967; Woollard, 1927) will be summarized. In the middle portion of the retina the ganglion cells form one continuous row, and the inner nuclear layer consists of five rows of cells, while the outer nuclear layer contains four rows. Cones predominate over rods in the receptor layer (Fig. 8). In the macular region the ganglion cell layer contains six to seven rows of nuclei. The inner nuclear layer consists of ten rows of cells, while the outer nuclear layer is narrow and contains only three to four rows of nuclei. The receptor layer consists almost entirely of short cones.

The fovea is about 0.66 mm in diameter. "It begins as a shallow depression," the ganglion cell layer, inner reticular layer, and inner nuclear layer all decreasing in size. Across the floor of the fovea the ganglion cell layer, inner reticular layer, and inner nuclear layer completely disappear, while the outer reticular and nuclear layers are continuous across the fovea (Woollard, 1927). In man the foveal cones are 70 μ long, the inner segments 1.5 μ thick, and the outer segments 1 μ thick. The entire foveal depression, measuring about 1.75 mm², is estimated to contain 100,000 to 115,000 cones (Polyak, 1957). The ratio of ganglion cells to receptors in the parafoveal region is 1:1.3, while in the extreme periphery it is 1:32 (Rohen and Castenholz, 1967). The fovea is also described by Rohen and Casenholz as being somewhat smaller and having steeper sides and a sharper center than in *Pan*. They report the ganglion cell layer and inner nuclear layer are also not completely absent in the fovea.

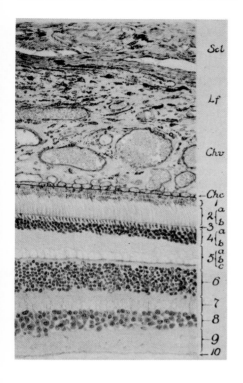

Figure 8. Vertical section through the tunics of human eyeball in the region of central area stained with hematoxylin and eosin. Upper half of figure shows portion of fibrous sclera containing pigment-bearing chromatophore cells and some blood vessels, more numerous in the choroid membrane, which is principally vascular, containing also some chromatophores, and terminating next to the retina in a choriocapillary layer composed of minute vessels. Lower half of figure shows retinal membrane made up of cellular and fibrous elements arranged in regular, parallel layers. *Chc,* choriocapillary layer; *Chv,* vascular layer of choroid membrane; *Lf,* lamina fusca; *Scl,* less pigmented portion of scleral membrane; *1,* pigmented epithelium of retina; *2,* bacillary layer; *3,* outer limiting membrane; *4,* outer nuclear layer; *5,* outer plexiform layer; *6,* inner nuclear layer; *7,* inner plexiform layer; *8,* ganglion cell layer; *9,* layer of optic nerve fibers; *10,* inner limiting membrane of retina. Approximately x 150. From Polyak, S. 1957. The Vertebrate Visual System. Courtesy University of Chicago Press.

Comparative Studies of the Ocular Fundus of Primates

In 1901 Johnson published a beautiful set of paintings (actually done by Mr. A. W. Head who worked with him) of the fundus of a variety of animal species. Included in these were the fundi of several primates. The surface morphology of the retina is shown very clearly in these illustrations—the nerve head with the blood vessels entering the eye and arching across the retina, the macular and foveal reflexes, and in some cases the nerve fibers near the papilla. A number of descriptions of primate fundi may be found in the literature, but they are rarely accompanied by such illustrations. More recently, Wolin and Massopust (1967) presented a series of photographs of the fundi of 14 primate species. From these two collections of fundus representations we may note certain characteristics which parallel those found in histological studies.

The ocular fundi of higher primates (the true monkeys and anthropoids) are, with one exception, basically like that of the human. The significant exception is the *Aotes* or owl monkey which has adopted a nocturnal pattern of life and which has an eye well adapted for this. The fundi of prosimians differ in certain respects from the human. The tree shrew (*Tupaia*), whose classification is still a subject of debate, reveals a fundus pattern generally unlike other prosimians, anthropoids, or human.

All of the Anthropoidea examined (including a number of species for which fundus photographs have not been published) with the exception of *Aotes* show the characteristic pattern of arcuate vessels and the central fovea and macular reflex (Plate I, a, b). Johnson (1901) says, "In fact with the exception of the colour of the fundus, the general characteristics found in man are common to *all* the Catarrhini (Old World monkeys), and all the Platyrrhini (New World monkeys)." Johnson also reported seeing a macula with a ring reflex, in *Aotes*, an observation which we have been unable to verify. Prince (1956) notes that foveas and macular areas are found in a wide range of vertebrate species, including many species with nocturnal habits. He points out that the macular area and even what appears to be a true fovea may be too shallow to detect grossly and can only be verified by histological study or micro-dissection. In most cases it is possible to visualize the choroidal vessels in some portion of the retina (but never in the central area) even though these do not always appear in the photographs (which include only the central fundus). In some cases the nerve fiber may also be seen, usually in the vicinity of the nerve head. In many cases, were it not for the differences in coloration of the retina, it would be difficult to differentiate between species on the basis of the fundus pattern (Plate I, a, b; see also Wolin and Massopust, 1967, Figs. 1-9).

The prosimians (excepting *Tupaia*) and *Aotes* show a somewhat similar vascular pattern, but except for *Tarsius* none show any macular or foveal reflex (Plate I, c, e, f). A central retinal (or central visual) area can be identified by the vascular pattern in every species of primate examined. Species which have predominantly rod retinas show a somewhat stippled pattern and an orange, yellow, or greenish yellow coloration. In the prosimians (again excepting *Tupaia*) and in *Aotes*, choroidal vessels are rarely visualized. They may sometimes be seen in the peripheral retina if it is not deeply pigmented.

Johnson (1901) stated, "In man and all the Simiae the disk is rosy pink or red; whilst in the Galagos and Loridae it is black or green." He also says that in the "Lemurs . . . it is a chalky white." Among the lemurs, we have examined *Lemur fulvis* and *Lemur catta*. In neither case would the description "chalky white" apply to the disk, nor does the disk appear particularly pink in *Aotes* (Plate I, c, e). In the lorises, galagos, and pottos, the disk may appear either black, greyish green, or pinkish gray, depending on the illumination employed. The retina (actually the tapetum) in those species examined is so brilliantly reflective that if one wishes to examine any details of the central fundus except the disk a relatively low level of illumination must be used, and the disk thus appears dark or even black (Plate I, f). If one, however, focuses directly on the disk to examine it in detail, a brighter light is employed, and the disk then takes on a lighter coloration.

Only in *Tarsius*, among the prosimians, may a fovea be visualized. It is farther lateral from the papilla than in the Anthropoidea and somewhat less distinct. The latter is due primarily to the more highly reflective character of the *Tarsius* retina (Plate I, d). If this retina is examined under dim illumination (not suitable for photography) the retina takes on a greyish hue, some of the detail is obscured, but a beautiful clear macular reflex may be observed. This is in contradiction to Johnson (1901), who stated, "This macula, which is bounded by a reflex ring, exists in all Simiae and *in no other mammals*, so that the macula ceases with the last of the Simiae."

Unfortunately, Johnson apparently never had the opportunity to examine the fundus of *Tarsius*. Ryerson (see Polyak, 1957, Fig. 149) on the other hand did examine this eye and illustrated it as showing both a macula and a fovea. His illustrations, which were painted on the basis of observation with a red-free light, differ somewhat from our photographs but do show many essential similarities.

In *Tupaia glis* the central retinal area may be seen far posterior and lateral to the nerve head (Plate I, g). The blood vessels which radiate like spokes of a wheel from the optic papilla branch around one portion of the temporal retina, leaving it relatively free of major vessels. This area in *Tupaia*, consistent with the more lateral orientation of the eyes, is located much farther from the nerve head than the equivalent area in the other prosimians.

Johnson offered a lengthy and detailed analysis of factors contributing to the diverse coloration of the fundus in different species. Not only the anatomy of the eye but also its state of adaptation at the time of examination must be taken into consideration, since some retinal pigments are bleached out by light.

As one proceeds outward from the neuroretina, the following layers are encountered. Just distal to, and often interdigitated with, the ends of the receptor outer segments there is sometimes found a layer of acicular pigment crystals. Next is the retinal epithelial layer containing pigment granules in varying degrees. Although these two types of pigments are not regularly distinguished by other investigators, Johnson (1901) stated that he had identified both types in all the mammalian eyes which he examined. This is followed by Bruch's membrane (lamina vitrea or glassy membrane). The next layer of importance is the choriocapillaris which contributes a reddish coloration, if not obscured by the pigment layer. In species with a tapetum, which is the next outer layer, the above mentioned pigments, Bruch's membrane, the choriocapillaris, and the tapetum determine the coloration of the fundus. In species which have no tapetum, there are additional layers which may contribute to the retinal appearance. There are a large elastic network with cells containing fusca pigment, the branches of the larger choroidal vessels, and another elastic network also containing fusca cells. These last three layers constitute about three quarters of the total thickness of the choroid. Finally, there is a densely pigmented "membrana fusca" of the sclera (Johnson, 1901). Johnson also stated that in species without a tapetum, "which show a red, reddish-brown, chocolate, or slatey color" the fusca pigment cells of the choroid contribute significantly to this coloration.

It is certainly the case that, aside from the occurrence or nonoccurrence of the macula and fovea, the variation in coloration of the retina is the most distinctive difference between the retinas of different primates.

Johnson (1901) also states, "in fine, the whole Fundus oculi affords a striking illustration of the working of progessive evolution, an example all the more valuable since it illustrates the direct modifying effect of external factors upon a highly-specialized organ, in the present case the continued influence of light upon the eye."

This statement, which is based upon observations of a wider variety of vertebrate eyes than just the primates, may be somewhat overdrawn. However, it contains a good deal of truth, and even within the primate order the funduscopic and histologic examinations of the retina reported here reflect in some degree the process of evolution.

Discussion

Many descriptions of retinal structure consist mainly of descriptions of the relative thickness of the various layers. Woollard (1926, 1927) made a point of describing the nuclear layers in terms of number of rows of nuclei and in many cases made judgments regarding the relative density of the nuclear elements. This constituted an important advance, giving us at least some information suggesting the relative functional relationships of the retinal layers.

Rohen and Castenholz (1967) found even this inadequate, and by systematically counting the number of nuclear rows in the retinal layers and the number of nuclear elements per 100 μ expanse of retina in selected comparable portions of the retina, they have provided another significant step toward our understanding of this structure. With these measures they are able to compute the ratio of ganglion cells to bipolar cells to receptor cells for different portions of the retina and to present these ratios for each of the 12 species of prosimians and the 9 species of anthropoids which they studied.

It is certainly desirable that all future studies of retinal histology should continue this practice so that more truly comparable data will be available.

The organization of the reticular layers, particularly the synaptic arrangements, is now being widely studied by electron microscopic techniques (see page 26). These relationships have been studied with the light microscope primarily in *Macaca mulatta*, *Pan troglodytes*, and *Homo sapiens*, and relatively little other comparative data is available.

The classic work on detailed retinal organization is of course contained in Polyak's two volumes (1941, 1957), while the photoreceptors were specifically dealt with by Detwiler (1943), and the ganglion cell layer by Van Buren (1963). Polyak's works, which review in great detail the varieties of nuclear elements and the complexity of synaptic relationships, are too extensive to permit review here and too well known to require it.

TAPETUM

Between the choroid and the pigment epithelial layer of many species is found a highly reflective membrane, the tapetum lucidum. This layer is most often considered a characteristic of the retina of nocturnal species, although it is found in ungulates as well as carnivores and nocturnal primates (Johnson, 1901). Even within the primates, some species which are not distinctively nocturnal in habit (e.g., *Lemur catta, Propithecus, Indri*) have a tapetum, while *Aotes* and *Tarsius*, which are nocturnal, appear not to have a tapetum.

The classical description of the tapetum (Johnson, 1901) states that the primates and carnivores have a tapetum cellulosum and ungulates have a tapetum fibrosum. This distinction between the two types of tapeta is apparently not nearly as clear as we might be led to suppose. A number of primates are described by some authors as having the fibrous type of tapetum, and in many instances there is not only disagreement between authors regarding the type of tapetum in a given species but even a change in classification by a given author from one publication to another, without any explanation of why such a change is made (see page 14).

PHOTORECEPTORS

The retinas of most primates contain two types of receptors: rods which are low intensity receptors for nocturnal or dim light function, and cones which are high intensity receptors for daylight vision and are color sensitive. It is generally accepted on the basis of physiological and spectrophotometric studies that three varieties of cones, selectively sensitive to red, green, and blue light, make up the cone population in trichromatic species.

We would expect some correlation between the retinal receptor structure and the behavioral patterns of a species. For the most part this is true. Species showing a marked incidence of cone receptors are predominantly diurnal in habit (e.g., most anthropoids, some lemurs, and *Tupaia*), while those having primarily rod (or pure rod) retinas are predominantly nocturnal in habit (e.g., *Aotes*, the lorises, some lemurs, and *Tarsius*). *Tupaia*, with a predominantly cone retina, has also been shown to have relatively good color discrimination (Shriver and Noback, 1967).

Within the Anthropoidea all the genera studied, *except Aotes*, are diurnal in habit and have a duplex retina. A duplex retina is here defined as one not only having rods and cones but also having central visual area containing a macular area and a fovea, the latter being both rod-free and avascular.

Differences in photoreceptors among the diurnal Anthropoidea are, so far as is known, differences of relative size and shape of the three main divisions (the outer segment, inner segment, and nucleus).

Enoch (1961, 1963) provided another dimension in the study of photoreceptor characteristics. By projecting a focused light beam through individual receptors and photographing the transmitted light through a microscope, he was able to demonstrate different "wave-guide modes" in the receptor elements. This technique offers possibilities both for the further study of color specificity of receptors within a given retina and for the comparative study of wave-guide modes among the retinas of different species.

Leach (1963) also notes that two types of cones may be detected in the human and monkey retina. The less numerous are found only in the macular region and because of their staining properties are termed "dark cones."

Such variations in size of photoreceptors have functional significance, since smaller receptor units make possible greater receptor density per unit area. Centrally, where 1:1 transmission of information is the rule, this provides for greater visual acuity. Peripherally, where convergence of a number of receptors on a ganglion is found, this makes possible greater sensitivity to low illumination and movement through spatial summation.

Aotes represents a special case among the Anthropoidea, since, as noted above, it is the only nocturnal genus in this suborder. Even with respect to the basic distinction between rods and cones, however, there is often disagreement. The controversy over the existence of cones in *Aotes* retina has been reviewed above. The same question has been raised numerous times regarding the occurrence of cones in other nocturnal species and with respect to the presence of rods in *Tupaia* retina.

Even using multiple criteria, such as length, width, and shape of inner and outer segments, staining properties of the nucleus, and shape of the synaptic endings, does not eliminate disagreement between different investigators. The shape of the receptor components and the staining properties of the nuclei are not uniform throughout the retina. Rods and cones in the central retina are much more alike than is the case in the periphery. The difference between synaptic endings is relative and not absolute. The biological variability which is found everywhere obscures the picture in the retina also. Species with presumably pure rod retinas are capable of efficient visual function in bright daylight. *Tupaia* does not appear to be altogether functionally blind in dim illumination. It appears highly likely that further investigation will reveal more in the way of transitional receptor functions or some greater degree of overlap of function between receptor types than has yet been demonstrated. Anatomic and physiologic investigations have not yet revealed the details of structure or the modes of function which would account for the complex and variable behavior which has been observed.

RELATIONSHIPS BETWEEN THE NUCLEAR LAYERS

In the nocturnal primates, the outer nuclear layer is generally larger (and consists of more nuclear rows) than the inner nuclear layer. In the diurnal species, these two layers tend to be equal, or the relationship is reversed, with the inner nuclear layer being larger, particularly in the central retina. Perhaps of greater importance is the relationship of receptor elements to ganglion cells. In nocturnal species the ratio of receptors to ganglion cells is quite high, so that even in the central visual area this ratio fails to come close to the almost 1:1 relationship found in the parafoveal region of the diurnal higher primates. Even in the diurnal species the ratio of receptors to ganglion cells is high in the peripheral retina. This similarity to the nocturnal species is not overly surprising, since the peripheral retina in higher primates is basically an achromatic, nocturnal retina.

A high ratio of receptors to bipolar and ganglion cells is presumably advantageous for nocturnal vision. It provides a mechanism for spatial summation of light energy falling on a larger expanse of retina, thus increasing sensitivity. This later organization results in a decrement in visual acuity, but this may be partially compensated for by an increase in sensitivity to moving stimuli, such sensitivity having recently been demonstrated in primates by Hubel and Wiesel (1968).

The more direct, nearly 1:1 transmission from receptor to ganglion cells in the foveal and parafoveal region is related to the higher visual acuity of this portion of the retina. The greater density of receptor elements in this area is of course also a contributing factor. The greater receptor density and some reduction in the ratio of receptors to bipolar cells appears to be characteristic of all primates. In spite of the disagreements in descriptions of various retinas, one or another investigator has come up with evidence for some degree of retinal centralization in each primate species so far studied.

VASCULAR SUPPLY

In all primates the outer or posterior portion of the retina is nourished via the choroidal circulation. In species with a relatively thin or transparent retina (and without any tapetum) these vessels may sometimes be visualized (Plate I, b; see also Wolin and Massopust, 1967, Figs. 2, 7, 9). The inner or anterior portion of the retina of primates receives nutriment via branches of the central retinal artery entering the eye by way of the optic nerve and distributing over the inner or vitreum surface of the retina. The return is via the central retinal vein. These vessels have a characteristic arcuate arrangement in all primates except *Tupaia* (Plate I, a, b).

In the diurnal monkeys and anthropoids the retinal arterioles and venules terminate short of the fovea. In some cases they can be seen extending a short distance into the larger macular area (Plate I, a, b; see also Wolin and Massopust, 1967, Figs. 2-5).

In the one nocturnal monkey and in the prosimians, the central visual area is easily defined by the termination of the surface vessels, leaving a vascular-free central retinal area (Plate I, c, d, e, f).

Even in *Tupaia*, whose place in the primate order is somewhat insecure, the central visual area is detectable by the vascular terminations although the retinal vascular pattern of this genus is otherwise quite unlike that of any other primate (Plate I, g).

The avascularity of the central visual area should be regarded as a relative rather than an absolute characteristic. Some species have been described as having capillaries or capillary loops extending into the foveal region, and we have seen cases in higher primates where a major retinal vessel runs directly across, and almost through, the center of the macular area (see Wolin and Massopust, 1967, Fig. 4). Such anatomical variability may be the exception, but it definitely does occur.

SIGNIFICANCE OF FOVEA

A controversy has been long standing as to whether or not the thinning of the retina to form a fovea is a useful or necessary optical device.

In nocturnal species without a specialized central retinal area, we find a thickening of the retina. This is due to both the elongation of the receptor cells and their greater density. Thus the outer nuclear layer is thickened by an increased number of cells, as may be, to a lesser extent, the inner nuclear and ganglion cell layer.

In the higher primates the increase in length of the receptor cells and their extremely high density in the central area tends to produce a similar effect. In addition to the tremendous increase in number of bipolar and ganglion cells required because of the trend toward 1:1 transmission as the central fovea is approached, an even greater thickening of the retina would result in these species if the displacement of the internal layers did not occur.

It is highly probable that up to a certain stage of development the formation of a fovea offers only slight optical advantage. With the development of a pure cone central area and with additional increase in bipolar and ganglion cells necessary for 1:1 transmission of impulses, it may indeed become important for such a development to occur. Had it not, it is possible that the increased potential for acuity made possible by the fine receptor pattern would have been dissipated by the optical diffusion of images through the greatly thickened retina.

Another factor which is directly related to this is the avascularity of the fovea region. Weale (1966) presents evidence that it is not the retinal neuroglia which interferes with visual acuity but the internal blood supply which supplies the neuroglia with nutriment.

If we combine the two arguments, we arrive at the following: Failure to develop a fovea in the higher primates (*ceteris paribus*) would result in a thickening, greater than that found in the prosimians, of the retina in the central visual region. This would further necessitate increased vascularization of this area. The combination of thickening of the retina and increased vascularization of this area would almost certainly result in some reduction of visual acuity.

Elliot-Smith (1928) interpreted developments throughout the visual system of higher primates which followed the development of the retina as "the new vision." Certainly this development resulted in a generally efficient visual system which, though lacking the exceptional acuity of some avians and somewhat less efficient as a light-gathering device than that of some carnivores, nevertheless combines the essential benefits of both systems. In addition, the evolution of the fovea in the primates parallels the massive development of the forebrain. With further comparative investigation of the finer details of retinal organization we may also expect to find other indices of increasing complexity of retinal organization as we progress through the primate order.

REFERENCES

Bierens de Haan, J. A., and M. J. Frima. 1930. Versuche über den Farbensinn der Lemuren. Z. Vergl. Physiol., 12:603-631.

Buettner-Janusch, J. 1966. Origins of Man. New York, John Wiley & Sons, Inc. *In* Castenholz, E. ed. 1965. Über die Struktur der Netzhautmitte bei Primaten. Z. Zellforsch., 65:646-661.

Detwiler, S. R. 1939. Comparative studies upon the eyes of nocturnal lemuroids, monkeys and man. Anat. Rec., 74:129-145.

———— 1943. Vertebrate Photoreceptors. New York, Macmillan.

Elliot-Smith, G. 1928. The new vision. Bowman Lecture. Trans. Ophthal. Soc. U.K., 48:64-85.

Enoch, J. M 1961 Visualization of wave-guide models in retinal receptors. Amer. J. Ophthal., 51:1107-1118.

———— 1963. Optical properties of the retinal receptors. J. Opt. Soc. Amer., 53:71-85.

Ferraz de Oliveira, L., and H. Ripps. 1968. The "area centralis" of the owl monkey (*Aotes trivirgatus*). Vision Res., 8:223-228.

Franz, V. 1911. Studien zur vergleichende Anatomie der Augen der Säugetiere. Arch. Vergl. Ophthal., 2:180-217.

Hamasaki, D. I. 1967. An anatomical and electrophysiological study of the retina of the owl monkey, *Aotes trivirgatus*. J. Comp. Neurol., 130:163-174.

Hill, W. C. O. 1953, 1955, 1957, 1960, 1962. Primates (Comparative Anatomy and Taxonomy), vols. 1-5. Edinburgh, University Press.

———— 1966. Primates (Comparative Anatomy and Taxonomy), vol. 6. New York, Interscience Publishers.

Hubel, R. H., and T. N. Wiesel. 1968. Receptive fields and functional architecture of monkey striate cortex. J. Physiol., 195:215-243.

Johnson, G. L. 1901. Contributions to the comparative anatomy of the mammalian eye, chiefly based on ophthalmoscopic examination. Phil. Trans. Roy. Soc. London, B194: 1-82.

Jones, A. E. 1965. The retinal structure of (*Aotes trivirgatus*) the owl monkey. J. Comp. Neurol., 125:19-27.

———— and G. H. Jacobs. 1963. Electroretinographic luminosity functions of the *Aotes* monkey. Amer. J. Physiol., 204:47-50.

Keefe, J. R., J. M. Ordy, and T. Samorajski. 1966. Prenatal development of the retina in a diurnal primate (*Macaca mulatta*). Anat. Rec., 154:759-784.

Kolmer, W. 1930. Zur Kenntnis des Auges der Primaten. Z. Anat. Entwiklungsgesch., 93:679-722.

Leach, E. H. 1963. On the structure of the retina of man and monkey. J. Roy. Micr. Soc., 82:135-143.

Marback, R. L., and A. R. Costa, Jr. 1962. Alguns dados relativos à estrutura da retina do sagüi (*Callithrix jacchus*). Folia Clin. Biol., 31:10-18.

Menner, E. 1931. Über die Retina einiger Kleinaffen aus der Familie der Callitrichidae und Cebidae. Zool. Anz., 95:1-12.

Michaelson, I. C. 1954. Retinal Circulation in Man and Animals. Springfield, Ill., Charles C Thomas, Publisher.

Napier, J. R., and P. H. Napier. 1967. A Handbook of Living Primates. New York, Academic Press, Inc.

Ordy, J. M., L. C. Massopust, Jr., and L. R. Wolin. 1962. Postnatal development of the retina, electroretinogram, and acuity in the rhesus monkey. Exp. Neurol., 5:364-382.

Polyak, S. 1936. Minute structure of the retina in monkeys and apes. Arch. Ophthal., 15:477-519.

———— 1941. The Retina. Chicago, University of Chicago Press.

———— 1957. The Vertebrate Visual System. Chicago, University of Chicago Press.

Prince, J. H. 1956. Comparative Anatomy of the Eye. Springfield, Ill., Charles C Thomas, Publisher.

Rochon-Duvigneaud, A. 1943. Les Yeux et la Vision des Vertébrés. Paris, Masson.

Rohen, J. W. 1962. Sehorgan. *In* Hofer, H., A. H. Schultz, and D. Starck, eds. Primatologia, Handbook of Primatology, vol. II/1, Lieferung 6, 1-210, Basel/New York, S. Karger.

———— 1966. Zur Histologie des Tarsiusauges. Graefe Arch. Klin. Exp. Ophthal., 169:299-317.

———— and A. Castenholz. 1967. Über die Zentralisation der Retina bei Primaten Folia Primat., 5:92-147.

Samorajski, T., J. M. Ordy, and J. R. Keefe. 1966. Structural organization of the retina in the tree shrew (*Tupaia glis*). J. Cell Biol., 28:489-504.

Shriver, J. W., and C. R. Noback. 1967. Color vision in the tree shrew (*Tupaia glis*). Folia Primat., 6:161-169.

Van Buren, J. M. 1963. The Retinal Ganglion Cell Layer. Springfield, Ill., Charles C Thomas, Publisher.

Walker, E. P., F. Warnick, K. I. Lange, H. E. Uible, S. E. Hamlet, M. A. Davis, and P. F. Wright. 1964. Mammals of the World, vol. 1. Baltimore, The Johns Hopkins Press.

Walls, G. L. 1963. The Vertebrate Eye and its Adaptive Radiation. New York, Hafner Publishing Co., Inc.

Weale, R. A. 1966. Why does the human retina possess a fovea? Nature, 212:255-256.

Wolin, L. R., and L. C. Massopust, Jr. 1967. Characteristics of the ocular fundus in primates. J. Anat., 101:693-699.

Woollard, H. H. 1926. Notes on the retina and lateral geniculate body in *Tupaia, Tarsius, Nycticebus* and *Hapale*. Brain, 49:77-104.

———— 1927. The differentiation of the retina in primates. Proc. Zool. Soc. London, No. I:1-17.

2

The Primary Optic Pathways and Nuclei of Primates*

Roland A. Giolli

Department of Human Morphology
University of California, Irvine
College of Medicine
Irvine, California 92664

and

Johannes Tigges

Yerkes Regional Primate Research Center,
and the Department of Anatomy
Emory University
Atlanta, Georgia 30322

Introduction

Until recently, knowledge of the organization of the primary optic projections of primates had been largely confined to the dorsal lateral geniculate nucleus, and, accordingly, the only in-depth review of this subject had been that of Walls (1953) dealing specifically with this terminal optic center. Recently, however, the advent of improved neurohistological staining procedures and the greater availability of a variety of primate species have occasioned a considerable increase in the volume of literature concerned with the primary optic projections of primates. Our main goal is to provide a crucially needed review of this recent literature. Whenever possible, it is planned to advance new concepts relevant to the comparative anatomical features of the optic projections. On the other hand, this review will offer only limited coverage of the functional aspects of these projections and, aside from a select number of references, will not delve into the literature on electron microscopy.

*We are greatly indebted to Miss Catherine S. Kalaha for invaluable technical assistance, to Miss Helene J. Oliver for secretarial help, and to Miss Sandra Wilks for the preparation of illustrative material. Appreciation is expressed for the financial support rendered by NIH grant FR-00165 to the Yerkes Regional Primate Research Center, by a McCandless grant to one of us (J. T.); and by a University Research Grant to the University of California, Irvine, College of Medicine.

As a second goal in this report we plan to introduce unpublished data concerning our studies on three species of prosimians and five species of anthropoids (See Table 1). In Table 1 it is seen that each of the experimental primates under investigation was sacrificed 3 to 180 days after unilateral ocular enucleation and its brain prepared according to one (or in the case of series 68-15, 68-17, 67-61, both) of the following two procedures: (1) The Nauta (Nauta and Gygax, 1954) or Fink-Heimer (1967) degeneration methods to show the course and terminal distribution of the primary optic fibers and (2) the transneuronal cell degeneration method to elucidate the rela-

TABLE 1

Data Pertaining to the Brain Series of the Present Research

Primate [a] (genus and species)	Identification number	Postenucleate survival (days) [b]	Plane of section	Histological methods	Primary optic nuclei studied [c]
PROSIMIANS					
Tupaia glis	67-17	7	transverse	Nissl, Fink-Heimer	All nuclei
	67-24	6	transverse	Nissl, Fink-Heimer	All nuclei
	67-25	4	transverse	Nissl, Fink-Heimer	All nuclei
Perodicticus potto	68-35	6	horizontal	Nissl, Fink-Heimer	Prt, SC, ADN
	68-37	8	horizontal	Nissl, Fink-Heimer	Prt, SC, ADN
	68-43	7	horizontal	Nissl, Fink-Heimer	Prt, SC, ADN
	68-21	N	horizontal	Nissl	Prt, SC, ADN
	68-36	N	horizontal	Nissl	Prt, SC, ADN
Nycticebus coucang	68-47	7	transverse	Nissl, Fink-Heimer	LGD (Tr.d.), AON
	68-50	3	transverse	Nissl, Fink-Heimer	LGD (Tr.d.), AON
ANTHROPOIDS					
Macaca cynomolgus	2PO14	14	transverse	Klüver-Barrera and Nauta-Gygax	Prt, AON
	3PO13	13	transverse	Klüver-Barrera and Nauta-Gygax	Prt, AON
	5PO12	12	transverse	Klüver-Barrera and Nauta-Gygax	Prt, AON
Macaca mulatta	68-16	90	transverse	Nissl	LGD (Tr.d.)
	68-17	180	sagittal transverse on chiasma	Nissl Fink-Heimer	LGD (Tr.d.)
Cercocebus atys	67-61	30	transverse transverse on chiasma	Nissl Fink-Heimer	LGD (Tr.d.)
Aotes trivirgatus	A-5	N	horizontal	Nissl	All nuclei
Ateles geoffroyi	68-14	90	transverse	Nissl	LGD (Tr.d.)
	68-15	180	sagittal transverse on chiasma	Nissl Fink-Heimer	LGD (Tr.d.)

[a] The brain series of *Macaca cynomolgus* was used by one of us (Giolli, 1963) in an earlier study of the accessory optic system.
[b] N denotes a normal brain series.
[c] AON, terminal accessory optic nuclei; LGD, dorsal lateral geniculate nucleus; Prt, pretectal nuclei; SC, superior colliculus; Tr.d., transneuronal cell degeneration study.

tionship of crossed and uncrossed retinal inputs within the dorsal lateral geniculate nucleus.

Optic Pathways

OPTIC NERVE FIBER COUNTS

The older literature dealing with fiber number in the optic nerves of primates has been reviewed by Clark (1942) and Polyak (1957), and therefore we will concern ourselves primarily with the literature of more recent years.

Essentially all available data on fiber number in the primate optic nerve are derived from studies on man and *Macaca mulatta*. In man, reduced silver preparations of optic nerve provided Bruesch and Arey (1942) with counts of 871,000 to 1,200,000 fibers and Kupfer et al. (1967) with an estimated 1,100,000 fibers with diameters of 0.5μ or greater. Comparable figures of 815,000 to 1,000,000 are given by Chacko (1948) for the myelinated fiber content of the human optic nerve.

The above estimates appear to bear little value as indicators of total retinofugal fiber population in the optic nerve of man. Van Buren (1963a) has shown that the number of ganglionic cells in the human retina (2,000,000) exceeds to a substantial degree (66 percent) the highest of the optic nerve counts (see Bruesch and Arey's count of 1,200,000 fibers).* Assuming that the aforementioned investigations provide reliable estimates of the optic nerve fiber population resolvable by light microscopy, an explanation for the reported difference between the number of retinal ganglionic cells and optic nerve fibers in man seems to rest on the premise that the calibers of a large proportion (about 40 percent) of the total optic nerve fibers are too fine to be resolved by light microscopy. This condition has been shown to apply to the albino rat, in which the light microscopic studies of Bruesch and Arey (1942) place the optic nerve fiber count at 74,000, while the electron microscopic studies of Forrester and Peters (1967) established a figure 58 percent higher (117,000 fibers).

In *Macaca mulatta*, Bruesch and Arey (1942) calculate the optic nerve fiber population in reduced silver preparations at 1,210,000 and in osmium preparations at 1,250,000. Their conclusion that the optic nerve of this monkey is an essentially myelinated fiber bundle is supported by the electron microscopic observations of Ogden and Miller (1966) on the optic nerve of this species.

OPTIC CHIASMA

In primates, semidecussation of the optic nerve appears to have evolved with the establishment of ocular frontality. Table 2 shows that non-tupaiid primates, i.e., forms possessing frontally positioned eyes, as a rule exhibit only 50 to 60 percent optic nerve decussation, whereas *Tupaia* has ocular lateralization and also an almost totally decussated optic nerve. At this juncture it seems appropriate to point out that the

---

* This discrepancy attains an even greater dimension if one is willing to accept Wolter and Lund's conclusion (1968) that 10 percent of the optic nerve fibers in man are retinopetal.

TABLE 2

Optic Fiber Decussation in Primates

Primate species	Degree of fibers decussated	Histological method	Authors
Tupaia glis	"overwhelming majority"	Nauta	Glickstein et al. (1966)
Tupaia glis	approx. 97%	Nauta-Gygax	Tigges (1966)
Tupaia glis	nearly complete	Nauta-Gygax	Campbell et al. (1967)
Tupaia glis	nearly complete	Nauta	Laemle (1967, 1968b)
Tupaia glis	approx. 90%	Fink-Heimer	present research
Galago crassicaudatus	50%	Glees	Campos-Ortega and Glees (1967a)
Galago crassicaudatus	approx. 50%	Nauta	Laemle (1967)
Galago crassicaudatus	50-60%	Fink-Heimer	Tigges and Tigges (1969)
Nycticebus coucang	approx. 50%	Nauta	Laemle (1967)
Nycticebus coucang	50-60%	Fink-Heimer	present research
Perodicticus potto	50-60%	Fink-Heimer	present research
Macaca mulatta	approx. 60%	Fink-Heimer	present research
Cercocebus atys	approx. 60%	Fink-Heimer	present research
Saimiri sciureus	"majority of fibers"	Nauta	Campos-Ortega and Glees (1967b)
Saimiri boliviensis, Saimiri madeirae, Saimiri sciurea	50-60%	Fink-Heimer	Tigges and Tigges (1968)
Ateles geoffroyi	50-60%	Fink-Heimer	present research
Homo sapiens	53%	Bodian	Kupfer et al. (1967)

primary optic system of *Tupaia* * resembles the corresponding system in rodents (Hayhow et al., 1962; rat) and lagomorphs (Giolli and Guthrie, 1968; rabbit) regarding not only the nearly total decussation of its optic nerve but also the organization of its primary optic nuclei.

The estimates presented in Table 2 on optic decussation among primates are based largely upon the relative degrees of orthograde degeneration in contralateral and ipsilateral optic tracts subsequent to eye enucleation. One is cautioned against the outright acceptance of these estimates, for the findings of orthograde degeneration studies on the optic pathways in cat (van Crevel and Verhaart, 1963) and *Saimiri* (Tigges and Tigges, 1968a) indicate a more rapid rate of disintegration in coarser than in finer calibrated fibers, leading one to assume that the quoted values in Table 2 carry with them errors implicit in the differential degeneration of optic fibers.

The retinotopic organization of the optic pathways of macaques is elucidated through the works of Brouwer and Zeeman (1926; Marchi degeneration method) and Hoyt and Luis (1962, 1963; Nauta degeneration method). It is concluded that more finely calibered optic fibers originate from the macula, lie centrally in the optic

---

* The taxonomic status of tupaiids remains unsettled. Tupaiids have on occasion been classified as primates (Simpson, 1945; Fiedler, 1956), subprimates (Remane, 1956), insectivores (McKenna, 1966), or as a group all their own (Van Valen, 1965). In his writings on primates, Hill (1953) refrains from any consideration of tupaiids. The primary optic pathways and nuclei of *Tupaia* are dealt with here in full recognition of the current taxonomc dilemma.

nerve, and rise to dorsal positions in the optic tracts, whereas coarse calibrated optic fibers spring from extramacular retina, lie peripherally in the optic nerve, and are located ventrally in the optic tracts.

ORTHOGRADE DEGENERATION

The process of orthrograde degeneration occurring in the optic nerve fibers following eye enucleation or optic nerve transection requires months to years for completion. Conclusions based upon several studies suggest that the actual period necessary is dependent upon the choice of histological staining procedure. In reduced silver preparations of the rabbit's optic nerve, Ramón y Cajal (1928) finds total fiber disappearance in only two and a half months, and van Crevel and Verhaart (1963) make the same observation in Häggqvist preparations of the cat's optic nerve after four to five months. By contrast, Nauta and Fink-Heimer degeneration studies indicate that the period necessary for total optic fiber disappearance is substantially longer. Goodman (1968) claims that 15 to 16 months are needed in rat, and Tigges and Tigges (1969a) stress that an excess of one year is required in *Saimiri*. Present Fink-Heimer degeneration studies on *Ateles* and *Macaca mulatta* show the persistence of numerous fragments of optic fibers for longer than six months. It seems reasonable to assume that the Nauta and Fink-Heimer degeneration methods stain a select group of optic fibers which by other silver methods or by the Häggqvist technique cannot be revealed.

TRANSNEURONAL DEGENERATION

Transneuronal degeneration, a most conspicuous feature of the primate visual system, is customarily described in terms of the degenerative cell changes occurring in the dorsal lateral geniculate nucleus following ocular enucleation (see below). Yet another type of transneuronal degeneration is demonstrated in the monkey's visual system by Van Buren (1963a, b). This worker sacrificed a Rhesus monkey four years after right occipital lobectomy and observed that the right optic tract had become severely atrophied (presenting a cross sectional area 44 percent that of the left optic tract) and that the ganglionic cells of the right hemiretinas had undergone severe atrophy. Support for Van Buren's finding of transneuronal cell degeneration is provided by the clinical observations of Haddock and Berlin (1950). In a patient having suffered gunshot wounds to both occipital lobes, Haddock and Berlin note only mild visual field changes after three and a half years but pronounced field changes after five and a half years.

RETINOPETAL FIBER SYSTEM

The existence of an elaborately organized retinopetal fiber system together with its nucleus of origin, the isthmo-optic nucleus, has been well documented in avians (consult review of Cowan and Wenger, 1968). Among mammals, retinopetal fibers have been described in cat (Granit, 1955; Brooke et al., 1965; Spinelli et al., 1965), monkey (Brooke et al., 1965), and man (Wolter, 1965; Wolter and Lund, 1968). Brooke and co-workers present electron microscopic evidence of retinopetal fibers in

the optic fiber and inner plexiform layers of the monkey's retina following optic nerve transection, and they propose that these fibers originate from the mammalian homolog to the isthmo-optic nucleus of avians. By studying reduced silver preparations of the human optic nerve on the side corresponding to eye enucleation, Wolter and Lund estimate that retinopetal fibers constitute a full 10 percent of the total fiber content in the human optic nerve.

Pregeniculate Nucleus (Ventral Lateral Geniculate Nucleus)

CYTOARCHITECTURE

The pregeniculate nucleus of non-tupaiid primates is homologous to the ventral lateral geniculate nucleus of other mammalian forms (Niimi et al., 1963). The distinction between these nuclei is purely topographic. Through an inward rotation and downward migration of the dorsal lateral geniculate nucleus, the ventral lateral geniculate nucleus is shifted from a position ventral to one rostrodorsal to the former nucleus. In this new position the ventral lateral geniculate nucleus acquires the name pregeniculate nucleus.

Niimi et al. (1963) divide the pregeniculate nucleus (and the ventral lateral geniculate nucleus) into external and internal layers. Their external layer seemingly corresponds in anthropoids to the "dichtes Praegeniculatum" of Balado and Franke (1937), in *Macaca* to the pars oralis of Olszewski (1952), and in man to the pars densa dorsalis and lateralis of Okamura (1957) and the n. praegeniculatus griseus of Hassler (1959). The internal layer of Niimi et al. is probably identical in anthropoids to the "lockeres Praegeniculatum" of Balado and Franke (1937), in *Macaca* to the pars caudalis of Olszewski (1952), and in man to the n. praegeniculatus fibrosus of Hassler (1959). In the present study, external and internal layers can be discerned in both the pregeniculate nucleus of *Perodicticus* and the ventral lateral geniculate nucleus of *Tupaia* (Fig. 1).

RETINOPREGENICULATE PROJECTION (RETINAL PROJECTION TO VENTRAL LATERAL GENICULATE NUCLEUS

It is Polyak (1957) who, in Marchi degeneration studies on *Macaca mulatta*, first describes a retinopregeniculate projection. This projection has more recently been demonstrated in Nauta and Fink-Heimer degeneration studies on *Galago* (Campos-Ortega and Clüver, 1968; Tigges and Tigges, 1969) and *Saimiri* (Campos-Ortega and Glees, 1967b) and in transneuronal cell degeneration studies on *Aotes* (Jones, 1966), but it has remained unobserved by Tigges and Tigges (1969) in Fink-Heimer degeneration studies on *Saimiri*. A retinal projection to the ventral lateral geniculate nucleus of *Tupaia* has been established through the Nauta and Fink-Heimer degeneration studies of Campbell et al. (1967).

Current Fink-Heimer degeneration studies reveal a retinal input to the external, but not the internal, layer of both the pregeniculate nucleus of *Perodicticus* and the ventral lateral geniculate nucleus of *Tupaia* (Fig. 1). In *Perodicticus*, contralateral

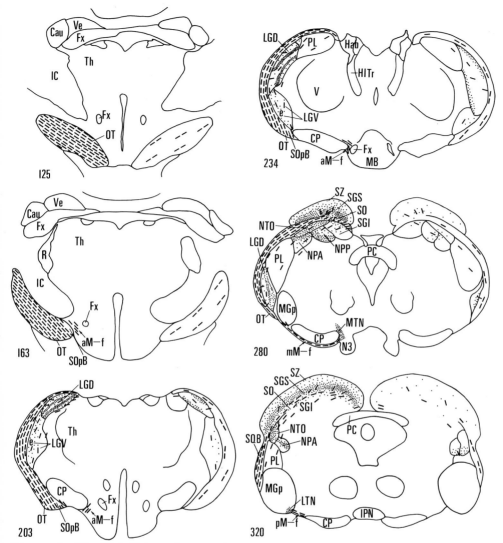

Figure 1. The Fink-Heimer degeneration pattern is seen seven days after right ocular enucleation in *Tupaia* 67-17. Transverse sections 125 through 320 are in rostrocaudal sequence, and each is identified by its serial number. The contralateral side lies on the left. Line segments denote relative densities of degenerating fibers, and dots depict relative densities of degenerating terminals.

Abbreviations to Figure 1.

aM-f, anterior M-fibers of accessory optic system; Cau, caudate nucleus; CP, cerebral peduncle; Fx, fornix; Hab, habenular nuclei; HItr, habenulointerpeduncular tract; IC, internal capsule; IPN, interpeduncular nucleus; LGD, dorsal lateral geniculate nucleus; LGV (e, i), ventral lateral geniculate nucleus (external and internal layers); LTN, lateral terminal nucleus of accessory optic system; MB, mammillary body; MGp, pars principalis, medial geniculate nucleus; mM-f, middle M-fibers of accessory optic system; MTN, medial terminal nucleus of accessory optic system; NPA. n. praetectalis anterior; NPP, n. praetectalis posterior; NTO, n. tractus opticus; N3, oculomotor nerve; OT, optic tract; PC, posterior commissure; PL, pulvinar; pM-f, posterior M-fibers of accessory optic system; R, thalamic reticular nucleus; SGI, str. griseum intermedium; SGS, str. griseum superficiale; SO, str. opticum; SOpB, supraoptic bundle; SQB, superior quadrigeminal brachium; SZ, str. zonale; Th, thalamus; V, ventral nuclei of thalamus; Ve, lateral ventricle.

and ipsilateral retinal inputs to the pregeniculate nucleus achieve a ratio of 3:2 and assume a crude differential pattern of representation, i.e., one in which contralateral and ipsilateral retinal inputs are partially overlapped and extend caudad and rostrad respectively (Fig. 2). In *Tupaia*, the pattern of terminal degeneration described in the ventral lateral geniculate nucleus by Campbell et al. (1967) is confirmed. Contra-

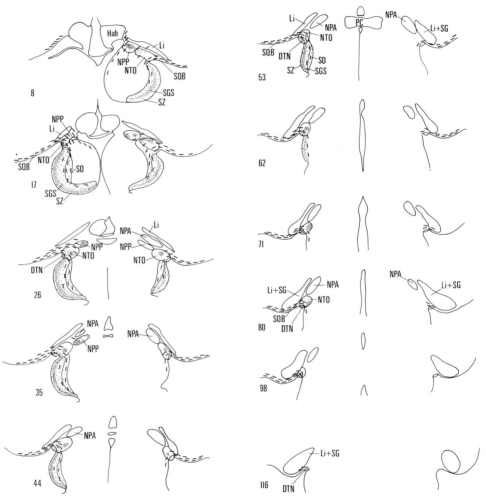

Figure 2. The Fink-Heimer degeneration pattern is seen eight days after right ocular enucleation in *Perodicticus* 68-37. Horizontal sections 8 through 116 are in dorsoventral sequence, and each is identified by its serial number. The contralateral side lies on the left. Line segments denote relative densities of degenerating fibers, and dots depict relative densities of degenerating terminals. DTN, dorsl terminal nucleus of accessory optic system; Hab, habenular nuclei; Li, n. limitans; NPA, n. praetectalis anterior; NPP, n. praetectalis posterior; NTO, n. tractus opticus; PC, posterior commissure; SG, suprageniculate nucleus; SGS, str. griseum superficiale; SO, str. opticum; SQB, superior quadrigeminal brachium; SZ str. zonale.

lateral and ipsilateral retinal inputs attain a ratio of 4:1 and appear to lack any differential pattern of representation (Fig. 1).

FUNCTIONAL CONSIDERATION

Polyak (1957) presents experimental-anatomical evidence in support of his claim that the retinopregeniculate projection constitutes a vital link in the pathway of the pupillary light reflex. This evidence is based upon Marchi degeneration studies on *Macaca mulatta*. It indicates that the retinopregeniculate fibers are among the finest of the degenerating optic nerve fibers seen after eye enucleation and that these fine fibers degenerate only after the production of retinal lesions which impinge upon the macula.* Furthermore, this evidence shows that the placement of lesions in the pregeniculate nucleus in *Macaca mulatta* is followed by the degeneration of a pregeniculomesencephalic tract of presumed termination within the nucleus of Edinger-Westphal.

Dorsal Lateral Geniculate Nucleus

CELLULAR LAMINATION

Cellular lamination as a structural feature characterizes the dorsal lateral geniculate nucleus (LGD) of primates, carnivores, artiodactyls, and the marsupial phalanger (*Trichosurus vulpecula*). Among primates the laminar plan is usually one consisting of six layers, but notable exceptions to this rule are the LGDs of *Tupaia glis, Tarsius,* and the platyrrhine monkeys (e.g., *Saimiri* and *Ateles*). In *Tupaia glis*, a majority of authors report a five layered LGD (Feremutsch, 1963; Tigges, 1966; Campbell et al., 1967; present research), although Hassler (1966) describes six layers and Glickstein (1967) identifies a sixth laminar component (his layer S). In the LGD of *Tarsius*, four cell layers are distinguished by Hassler (1966), and only the magnocellular set of laminae are reported to exist in the predominantly unlaminated geniculates of *Saimiri* (Clark, 1941; Doty et al., 1966; Campos-Ortega and Glees, 1967b; Tigges and Tigges 1969a) and *Ateles* (Clark, 1941; Jones, 1964).

Besides its traditional six laminae, the primate LGD has on occasion been found to possess an additional cell layer sandwiched between the optic tract and lamina 1. Hassler's term (1959) for this layer, "nullte Schicht," seems appropriate because it is in harmony with the established rule for numbering geniculate laminae, viz., in a central direction from the optic tract. Accordingly, we designate this layer as lamina 0 and note that Tigges and Tigges (1969) have also adopted this terminology.

The discovery of lamina 0 is to be credited to Balado and Franke (1937) who, using the term "6. Schicht," † describe this lamina in the LGDs of *Macaca, Cebus,*

---

* It should also be noted that the macula is the retinal zone found to elicit by far the most vigorous pupillary constriction upon photic stimulation (Hess, 1907).

† Balado and Franke number LGD laminae toward the optic tract and not away from this tract as is currently the custom. In addition, these investigators consider the paired magnocellular laminae together as comprising their lamina 5. It is thus apparent that lamina 6 (i.e., 6. Schicht) of the Balado and Franke nomenclature and lamina 0 of the present report are homologous.

Cercocebus, Pan, and *Pongo.* Lamina 0 has since been identified with certainty in the LGDs of *Galago* (Tigges and Tigges, 1969), *Saimiri* (Tigges and Tigges, 1969a), and man (Hassler, 1959), and it appears to correspond to a supernumerary layer observed regularly in *Aotes* (Jones, 1966) but inconsistently among specimens of *Macaca mulatta* (Clark, 1941). In the present study lamina 0 can be discerned in two specimens of *Ateles* (see Fig. 3), two of *Nycticebus,* and one of *Macaca mulatta* (Fig. 4), but it is unidentifiable in a specimen each of *Macaca mulatta* and *Cercocebus.* From the forgoing account it can be reasonably assumed that lamina 0 represents an incipient feature of geniculate organization whose occurrence among primates is by no means uncommon.

RETINOGENICULATE PROJECTION

The LGDs of rat (Hayhow et al., 1962), rabbit (Giolli and Guthrie, 1969), and hedgehog (Campbell et al., 1967) exhibit a concealed lamination which is based upon a partial or complete segregation of crossed and uncrossed retinal inputs in the absence of any apparent cellular lamination. Concealed lamination, also found in the undifferentiated parvocellular mass of the LGDs of platyrrhine monkeys, e.g., *Saimiri* (Doty et al., 1966; Campos-Ortega and Glees, 1967b; Tigges and Tigges, 1969a) and *Ateles* (Clark, 1941; Jones, 1964) is a feature essentially lacking in the LGDs of other primate groups.

Complete monocular isolation is an outstanding characteristic of the retino-geniculate input of primates. Among anthropoids, a pattern in which the contralateral retina innervates laminae 1, 4, and 6 while the ipsilateral retina innervates laminae 2, 3, and 5 has been established both through Nauta and Glees degeneration studies (*Saimiri:* Campos-Ortega and Glees, 1967b; *Macaca* and *Papio:* Glees, 1961) and transneuronal cell degeneration studies (*Saimiri:* Doty et al., 1966; Tigges and Tigges,

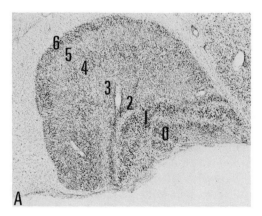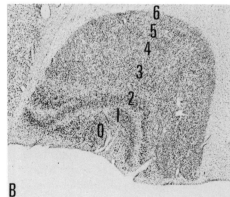

Figure 3. Transverse Nissl sections through the central portions of the dorsal lateral geniculate nuclei of *Ateles* 68-14. The pattern of transneuronal cell degeneration is seen in (A) right ipsilateral and (B) left contralateral nucleus 90 days after right ocular enucleation, x 12. Degeneration is located in laminae 2, 3, and 5 ipsilaterally and laminae 1, 4, and 6 contralaterally as typical of anthropoids. In addition, lamina 0 is discernible and noted to be degenerated ipsilaterally.

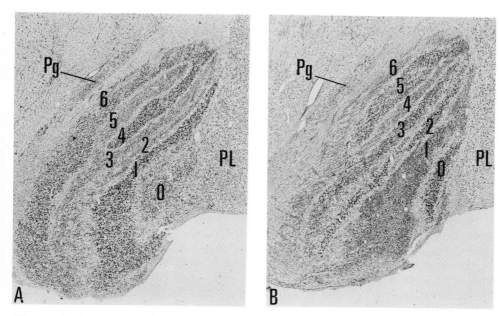

Figure 4. Parasagittal Nissl sections through the central portions of the dorsal lateral geniculate nuclei of *Macaca mulatta* 68-17. The pattern of transneuronal cell degeneration is seen in (A) right ipsilateral and (B) left contralateral nucleus 180 days after right ocular enucleation, x 10. The typical anthropoid pattern is shown, i.e., ipsilateral degeneration in laminae 2, 3, and 5 and contralateral degeneration in laminae 1, 4, and 6. As with *Ateles* (see Figure 3), lamina O also is identifiable and found to be degenerated ipsilaterally. Pg, pregeniculate nucleus; PL, pulvinar.

1969a; *Ateles:* Jones, 1964; *Macaca:* Minkowski, 1920; Matthews et al., 1960; Glees, 1961). Current transneuronal cell degeneration studies further show this basic pattern of retinogeniculate input * in *Ateles* (Fig. 3), *Macaca mulatta* (Fig. 4), and *Cerco-cebus*.

In the prosimian LGD, complete monocular isolation has been demonstrated through Nauta and Fink-Heimer degeneration studies (*Galago* †: Laemle, 1968a; Tigges and Tigges, 1969; *Nycticebus:* Laemle, 1968a) and transneuronal cell degeneration studies (*Galago:* Hassler, 1965, 1966; Tigges and Tigges, 1969; *Microcebus, Cheirogaleus, Loris:* Hassler, 1965, 1966; *Nycticebus:* present research). The established pattern of retinogeniculate input among prosimians (i.e., contralateral input to laminae 1, 5, and 6, ipsilateral input to laminae 2, 3, and 4) differs from that seen in anthropoids, but the reason for this difference is as yet unknown.

Complete monocular isolation as a feature of retinogeniculate organization does not apply to *Tupaia glis.* Of the five laminae usually described in this species, three

---

* The basic pattern of retinogeniculate input denoted here does not take into account lamina 0 with its ipsilateral retinal input. Discussion of the retinal innervation of lamina 0 is to follow in the text.
† In Nauta and Glees degeneration studies on the LGD of *Galago,* however, Campos-Ortega and Glees (1967a) and Campos-Ortega and Clüver (1968) describe a binocular innervation of their lamina 3.

(2, 3, and 4) undisputedly receive monocular input, but two (1 and 5) notably possess binocular input (Tigges, 1966; Campbell et al., 1967; present research: Fig. 1). In terms of function, however, the significance of the binocular innervation of the tupaiid LGD is open to question. The contralateral retinal input is quite minute, and, in fact, it is of such minor dimensions as to have been unidentifiable to Glickstein (1967) in his Nauta and transneuronal cell degeneration studies on this species.

In addition to their usual compliment of laminae, the LGDs of several groups of primates have been found to contain a lamina 0 (see below). Lamina 0 recently has been shown to receive ipsilateral retinal innervation in Fink-Heimer degeneration studies on *Galago* (Tigges and Tigges, 1969) and in transneuronal cell degeneration studies on *Saimiri* (Tigges and Tigges, 1969a), *Ateles* (present research: Fig. 3), *Macaca mulatta* (present research: Fig. 4), and *Nycticebus* (present research).

Studies indicate that the initial appearance of transneuronal cell degeneration in the primate LGD varies with the particular form being investigated. Following ocular enucleation, cell degeneration is discernible in the LGDs of *Nycticebus* (present research) and *Macaca mulatta* (Matthews et al., 1960) after 3 and 4 days respectively. On the other hand, cell degeneration is reported to make its first appearance after a lapse of 10 to 30 days following eye removal in *Saimiri* (Doty et al., 1966; Campos-Ortega and Glees, 1967b), and in man (Kupfer, 1965) it is barely evident 30 days postenucleate. Speculation is open as to the mechanism underlying these different rates of cell degeneration, but it seems conceivable that they are dependent upon the ability of nonoptic neurons to sustain geniculate cells.

CORRELATES OF LGD LAMINATION

Experiments conducted in the past by scientists of such eminence as Minkowski (1920), Brouwer and Zeeman (1925, 1926), and Clark and Penman (1934) elucidate many facets of retinogeniculate organization in primates. It is through such experiments that each geniculate has been shown to relate to the contralateral half of the visual field, that each geniculate lamina has been noted to receive retinal input from one or the other retina, and that corresponding points on the retinas have been demonstrated to project upon strips of geniculate cells radially oriented through all laminae. However, while the lamination found in other areas of the nervous system, notably the cerebral cortex, the superior colliculus, and the retina, is known to accomplish a segregation of functionally distinct cellular types, the body of data on retinogeniculate organization has done little to establish the *raison d' etre* for geniculate lamination.

During the 1940's Clark developed his theory on the functional basis of geniculate lamination in primates (see literature review by Walls, 1953). This theory states that geniculate laminar organization serves to segregate retinogeniculate components concerned with color vision. It is Walls (1953), who in a well-documented critique, puts a quietus to this theory. He presents a body of evidence to repudiate the theory, and the following are several of the points of comparative anatomical interest used in his argument: (1) There are primates without any demonstrable color vision to speak of, e.g., *Lemur mongoz*, which possess a six-layered geniculate; (2) the pure-rod prosimians *Galago*, *Perodicticus*, and *Microcebus* each has a six-layered geniculate;

and (3) among the nonprimates there is *Trichosurus vulpecula* which exhibits a geniculate of six well-developed laminae but lacks color vision.

A relationship between nocturnality and geniculate laminar structure is indicated from at least two lines of investigation. In studies on a series of primates, Hassler (1966) finds the magnocellular, but not the parvocellular, laminae to be larger and to contain greater numbers of cells in nocturnal as compared with diurnal forms. And in transneuronal cell degeneration studies, Jones (1966) identifies only four laminae in the LGD of the nocturnal platyrrhine *Aotes,* while other workers find six or seven laminae in the LGDs of diurnal platyrrhine monkeys (*Saimiri:* Doty et al., 1966; Tigges and Tigges, 1969a; *Ateles:* Jones, 1964; present research: Fig. 3).

WALLS' THEORY OF LGD LAMINATION

In 1953 Walls announced his brilliant *diageniculate path theory,* stating that the laminar structuring of the dorsal lateral geniculate nucleus allows for a segregation of functionally incompatible optic fiber types. Walls bases his theory upon experimental and ophthalmological evidence. The theory receives added support through the work of DeValois and Jones (1961), showing that cells of each of the three pairs of laminae in *Macaca mulatta* elicit a particular response to photic stimulation. On the other hand, it is unsubstantiated by Hubel and Wiesel (1964), who are unable to discern response differences between the pairs of parvocellular laminae in this species. As it stands, the theory offers a plausible and most refreshing explanation for geniculate lamination. It now remains for future experimentation to test the theory's validity.

Pretectal Nuclei

CYTOARCHITECTURE

In the present text, we follow the nomenclatural scheme of Rose (1942) in the sheep and confine our discussion to pretectal nuclei of known retinal innervation among mammals, viz., nn. tractus opticus, praetectalis anterior, and praetectalis posterior. Nucleus tractus opticus appears to correspond in man to n. lentiformis mesencephali pars magnocellularis of Kuhlenbeck and Miller (1949); in *Macaca* to the n. of the optic tract and n. suprageniculatus of Aronson and Papez (1934) or to a portion of regio pretectalis of Olszewski (1952); and in *Saimiri* to n. limitans of Emmers and Akert (1963). The retinal innervation of n. limitans as described in *Galago* (Campos-Ortega and Clüver, 1968) and *Saimiri* (Campos-Ortega and Glees, 1967b; Tigges and Tigges, 1969a) seems to lie within the boundaries of n. tractus opticus.

Nucleus praetectalis anterior of the present report is in man probably homologous to n. praetectalis of Kuhlenbeck and Miller (1949); in *Macaca* to n. prectectalis of Aronson and Papez (1934) and n. pretectalis anterior of Olszewski (1952); and in *Saimiri* to area praetectalis of Emmers and Akert (1963). Nucleus praetectalis posterior of the current report seemingly corresponds in man to n. dentiformis mesencephali pars parvocellularis of Kuhlenbeck and Miller (1949) and in *Saimiri* to n. praetectalis of Emmers and Akert (1963). The retinal innervation which Campos-Ortega and Clüver (1968) assign to their medial pretectal nucleus in *Galago* is probably confined to n. praetectalis posterior.

Kruger (1959) reports that the pretectal nuclear grouping is smaller and is less well developed in primates than in other major groups of mammals. A comparison of the pretectal nuclei as they appear in rabbit (Fig. 5) and in *Perodicticus* (Fig. 6) serves to illustrate this point. Nucleus tractus opticus, n. praetectalis anterior, and n. praetectalis posterior are seen to be enormous in rabbit but relatively small and unimposing in *Perodicticus*. In *Tupaia* these nuclei are well developed (Fig. 1) and therefore resemble the corresponding centers of nonprimate mammals rather than non-tupaiid primates.

RETINOPRETECTAL PROJECTION

Among mammals, the retinopretectal projection and its nuclei of termination show a parallel course of development. Nauta and Fink-Heimer degeneration studies reveal that rat (Hayhow et al., 1962), rabbit (Giolli and Guthrie, 1968), and *Tupaia* (Tigges, 1966; Campbell et al., 1967; present research) each has a massive retinopretectal projection providing innervation to three large, conspicuous nuclei, viz., nn. tractus opticus, praetectalis anterior, and praetectalis posterior (see Fig. 1 on *Tupaia*). By contrast, in our analysis of comparable studies on non-tupaiid primates we find a considerable reduction in the size of the retinopretectal projection in *Galago* (Campos-Ortega and Clüver, 1968; Tigges and Tigges, 1969), *Perodicticus* (present research), *Saimiri* (Campos-Ortega and Glees, 1967b; Tigges and Tigges, 1969a), and *Macaca cynomolgus* (present research). Furthermore we note in these forms a significant diminution in the extent of the retinopretectal input; i.e., in prosimians (*Galago* and

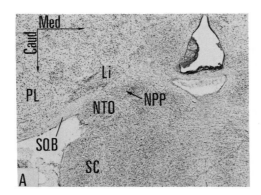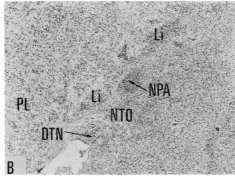

Figure 5. Horizontal Nissl sections through the pretectal nuclear grouping of the rabbit. Section (A) passes dorsal, section (B) ventral, through the nuclear grouping, x 11. The well-developed nature of the pretectal nuclei in rabbit does not characterize the corresponding centers of monkey (compare Fig. 5 with Fig. 6). LGD, dorsal lateral geniculate nucleus; MGd, pars dorsalis, medial geniculate nucleus; NPA, n. praetectalis anterior; NPP, n. praetectalis posterior; NSP, n. suprageniculatus praetectalis; NTO, n. tractus opticus; SC, superior colliculus; SQB, superior quadrigeminal brachium.

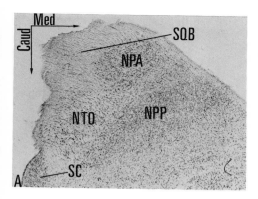
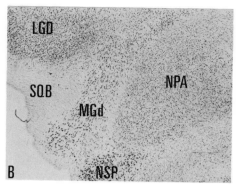

Figure 6. Horizontal Nissl sections through the pretectal nuclear grouping of *Perodicticus* 68-37. Section (A) passes dorsal, section (B) ventral, through the nuclear grouping, x 11. A comparison of Figure 5 with Figure 6 illustrates that corresponding pretectal nuclei are substantially larger and more highly developed in rabbit than in *Perodicticus*. DTN, dorsal terminal nucleus of accessory optic system; Li, n. limitans; NPA, n. praetectalis anterior; NPP, n. praetectalis posterior; NTO, n. tractus opticus; PL, pulvinar; SC, superior colliculus; SQB, superior quadrigeminal brachium.

Perodicticus) this input includes only n. tractus opticus and n. praetectalis posterior, and in anthropoids (*Saimiri* and *Macaca cynomolgus*) it is limited entirely to n. tractus opticus.

From current Fink-Heimer studies it is estimated that the contributions of contralateral and ipsilateral retinas to the retinopretectal ~ction achieve a ratio of 10:1 in *Tupaia* (Fig. 1) and 3:2 in both *Perodi~* ?) and *Macaca cynomolgus*. The contralateral and ipsilateral retinal · ese forms are differentially represented, and this is to be seen · ceptionally dense network of terminal degeneration i~ ?dicticus is particularly noteworthy (Fig. 7).

*FU^*

ERRATUM

PAGES 42 AND 43: The photomicrographs for Figures 5 and 6 are reversed.

he first to demon-
~ciated with the
~ö5). Their discovery
~ree decades the publication
~inopretectal projection in either
~t al., 1962; Meikle and Sprague, 1964;

o~
no~
Sim~

~tectal region of the mammalian brain participates
in visu~ ~ence, Thompson et al. (1963) report that bilateral
destructi~ ~tal region in rat and cat impairs a conditioned avoidance
response ~ ~y a light cue. And from experiments designed to show the effect
of subcorti~ ~ lesioning on visual behavior in monkey (after total striate-prestriate
cortical ablation), Pasik and Pasik (1965) and Pasik (1966) conclude that extra-

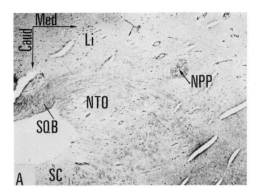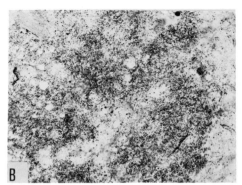

Figure 7. (A) Fink-Heimer section through the left contralateral pretectal region eight days after right eye enucleation in *Perodicticus* 68-37, x 24. This section is contiguous with the Nissl section represented in Figure 6A. Comprison of Figure 6A with 7A reveals that the dense network of degeneration indicated by an arrow in Figure 7A is confined to n. praetectalis posterior. (B) Detail from (A) showing that the dense network of Fink-Heimer degeneration within n. praetectalis posterior consists largely of degenerating fiber terminals, x 270. Li, n. limitans; NPP, n. praetectalis posterior; NTO, n. tractus opticus; SC, superior colliculus; SQB, superior quadrigeminal brachium.

geniculate vision requires the integrity of the lateral pretectal area but is unaffected by destruction of either the medial pretectal area or the superior colliculus.

Superior Colliculus

RETINOCOLLICULAR PROJECTION

Current knowledge of mammalian retinocollicular organization has been gained largely through investigations on nonprimate mammals (Hayhow et al., 1962; Meikle and Sprague, 1964; Siminoff et al., 1966) and *Tupaia* (Tigges, 1966; Campbell et al., 1967). In non-tupaiid primates the literature on this subject is relatively scant, and the observations of different researchers stand at odds. In *Saimiri*, Campos-Ortega and Glees (1967b; Nauta and Glees degeneration methods) report that the retino-collicular input is restricted to str. opticum, but Tigges and Tigges (1969a; Fink-Heimer degeneration method) present evidence favoring the view that this input is distributed over str. opticum, str. griseum superificale, and str. zonale. In *Galago*, Campos-Ortega and Clüver (1968; Nauta and Glees degeneration methods) describe the retinocollicular input as being scattered over str. opticum, str. griseum superificale, and str. zonale. Tigges and Tigges (1969; Fink-Heimer degeneration method), on the other hand, observe that, in large measure, this input forms a set of concealed laminae residing within str. griseum superificale.

The Fink-Heimer degeneration method is utilized in the present study to examine the retinocollicular projections of *Tupaia* and *Perodicticus*. In *Tupaia* the organizational plan as basically presented by Campbell et al. (1967) is confirmed. The contralateral input is massive, the ipsilateral one minute, and each input occupies the superficial four strata, viz., str. griseum intermedium, str. opticum, str. griseum superificale, and str. zonale (Fig. 1). In *Perodicticus* the contralateral and ipsilateral retino-collicular inputs attain a ratio of 2:1 (Fig. 2). These inputs in *Perodicticus*, as in a majority of mammals heretofore studied, provide innervation to the superficial three collicular strata. However, the representational pattern of these inputs in *Perodicticus* differs from the generalized mammalian case and resembles that noted in *Galago* (Tigges and Tigges, 1969). Specifically, retinocollicular innervation is heavily concentrated in the outer portion of str. griseum superificale rather than tending to be evenly distributed over the superifcal strata. The contralateral and ipsilateral retino-collicular inputs endow str. griseum superificale with a set of concealed, partially overlapping laminae (compare the two sides of the brain in Figs. 2 and 8) which in Figures 8A, B are denoted as substrata A and B respectively. It remains for future study to determine whether this special type of retinocollicular organization is unique to nocturnal prosimians or whether it is shared by either diurnal prosimians (e.g., *Lemur mongoz*) or the nocturnal anthropoid *Aotes*.

FUNCTIONAL CONSIDERATION

Current knowledge of the role of the superior colliculus in visually guided behavior has evolved largely from ablation type experiments. It has been shown that

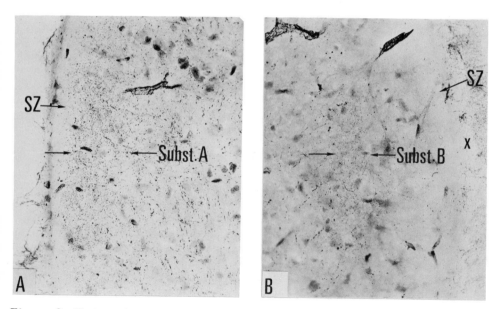

Figure 8. Horizontal sections through (A) left contralateral and. (B) right ipsilateral superior colliculus eight days after right ocular enucleation in *Perodicticus* 68-37, x 169. Differential innervation of str. griseum superficale by (A) contralateral and (B) ipsilateral retinal inputs results in a concealed laminar organization. Comparison of (A) with (B) indicates that the contralateral lamina (substratum A) is centered immediately superficial to the ipsilateral lamina (substratum B). The x in (B) lies at the surface of the superior colliculus. SZ, str. zonale.

visual discrimination remains essentially unimpaired following ablation of the striate cortex in rodents (Lashley, 1931; Ten Cate and van Herk, 1934) and in *Tupaia* (Snyder et al., 1966; Snyder and Diamond, 1968). In monkey, on the other hand, the classical studies of Klüver (1942) indicate that an animal deprived of its striate cortex is unable to discriminate visually much more than "total luminous energy," although the more recent investigations of Humphrey and Weiskrantz (1967) seem to cast some doubt on this conclusion by establishing that destriate monkeys can be taught to localize visual events in space.

Recent studies on monkeys provide evidence that the superior colliculus functions in the detection of movement. Humphrey (1968) reports that unit responses recorded in the monkey's colliculus to various types of visual stimuli are, with rare exceptions, to movement, and Anderson and Symmes (1968) find that the ability of monkeys to respond differentially to the rate of movement is dependent upon the integrity of the superior colliculus. From studying the unit responses in the superior colliculus of monkey to visual stimulation with red and blue light, Wolin et al. (1966) conclude that the colliculus functions in color discrimination. However, this finding remains unsubstantiated by the results of collicular ablation experiments on monkeys (Anderson and Symmes, 1969).

One of the functions attributed to the superior colliculus has been that of oculomotor control. As early as 1870, Adamük had demonstrated that electrical stimulation of the superior colliculus in dog and cat induces conjugate eye movements, and this finding, since confirmed in these species, has led to the hypothesis that a gaze center exists in the superior colliculus. Notwithstanding this finding, superior collicular ablation in both nonprimate mammals (see review of Pasik and Pasik, 1964) and primates (Pasik and Pasik, 1964; Anderson and Symmes, 1969) fails to produce any apparent oculomotor deficit.

Accessory Optic System

ACCESSORY OPTIC PROJECTION

An accessory optic system composed of crossed retinal fibers together with their pretectal and tegmental nuclei of termination has been amply described in a variety of mammalian forms (see reviews of Marg, 1964; Tigges, 1966; Hayhow, 1966).

The use of several different terminologies in describing the components of the mammalian accessory optic system had in the past resulted in a great deal of confusion. It was with the purpose of providing a clear understanding of the anatomical organization of this system that Hayhow and co-workers (Hayhow et al. 1960; Hayhow, 1966) devised their nomenclatural scheme (Fig. 9). According to this scheme the accessory optic system may consist of as many as two pairs of fiber groups (inferior and superior accessory optic fasciculi) together with three pairs of terminal nuclei (medial, lateral, and dorsal terminal nuclei), and a fully developed accessory optic system of this sort is to be found in the rat (Hayhow et al., 1960), rabbit (Giolli and Guthrie, 1969), and *Tupaia* (Tigges, 1966; Campbell et al., 1967; present research). Furthermore, in compliance with this scheme the cat, which lacks an inferior fasciculus

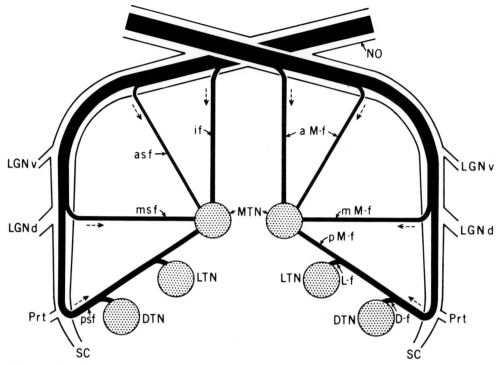

Figure 9. Diagrammatic representation of the organizational scheme of the accessory optic system as proposed by Hayhow and co-workers (1960, 1966) on the left and Tigges and Tigges (1969b) on the right. Broken arrows denote the direction of nerve propagation.

Abbreviations to Figure 9.

DTN, dorsal terminal nucleus of accessory optic system; LGNd, dorsal lateral geniculate nucleus; LGNv, ventral lateral geniculate nucleus; LTN, lateral terminal nucleus of accessory optic system; MTN, medial terminal nucleus of accessory optic system; NO, optic nerve; Prt, pretectal nuclei; SC, superior colliculus.

Left: scheme of Hayhow et al.	*Right: scheme of Tigges and Tigges*
if, inferior fasciculus	aM-f, anterior M-fibers
asf, anterior fibers, superior fasciculus	mM-f, middle M-fibers
msf, middle fibers, " "	pM-f, posterior M-fibers
psf, posterior fibers, " "	L-f, L-fibers
	D-f, D-fibers

(Hayhow, 1959), possesses a moderately reduced accessory optic system, and primates, which lack all components other than a foreshortened superior fasciculus innervating a lateral (and in some cases also a dorsal) terminal nucleus, have a markedly reduced system (Giolli, 1963; Campos-Ortega and Glees, 1967b; Campos-Ortega and Clüver, 1968; Tigges and Tigges, 1968, 1969a, b).

A second organizational scheme, one based upon the termination of accessory optic fibers, has recently been proposed by Tigges and Tigges, (1969b). This scheme (Fig. 9) depicts M-, L-, and D-fibers as terminating respectively in medial, lateral, and dorsal terminal nuclei. Comparison of the scheme of Hayhow and co-workers

with that of Tigges and Tigges brings out the following relationships (see Fig. 9):
The inferior fasciculus and the anterior and middle portions of the superior fasciculus
consist of M-fibers, while the posterior portion of the superior fasciculus is composed
of M-, L-, and D-fibers.

Great surprise has been expressed at Giolli's observation (1963; Nauta degeneration method) of an accessory optic system in *Macaca cynomolgus* which, contrary
to the condition in nonprimate mammals, is of drastically reduced dimensions and is
entirely wanting in M-fibers (see Hayhow, 1966). More recently, a reduced accessory
optic system of this type has been found in *Galago* (Campos-Ortega and Clüver, 1968;
Tigges and Tigges, 1968, 1969b; Laemle, 1968), *Perodicticus* (present research),
Nycticebus (Laemle, 1968; present research), and *Saimiri* (Campos-Ortega and Glees,
1967b; Tigges and Tigges, 1969a).

In *Tupaia*, the present findings are in accordance with the conclusions of Campbell et al. (1967) in showing the existence of a fully developed accessory optic system,
i.e., a system composed of two pairs of fiber groups and three pairs of terminal nuclei.
In keeping with the organizational plan of its entire primary optic system, *Tupaia*
has an accessory optic system which resembles that of rodents and lagomorphs rather
than non-tupaiid primates.

FUNCTIONAL CONSIDERATION

The content of the melatonin-forming enzyme hydroxyindole-O-methyl transferase
(HIOMT) in the rat pineal is subjected to a 24-hour rhythm (Axelrod et al., 1965)
which Moore et al. (1967) find to be interrupted by the selective destruction of the
bundle of anterior M-fibers. Quay (1966) reports a comparable 24-hour rhythm in
the HIOMT content of the pineal of *Macaca mulatta*. In monkey, however, anterior
M-fibers are lacking, and it is not apparent which primary optic projection is concerned
with the regulation of this rhythm.

Reference has already been made to the observation (Pasik and Pasik, 1965;
Pasik, 1966) that the lateral pretectal region, but neither the medial pretectal region
nor the superior colliculus, is concerned with extrageniculate vision in monkeys. In
a more current report Pasik (1968) offers reasonable assurance that it is the accessory
optic system which represents that portion of the lateral pretectal region implicated in
extrageniculate vision.

Giolli (1963) notes that the accessory optic fibers in *Macaca cynomolgus* arise
from the contralateral retina and are among the finest of the optic nerve fibers. He
postulates that the accessory optic fibers form part of an intercalated fiber system
whose input to the brain stem reticular formation affords one means of alerting to
objects within the central-temporal visual fields.

Other data of functional nature are presently unavailable on the accessory optic
system of primates. However, in the rabbit this system has yielded to electrophysiological study. Many of the physiological properties of this system have been elucidated
by Hamasaki and Marg (1960, 1962). In addition, Walley (1967) finds that the
rabbit accessory optic system is specialized for detecting movement directed vertically
within its visual fields, and Hill and Marg (1963) present evidence indicating that
this system in rabbit does not function in color discrimination.

Retinohypothalamic System

RETINOHYPOTHALAMIC PROJECTION

The existence of a retinohypothalamic projection in mammals has been a much debated subject which recently has been reviewed by Meikle and Sprague (1964), Feldman (1964), and Kiernan (1967). The vast majority of experimental-anatomical data argues against the existence of a mammalian retinohypothalamic projection, but a fair number of reports suggest the presence of such a projection, and figured prominently among these reports is the name of Frey (1950). From Marchi degeneration studies, this investigator describes his "dorsale hypothalamische Wurzel" splitting from the optic chiasma and terminating in the periventicular grey. Several authors have expressed the view (see Knoche, 1960) that Frey is mistakenly identifying the dorsalmost portion of the optic chiasma and not a retinohypothalamic fiber bundle.

It is in normal and experimental * brain series of several mammalian forms that Knoche (1956, 1957, 1960) and Blümcke (1958), both using the Bielschowsky silver method, describe their "retino-hypothalamische Bahn." These workers propose that the fibers in this bundle originate from the autonomic cells demonstrated in the retinal ganglionic cell layer by Becher (1954). The experimental evidence for the presence of this fiber bundle, i.e., the occurrence of fragmented and swollen fibers in Bielschowsky silver preparations, is, however, suspect. It seems probable that Knoche and Blümcke mistake incompletely impregnated normal fibers for degenerating ones, and it is noteworthy that in preparations stained by the closely related Glees silver method, Cowan and Powell (1956) report seeing fibers with degenerative appearances in central hypothalamic nuclei in normal monkey and man.

The existence of a complex system of retinohypothalamic neurons projecting to a variety of hypothalamic termini is suggested from the studies of Di Virgilio and Lavenda (1964) in reduced silver preparations of normal cat brains and of Ban et al. (1965) in Marchi series of experimental rabbit brains.

Among primates, Knoche (1956, 1957, 1960) alone describes a retinohypothalamic projection, and this he does in Bielschowsky series of normal human brain. Other studies using the Nauta or Fink-Heimer degeneration methods fail to show the presence of a retinal input to the hypothalamus in *Tupaia* (Tigges, 1966; present research), *Galago* (Campos-Ortega and Clüver, 1968; Laemle, 1968a; Tigges and Tigges, 1969), *Perodicticus* (present research), *Nycticebus* (Laemle, 1968a; present research), *Saimiri* (Campos-Ortega and Glees, 1967b), and *Macaca cynomolgus* (Giolli, 1963).

FUNCTIONAL CONSIDERATION

The present article will not include a review of the literature pertaining to the influence of light upon neuroendocrine function. It is therefore recommended that the interested reader consult the surveys on this subject edited by Hague (1964) and by Martini and Ganong (1966, 1967).

---

* The term "experimental" denotes the use of animals in which unilateral ocular enucleation had been performed prior to sacrifice.

REFERENCES

Adamük, E. 1870. Über die Innervation der Augenbewegungen. Zbl. Med. Wiss., 8:65-67.

Anderson, K. V., and D. Symmes. 1969. The superior colliculus and higher visual functions in the monkey. Brain Res. 13:37-52.

Aronson, L. R., and J. W. Papez. 1934. Thalamic nuclei of *Pithecus* (*Macacus*) *rhesus*. II. Dorsal thalamus. Arch. Neurol. Psychiat., 32:27-44.

Axelrod, J., R. J. Wurtman, and S. H. Snyder. 1965. Control of hydroxyindole-O-methyl transferase activity in the rat pineal gland by environmental lighting. J. Biol. Chem., 240:949-954.

Balado, M., and E. Franke. 1937. Das Corpus geniculatum evternum. Eine anatomisch-klinische Studie. Monogr. Gesamtgeb. Neurol. Psychiat. Foerster, O., ed. Heft 62.

Ban, T., T. Oki, and K. Zyo. 1965. An experimental study of the accessory optic system in the rabbit. Okajima Folia Anat. Jap., 40:625-645.

Becher, H. 1954. Über ein vegetatives, zentralnervöses Kerngebiet in der Netzhaut der Menschen und der Säugetiere. Acta Neuroveg. Wien), 8:421-436.

Blümcke, S. 1958. Zur Frage einer Nervenfaserverbindung zwischen Retina und Hypothalamus. 1. Anatomische und experimentelle Untersuchungen an Meerschweinchen und Katzen. Z. Zellforsch., 48:261-282.

Brooke, R. N. L., J. de C. Downer, and T. P. S. Powell. 1965. Centrifugal fibres to the retina in the monkey and cat. Nature (London), 207:1365-1367.

Brouwer, B., and W. P. C. Zeeman. 1925. Experimental anatomical investigations concerning the projection of the retina on the primary optic centres in apes. J. Neurol. Psychopath., 6:1-10.

———— and W. P. C. Zeeman. 1926. The projection of the retina in the primary optic neuron in monkeys. Brain, 49:1-35.

Bruesch, S. R., and L. B. Arey. 1942. The number of myelinated and unmyelinated fibers in the optic nerve of vertebrates. J. Comp. Neurol., 77:631-665.

Campbell, C. B. G., J. A. Jane, and D. Yashon. 1967. The retinal projection of the tree shrew and hedgehog. Brain Res., 5:406-418.

Campos-Ortega, J. A., and P. F. de V. Clüver. 1968. The distribution of retinal fibres in *Galago crassicaudatus*. Brain Res., 7:487-489.

———— and P. Glees. 1967a. The termination of ipsilateral and contralateral optic fibers in the lateral geniculate body of *Galago crassicaudatus*. J. Comp: Neurol., 129:279-284.

———— and P. Glees. 1967b. The subcortical distribution of optic fibers in *Saimiri sciureus* (squirrel monkey). J. Comp. Neurol., 131:131-142.

Chacko, L. W. 1948. An analysis of fibre-size in the human optic nerve. Brit. J. Ophthal., 32:457-461.

Cowan, W. M., and T. P. S. Powell. 1956. A note on terminal degeneration in the hypothalamus. J. Anat., 90:188-192.

———— and E. Wenger. 1968. The development of the nucleus of origin of centrifugal fibers to the retina in the chick. J. Comp. Neurol., 133:207-240.

Clark, W. E. Le Gros 1941. The lateral geniculate body in the platyrrhine monkeys. J. Anat., 76:131-140.

———— 1942. The visual centres of the brain and their connexions. Physiol. Rev., 22:205-232.

———— and G. G. Penman. 1934. The projection of the retina in the lateral geniculate body. Proc. Roy. Soc. [Biol.], 114:291-313.

Crevel, H. van, and W. J. C. Verhaart. 1963. The rate of secondary degeneration in the central nervous system. II. The optic nerve of the cat. J. Anat., 97:451-464.

DeValois, R. L., and A. E. Jones. 1961. Single-cell analysis of the organization of the primate color-vision system. *In* Jung, R., and H. Kornhuber eds. The Visual System: Neurophysiology and Psychophysics. Berlin, Göttingen, and Heidelberg, Springer Verlag, pp. 178-191.

Di Virgilio, G., and N. Lavenda. 1964. Preuves d'une représentation retinienne dans l'hypothalamus. Acta Opthal., 42:939-950.

Doty, R. W., M. Glickstein, and W. H. Calvin. 1966. Lamination of the lateral geniculate nucleus in the squirrel monkey, *Saimiri sciureus.* J. Comp. Neurol., 127:335-340.

Emmers, R., and K. Akert. 1963. A Stereotaxic Atlas of the Brain of the Squirrel Monkey (*Saimiri sciureus*). Madison, University of Wisconsin Press.

Feldman, S. 1964. Visual projections to the hypothalamus and preoptic area. Ann. N. Y. Acad. Sci., 117:53-68.

Feremutsch, K. 1963. Thalamus. *In* Hofer, H., A. H. Schultz, and D. Starck, eds. Primatologia II/2/6. Basel, Karger, pp. 2-226.

Fiedler, W. 1956. Übersicht über das System der Primaten. *In* Hofer, H., A. H. Schultz, and D. Starck, eds. Primatologia I/I. Basel, Karger, pp. 1-266.

Fink, R. P., and L. Heimer. 1967. Two methods for selective silver impregnation of degenerating axons and their synaptic endings in the central nervous system. Brain Res., 4:369-374.

Forrester, J., and A. Peters. 1967. Nerve fibres in the optic nerve of rat. Nature, 214: 245-247.

Frey, E. 1950. Neue anatomische und experimentelle Ergebnisse über das optische Gebiet im Hypothalamus. Schweiz. Arch. Neurol. Psychiat., 66:67-86.

Giolli, R. A. 1963. An experimental study of the accessory optic system in the *Cynomolgus* monkey. J. Comp. Neurol., 121:89-107.

———— and M. D. Guthrie. 1969. The primary optic projections in the rabbit. An experimental degeneration study. J. Comp. Neurol. 36:96-126.

Glees, P. 1961. Terminal degeneration and trans-synaptic atrophy in the lateral geniculate body of the monkey. *In* Jung, R., and H. Kornhuber, eds. The Visual System: Neurophysiology and Psychophysics. Berlin, Göttingen, and Heidelberg, Springer Verlag, pp. 104-110.

Glickstein, M. 1967. Laminar structure of the dorsal lateral geniculate nucleus in the tree shrew (*Tupaia glis*). J. Comp. Neurol., 131:93-102.

———— W. Calvin, and R. W. Doty. 1966. Laminar structure of the dorsal lateral geniculate body of *Saimiri* and *Tupaia.* Anat. Rec., 154:348.

Goodman, D. C. 1968. Personal communication.

Granit, R. 1955. Centrifugal and antidromic effects on ganglion cells of retina. J. Neurophysiol., 18:388-411.

Haddock, J. N., and L. Berlin. 1950. Transsynaptic degeneration in the visual system. Arch. Neurol. (Chicago), 64:66-73.

Hague, E., ed. 1964. Photo-neuro-endocrine effects in circadian systems. Ann. N. Y. Acad. Sci., 117:1-645.

Hamasaki, D., and E. Marg. 1960. Electrophysiological study of the posterior accessory optic tract. Amer. J. Physiol., 199:522-528.

———— and E. Marg. 1962. Microelectrode study of accessory optic tract. Amer. J. Physiol., 202:480-486.

Hassler, R. 1959. Anatomy of the thalamus. *In* Schaltenbrand, G., and P. Bailey, eds. Introduction to Stereotaxis with an Atlas of the Human Brain. Stuttgart, Thieme Verlag, 1:230-290.

———— 1965. Die zentralen Systems des Sehens. Berlin. Ophthal. Ges., 66:229-251.

———— 1966. Comparative anatomy of the central visual systems in day- and night-active primates. *In* Hassler, R., and H. Stephan, eds. Evolution of the Forebrain. Stuttgart, Thieme Verlag, pp. 419-434.

Hayhow, W. R. 1959. An experimental study of the accessory optic system in the cat. J. Comp. Neurol., 113:281-313.

———— 1966. The accessory optic system in the marsupial phalanger, *Trichosurus vulpecula.* An experimental degeneration study. J. Comp. Neurol., 126:653-672.

———— A. Sefton, and C. Webb. 1962. Primary optic centers in the rat in relation to the terminal distribution of the crossed and uncrossed optic nerve fibers. J. Comp. Neurol., 118:295-322.

———— C. Webb, and A. Jervie. 1960. The accessory optic fiber system in the rat. J. Comp. Neurol., 115:187-215.

Hess, C. 1907. Untersuchungen über die Ausdehnung des pupillomotorisch wirksamen Bezirkes der Netzhaut und über die pupillomotorischen Aufnahmeorgane. Arch. Augenh., 58:182-205.

Hill, R. M., and E. Marg. 1963. Single-cell responses of the nucleus of the transpeduncular tract in rabbit to monochromatic light on the retina. J. Neurophysiol., 26:249-257.

Hill, W. C. O. 1953. Primates. Comparative Anatomy and Taxonomy. I. Strepsirhini. Edinburgh, University of Edinburgh Press.

Hoyt, W. F., and O. H. Luis. 1962. Visual fiber anatomy in the infrageniculate pathway of the primate. Uncrossed and crossed retinal quadrant fiber projection studied with the Nauta stain. Arch. Ophthal. (Chicago), 68:94-106.

———— and O. H. Luis. 1963. The primate chiasma. Details of visual fiber organization studied by silver impregnation techniques. Arch. Ophthal. (Chicago), 70:69-85.

Hubel, D. H., and T. N. Wiesel. 1964. Responses of monkey geniculate cells to monochromatic and white spots of light. Physiologist, 7:162.

Humphrey, N. K. 1968. Responses to visual stimuli of units in the superior colliculus of rats and monkeys. Exp. Neurol., 20:312-340.

———— and L. Weiskrantz. 1967. Vision in monkeys after the removal of the striate cortex. Nature (London), 215:595-597.

Jones, A. E. 1964. The lateral geniculate nucleus of Ateles ater. J. Comp. Neurol., 123:205-210.

———— 1966. The lateral geniculate complex of the owl monkey Aotes trivirgatus. J. Comp. Neurol., 126:171-180.

Kiernan, J. A. 1967. On the probable absence of retino-hypothalamic connections in five mammals and an amphibian. J. Comp. Neurol., 131:405-408.

Klüver, H. 1942. Functional significance of the geniculostriate system. Biol. Symp., 7:253-299.

Knoche, H. 1956. Morphologisch-experimentelle Untersuchungen über eine Faserverbindung der Retina mit den vegetativen Zentren des Zwischenhirns und mit Hypophyse. Z. Zellforsch., 45:201-264.

———— 1957. Die retino-hypothalamische Bahn von Mensch, Hund und Kaninchen. Z. Mikr. Anat. Forsch., 63:461-486.

———— 1960. Ursprung, Verlauf und Endigung der retino-hypothalamischen Bahn. Z. Zellforsch., 51:658:704.

Kruger, L. 1959. The thalamus of the dolphin (Tursiops truncatus) and comparison with other mammals. J. Comp. Neurol., 111:133-194.

Kuhlenbeck, H., and R. N. Miller 1949. The pretectal region of the human brain. J. Comp. Neurol., 91:369-408.

Kupfer, C. 1965. The distribution of cell size in the lateral geniculate nucleus of man following transneuronal cell atrophy. J. Neuropath. Exp. Neurol., 24:653-661.

———— L. Chumbley, and J. de C. Downer. 1967. Quantitative histology of optic nerve, optic tract and lateral geniculate nucleus of man. J. Anat., 101:393-401.

Laemle, L. K. 1967. Retinal projections of Tupaia, Nycticebus, Galago and Saimiri. Anat. Rec., 157:273-274.

———— 1968a. Visual pathways of the lemurs. Anat. Rec., 160:380-381.

———— 1968b. Retinal projections of Tupaia glas. Brain, Behavior and Evolution. 1:473-499.

Lashley, K. S. 1931. The cerebral areas necessary for pattern vision in the rat. J. Comp. Neurol., 53:419-478.

Magoun, H. W., and S. W. Ranson. 1933. The central path of the pupillo-constrictor reflex in response to light. Arch. Neurol. (Chicago), 30:1193.

———— and S. W. Ranson. 1935. The afferent path of the light reflex. A review of the literature. Arch. Ophthal. (Chicago), 13:862-874.

Marg, E. 1964. The accessory optic system. Ann. N. Y. Acad. Sci., 117:35-52.

Martini, L., and W. F. Ganong, eds. 1966-67. Neuroendocrinology. New York and London, Academic Press, Inc. 2 vols.

Matthews, M. R., W. M. Cowan, and T. P. S. Powell. 1960. Transneuronal cell degeneration in the lateral geniculate nucleus of the macaque monkey. J. Anat., 94: 145-169.

McKenna, M. C. 1966. Paleontology and the origins of the primates. Folia Primat. (Basel), 4:1-25.

Meikle, T. H., and J. M. Sprague. 1964. The neural organization of the visual pathways in the cat. Int. Rev. Neurobiol., 6:149-189.

Minkowski, M. 1920. Über den Verlauf, die Endigung und die zentrale Repräsentation von gekreuzten und ungekreuzten Sehnervenfasern bei einigen Säugetieren und beim Menschen. Schweiz. Arch. Neurol. Psychiat., 6:201-252.

Moore, R. Y., A. Heller, R. J. Wurtman, and J. Axelrod. 1967. Visual pathway mediating pineal response to environmental light. Science. 155:220-223.

Nauta, W. J. H., and P. A. Gygax. 1954. Silver impregnation of degenerating axons in the central nervous system. A modified technic. Stain Techn., 29:91-93.

Niimi, K., T. Kanaseki, and T. Takimoto. 1963. The comparative anatomy of the ventral nucleus of the lateral geniculate body in mammals. J. Comp. Neurol., 121: 313-324.

Ogden, T. E., and R. F. Miller. 1966. Studies on the optic nerve of the rhesus monkey: nerve spectrum and physiological properties. Vision Res., 6:485-506.

Okamura, N. 1957. On the development of the medial and lateral geniculate body in man. (In Japanese). Arb. II. Abt. Anat. Inst. Univ. Tokushima, 2:129-216.

Olszewski, J. 1952. The Thalamus of the *Macaca mulatta*. New York, Karger.

Pasik, P., and T. Pasik. 1964. Oculomotor functions in monkeys with lesions of the cerebrum and the superior colliculi. *In* Bender, M. B., ed. The Oculomotor System. New York, Harper & Row, Publishers. pp. 40-80.

———— and T. Pasik. 1965. Visual behavior of monkeys with occipital lobe lesions. 8th Int. Cong. of Neurol., pp. 127-130.

Pasik, T. 1966. Extrageniculate vision in the monkey: critical structure. Fed. Proc., 25:574.

———— 1968. Extrageniculate vision in the monkey: importance of the accessory optic system (A. O. S.), Fed. Proc., 27:637.

Polyak, S. 1957. The Vertebrate Visual System. Klüver, H., ed. Chicago, University of Chicago Press.

Quay, W. B. 1966. 24-hour rhythms in pineal 5-hydroxytryptamine and hydroxyindole-O-methyl transferase activity in the macaque. Proc. Soc. Exp. Biol. Med., 121:946-948.

Ramón y Cajal, S. 1928. Degeneration and Regeneration in the Nervous System. London, Oxford University Press, vol. 2.

Remane, A. 1956. Paläontologie und Evolution der Primaten. Besonders der Nichthominiden: *In* Hofer, H., A. H. Schultz, and D. Strack, eds. Primatologia I/2. Basel, Karger, pp. 267-378.

Rose, J. E. 1942. The thalamus of the sheep: Cellular and fibrous structure and comparison with pig, rabbit and cat. J. Comp. Neurol., 77:469-524.

Siminoff, R., H. O. Schwassmann, and L. Kruger. 1966. An electrophysiological study of the visual projection to the superior colliculus of the rat. J. Comp. Neurol., 127: 435-444.

———— H .O. Schwassmann, and L. Kruger. 1967. Unit analysis of the pretectal nuclear group in the rat. J. Comp. Neurol., 130:329-342.

Simpson, G. G. 1945. The principles of classification and a classification of mammals. Bull. Amer. Mus. Nat. Hist., 85:1-350.

Snyder, M., and I. T. Diamond. 1969. The organization and function of the visual cortex in the tree shrew. Brain, Behavior and Evolution. 1:244-288.

———— W. Hall, and I. T. Diamond. 1966. Vision in tree shrews (*Tupaia glis*) after removal of striate cortex. Psychon. Sci., 6:243-244.

Spinelli, D. N., K. H. Pribram, and M. Weingarten. 1965. Centrifugal optic nerve responses evoked by auditory and somatic stimulation. Exp. Neurol., 12:303-319.

Ten Cate, J., and A. W. H. van Herk. 1934. Beobachtungen an Kaninchen nach Exstirpationen im Neopallium. Arch. néerl. Physiol., 18:337-386.

Thompson, R., H. Lesse, and I. Rich. 1963. Dissociation of visual and auditory habits following pretectal lesions in rats and cats. J. Comp. Neurol., 121:161-171.

Tigges, J. 1966. Ein experimenteller Beitrag zum subkortikalen optischen System von *Tupaia glis*. Folia Primat., 4:103-123.

———— and M. Tigges. 1968. The accessory optic system in *Galago crassicaudatus* (primates). Anat. Rec., 160:441.

———— and M. Tigges. 1969a. The accessory optic system and other optic fibers of the squirrel monkey. Folia Primat. 10:245-262.

———— 1969b. The accessory optic system in *Erinaceus* (Insectivora) and *Galago* (Primates). J. Comp. Neurol., 137:59-70.

Tigges, M., and J. Tigges. 1969. Retinal projection in *Gallago crassicaudatus* (Primates). Anat. Rec., 163:274-275.

Van Buren, J. M. 1963a. The Retinal Ganglion Cell Layer. Springfield, Ill., Charles C Thomas, Publisher.

———— 1963b. Trans-synaptic retrograde degeneration in the visual system of primates. J. Neurol. Neurosurg. Psychiat., 26:402-409.

Van Valen, L. 1965. Treeshrews, primates, and fossils. Evolution, 19:137-151.

Walley, R. E. 1967. Receptive fields in the accessory optic system of the rabbit. Exp. Neurol., 17:27-43.

Walls, G. L. 1953. The lateral geniculate nucleus and visual histophysiology. Berkeley and Los Angeles, Univ. Calif. Publ. Physiol., 9:1-100.

Wolin, L. R., L. C. Massopust, and J. Meder. 1966. Differential color responses from the superior colliculus of squirrel monkeys. Vision Res., 6:637-644.

Wolter, J. R. 1965. The centrifugal nerves in the human optic tract, chiasm, optic nerve, and retina. Trans. Amer. Ophthal. Soc., 63:678-707.

———— and O. E. Lund. 1968. Reaction of centrifugal nerves in the human retina. Amer. J. Ophthal., 66:221-232.

3

Structural and Functional Aspects of the Visual Pathways of Primates*

CHARLES R. NOBACK *and* LOIS K. LAEMLE †

Departments of Anatomy,
College of Physicians and Surgeons,
Columbia University,
New York, New York 10032
and
Albert Einstein College of Medicine
of Yeshiva University,
Bronx, New York 10461

Introduction

Recent investigations have contributed significantly to a more meaningful appreciation of the dynamics of the optic pathways in primates—an order of mammals comprised of species basically oriented and geared to the visually sensed environment. The primary purpose of this review is to present some major advances in the neuro-ultrastructure, neuroanatomy, and neurophysiology as they relate to the structure and function of the retina, the retinogeniculate pathway, the dorsal lateral geniculate body, and the visual cortex. Essentially all of these advances have been based upon studies of but a few species of primates. As a consequence, future researches must be made on the many diverse groups of prosimians and simians before a relatively complete account of the optic system in the primates will be attained.

The Retina

DERIVATION OF THE RETINA

The retina and certain adjacent regions of the iris and the ciliary body are embryologically derived from the optic cup, an outgrowth of the neural tube. The

* This review was supported by United States Public Health Service Grants NB-3473, 5TI-GM-256 and GM-00102.
† With the assistance of Derwent Grubb.

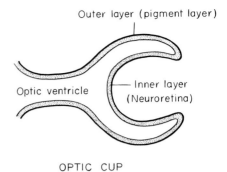

OPTIC CUP

Figure 1. The optic cup, an outgrowth of the forebrain, comprises an outer layer, which differentiates into the pigment epithelium of the retina, and an inner layer, which differentiates into the neuroretina. Note the optic ventricle which, in the embryo, is continuous with the ventricular system.

inner layer and the outer layer of the optic cup are composed of ependymal cells. The cavity between these two layers of the optic cup is the optic ventricle, which is continuous with the ventricle of the embryonic brain (Fig. 1). Adjacent ependymal cells are attached to each other at their luminal surfaces (facing the original optic ventricle) by the juxtaluminal junctional complexes consisting of terminal bars and tonofibrils. The outer layer of the optic cup differentiates into the pigment layer of the retina and the inner layer into the neural retina (neuroretina).

During subsequent development, the optic ventricle becomes totally obliterated by the interdigitation of cytoplasmic extensions of the pigment cells with extensions of the rods, cones, and glial cells of Müller of the receptor layer of the retina. The site of the original luminal lining of the optic ventricle persists in the fully differentiated retina as (1) the external limiting membrane, the junctional complexes between adjacent cells of the pigment epithelium; and (2) the internal limiting membrane, actually the junctional complexes between the rods, cones, and glial cells of Müller (Fig. 2). The ventricular lumen is indicated by the region within the retina between the external limiting membrane and the internal limiting membrane (Cohen, 1963, 1965).

PIGMENT EPITHELIUM (Fig. 2)

The interface between the pigment epithelium and the receptor layer of the neuroretina is filled by a laminar film of mucoid substance. Only at the optic disk and the ora serrata are there structural connections between these two layers (Cohen, 1963). A cleavage of the retina (detached retina) may occur at the pigment epithelium—receptor layer junction. This retinal detachment "recreates" the cavity of the original optic ventricle.

The pigment granules of the pigment epithelium, a form of melanin, are synthesized within the endoplasmic reticulum of these cells (Moyer, 1961). The pigment granules are concentrated in the inner portions of the cells (adjacent to the receptor layer), including the microtubular (microvilli) processes that interdigitate between the outer segments of the rods and cones. It has not been established whether the pigment granules within the microtubules are redistributed during adaptation to the cell proper by intracellular streaming or by the retraction of the tubules. The pigment absorbs light rays.

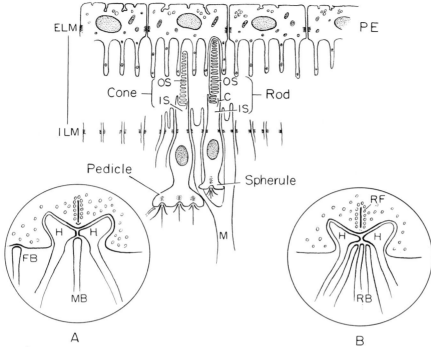

Figure 2. Schematic diagram of the ultrastructural organization of part of the retina, illustrating the relation of pigment epithelium, rods, cones, and Müller's cells. Insert A illustrates synaptic contacts of a cone pedicle with horizontal cells, midget bipolar cells, and flat bipolar cell. Insert B illustrates synaptic contacts of a cone spherule with rod bipolar cells and horizontal cells. The inner limiting membrane and outer limiting membrane are actually the lines of tight junctions. The region between these two membranes represents the original optic ventricle. C, cilium; ELM, external limiting membrane; FB, dendrite of flat bipolar cell; H, terminal of horizontal cell; ILM, internal limiting membrane; IS, inner segment; M, Müller's cell; MB, dendrite of midget biopolar cell; OS, outer segment; PE, pigment epithelium; RB, dendrite of rod bipolar cell; RF ribbon filament. Adapted from Dowling, J. E., and B. B. Boycott. 1966. Proc. Roy. Soc. Biol., 166: 80-111; and Cohen, A. I. 1963. Biol. Rev., 38:427-459.

RECEPTORS: RODS AND CONES (Fig. 2)

The primary receptors are the rods (rod cells) and the cones (cone cells). The rods are generally thin cylindrical cells, especially in the periphery of the retina; they respond to weak light stimuli. The cones are often broader, with a thick inner segment and a conical outer segment specialized to respond to bright light and differentially to various wavelengths. Cones have a functional role in fine detail discrimination and in color vision. The precise identification of a rod and a cone exclusively on the basis of morphological criteria may be tenuous, and it may have to be modified or reevaluated (Pedler and Tilly, 1965; and others).

Each rod (or cone) is composed of an outer segment, narrow neck, inner segment, fiber with a body, and a synaptic base (Fig. 2). The photopigments are present in the outer segments of the rods and cones. Within these segments, the transduction and the genesis of the generator (receptor) potential take place. Transduction consists of the photochemical reactions in response to the stimulation by light. The outer segment is composed of a series of stacked laminated disks, which are derived by the infolding of the plasma membrane of the segment. Some disks in the cones retain their continuity with the plasma membrane, while others are pinched off from their plasma membrane (Cohen, 1961, a, b, c; and others). The photopigments are bound to the membranes of these disks. The disk membranes are constantly renewed. The photopigments are synthesized in the inner segment of rods and cones and then incorporated into the disk membrane at the base of the outer segment. The pigment and disk membrane are gradually displaced toward the apex of the outer segments, where they are ingested by the pigment cells (Young, 1967, in rat; Hall, Bok and Bacharach, 1969, in frog). The light-trapping efficiency of the outer segment is enhanced (1) by an increase in the amount of disk membrane and photopigment, and (2) by the orientation of the chromatophores of the photopigment molecules in the plane of the disks (Wald, Brown, and Gibbons, 1963). Rhodopsin is the photopigment of the rods of primates with a maximum scotopic sensitivity at about 500 nm (Wald and Brown, 1958; Wald, 1968).

The cones of man and the macaque monkey contain three photopigments, with each cone containing only one pigment (Marks, Dobelle, and MacNichol, 1964; Brown and Wald, 1964). The three pigments in the cones of man and of the macaque monkey are probably identical. Their peak maximum absorptions at approximately 435 nm, 535 nm, and 565 nm are respectively the blue, green, and red portions of the spectrum. The cones are called blue cones, green cones, and red cones. The red-sensitive pigment in man and in the macaque monkey is apparently iodopsin (Wald, 1968).

The narrow neck or connecting zone contains a true cilium which extends into the outer segment. The outer segment has been considered to be a modified cilium. Each cilium is composed of the typical nine pairs of circumferential filament doublets without the central pair of fibrils. It terminates in the outer end of the inner segment as a centriole (basal body) with a nearby secondary centriole. Mitochondria are numerous in the distal portion of the inner segment.

Each rod fiber (or cone fiber) is a protoplasmic extension that terminates as the synaptic base of the cell. The base of the cone is called a pedicle or end foot and that of a rod is called a spherule or end bulb. The pedicles and the spherules are in direct contact with each other (Cohen, 1965). These are interpedicle contacts, interspherule contacts and pedicle-spherule contacts. Granit (1962) states that rods and cones can be pragmatically distinguished (1) anatomically, by the presence of pedicles in cones and spherules in rods, and (2) physiologically, by the differences in their spectral response curves and adaptive properties.

NEURONS OF THE RETINA (Figs. 2, 3)

Several types of neurons are located in the retina of the primates: (1) bipolar neurons, (2) interneurons, and (3) ganglion cells. These neurons and their interconnections and linkages have been characterized on the basis of ultrastructural and

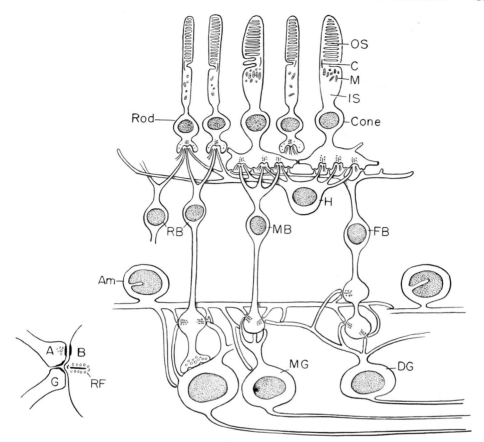

Figure 3. Schematic diagram of the ultrastructural organization of the retina. Insert on lower left illustrates dyad synaptic contacts of bipolar terminal, ganglion cell dendrite, and amacrine cell process. A, amacrine cell terminal; Am, amacrine cell; B, bipolar cell terminal; C, cilium of cone; DG, diffuse ganglion cell; FB, flat bipolar cell; G, ganglion cell terminal; H, horizontal cell; IS, inner segment; M, mitochondria; MB, midget bipolar cell; MG, midget ganglion cell; OS, outer segment; RB, rod bipolar cell; RF, ribbon filament. Adapted from Dowling, J. E., and B. B. Boycott. 1966. Proc. Roy. Soc. Biol., 166:80-111.

microscopical analyses of the retina of man and the macaque monkey (Missotten, 1965; Dowling and Boycott, 1966; Dowling, 1968; Boycott and Dowling, 1969; and others). The bipolar cells may be classified into three basic types: (1) rod (mop) bipolar cell (moplike tuft endings in the light microscope, Polyak, 1941), (2) midget bipolar cell, and (3) flat bipolar cell (Dowling and Boycott, 1966; and others). The types of interneurons include (1) the horizontal cell of the outer plexiform layer and (2) the amacrine cell (anaxonic neuron, cell without an axon) of the inner plexiform layer. The two basic types of ganglion cells are (1) the midget ganglion cell and (2) the diffuse ganglion cell.

Depending upon one's preference, the rods and cones may be classified as neurons of the retina or as neuroepithelial cells comparable to the hair cells of the organ of Corti of the ear. Apparently the many cell types previously described in the retina can be classified into one of the above cell types (Dowling and Boycott, 1966).

Synaptic organization of the pedicles of the cones and the spherules of the rods. Each cone pedicle has several invaginations. Within each invagination, three processes (triad) are usually found (Figs. 2, 3). The lateral two processes of the triad are the terminals of the horizontal cells (Missotten, 1960), and each lateral process of a triad is derived from a different horizontal cell. The central process is the dendritic terminal of a midget bipolar cell. This central process assumes a less deep position in the invagination (Missotten et al., 1963). The base of each pedicle makes superficial contacts with the dendritic terminals of processes of the flat bipolar cells. These synaptic contacts are not incorported within any triad.

Each rod spherule has a single invagination. Within each invagination are four to seven processes. The most common organization is that of two lateral processes (from the horizontal cells) and two or three central processes from rod bipolar cells (Missotten et al., 1963).

The spherules and pedicles contain presynaptic neurosecretory vesicles and synaptic ribbons (ribbon filament). Each ribbon points directly between two postsynaptic processes within the invaginations. This is assumed to be a synaptic complex (Missotten, 1960).

Bipolar cells (Fig. 3). Within the outer plexiform layer, each rod bipolar cell makes its synaptic contact as the central process of a triad associated with a rod spherule. Each rod spherule receives processes from several bipolar cells, and, in turn, each bipolar cell has processes which extend to several rod cell triads (Dowling and Boycott, 1966). Within the inner plexiform layer, the rod bipolar cells make axodendritic and axosomatic synaptic contacts with the diffuse ganglionic cells.

Each midget bipolar cell of the central retina makes synaptic contacts with only one cone. However, it does make synaptic contacts as the central element of several triads of each cone. Each midget bipolar cell makes numerous axodendritic synaptic contacts with one midget ganglion cell. It does not make any axosomatic synapses. Some synaptic contacts may be made with diffuse ganglion cells.

Each flat bipolar cell makes synaptic contacts with only the bases of the pedicles of cones. Each of these cells synapses with from five to nine cones—seven is the average in the macaque monkey (Dowling and Boycott, 1966). All contacts are superficial, and none are incorporated within a triad. The flat bipolar cells make axodendritic synaptic contacts with diffuse ganglion cells.

In summary, rods make synaptic contacts only with rod bipolar cells and horizontal cells, and cones make synaptic contacts only with midget bipolar cells, diffuse bipolar cells, and horizontal cells.

Interneurons (Fig. 3). The nerve fibers of the horizontal cells of the outer plexiform layer terminate as the lateral processes of the invaginations in the cone pedicles and the rod spherules. It is not possible to determine whether each process is a dendrite or an axon (Dowling and Boycott, 1966). The horizontal cells may be similar to amacrine cells, with each process being capable of both receiving and transmitting stimuli.

The amacrine cells have processes which make synaptic contacts in the inner plexiform layer with (1) each type of bipolar cell, (2) the processes of other amacrine cells, and (3) the dendrites and cell bodies of the ganglion cells. A characteristic synaptic complex of the inner plexiform layer is the dyad (Fig. 3). This is a complex comprised of three processes: amacrine cell process, ganglion cell dendrite, and bipolar cell axon terminal (Dowling and Boycott, 1966). Within the cytoplasm of the bipolar terminal is a synaptic ribbon. In this complex, the bipolar cell acts as a presynaptic neuron influencing, in the region of the synaptic ribbon, both the ganglion cell and the amacrine cell, while the amacrine cell also can act as a presynaptic terminal influencing the bipolar terminal. In this dyad, the bipolar terminal and the amacrine cell process form reciprocal synaptic contacts or junctions. These reciprocal contacts in the primate retina may have a significant role in visual adaptation (Dowling, 1967). In the Rhesus monkey, the amacrine cells contact other amacrine cells. In contrast, horizontal cells do not contact other horizontal cells.

Ganglion cells (Fig. 3). Each midget ganglion cell makes several synaptic contacts with but one midget bipolar cell. Each diffuse ganglion cell makes synaptic contacts with all types of bipolar cells (Dowling and Boycott, 1966). The ganglion cells have axons which project to the diencephalon and the midbrain.

Synaptic contacts. Many of the contacts between the cells of the retina do not exhibit the classical ultramicroscopic morphological features of typical synapses. On the assumption that the contacts are actually synapses, they are called synaptic contacts. As calculated by Dowling and Boycott (1966), the total number of synaptic contacts in the parafoveal area of the retina is approximately 2,900,000 contacts per square millimeter in man and 2,100,000 per square millimeter in the Rhesus monkey.

FUNCTIONAL ASPECTS OF THE RETINA

Light waves trigger the sequence of the transduction and the generation of the receptor potential in the rods and cones. Further processing occurs within the neuroretina. Ultimately the ganglion cells are adequately stimulated to project stimuli to the central nuclei of the diencephalon and midbrain. Only a few selected aspects of this activity will be discussed.

The delineated area in the visual field that may stimulate a ganglion cell of the retina (a neuron of the dorsal lateral geniculate body or a neuron of the visual cortex) is called the receptor field of that neuron ("cell's eye view of the environment"). The concept of receptive fields is analyzed by Jacobs (1969). In the retina the receptor field comprises those receptors (rods and cones) and other retinal neurons which influence one ganglion cell of the retina. The retina is a composite of as many receptor fields as there are ganglion cells. Each receptor field is roughly organized in two zones: a small circular zone, called the center, surrounded by a concentric zone, called the periphery or the surround. These two zones are functionally antagonistic (Kuffler, 1953).

With regard to the responses in the light-adapted eye, two general types of receptor fields include (1) receptor fields with an on-center and an off-surround and (2) receptors with an off-center and an on-surround. The on-center off-surround receptor field of a ganglion cell of the retina consists of a center which fires vigorously when the illumination comes on (or goes off) and of a surround which gives an antagonistic response (mutual inhibition between the two zones). The off-center on-surround receptor field responds in the opposite way. An intermediate zone between the center and the surround has been described (Kuffler, 1953). If the light stimuli are presented to the entire field of on and off zones, each stimulus tends to inhibit the response of the other.

The two types of receptive fields are apparently present in equal numbers in the retina of the spider monkey (Hubel and Wiesel, 1960). In this species the total size of each receptive field appears to be approximately the same over the entire retina. However, the relative size of the center to the surround changes. The closer to the fovea, the smaller is the size of the center zone of the receptor field. The size of the antagonistic surround appears to be the same from the periphery of the retina to the fovea. In the fovea, the center of the receptive fields may be the diameter of a foveal cone. In the Rhesus monkey, field centers as small as 2 degrees of arc (10 μ) have been reported at 1 or 2 degrees from the fovea (Wiesel and Hubel, 1966).

On the basis of the known ultramicroscopic morphology of the retina, the anatomical organization of the center surround receptive field has been proposed by Dowling and Boycott (1966). The on-center off-surround receptive field is taken as an example. The center of a receptive field is composed of a ganglion cell and the bipolar cells with which it is directly in synaptic contact (Fig. 3). The rod–bipolar cell–ganglion cell linkage apparently supplies the adequate stimulus for a ganglion cell to fire. The surround of this receptive field comprises the rod–bipolar cell–amacrine cell–ganglion cell linkage with the ganglion cell of the center of the receptive field. The bipolar cells of the surround do not have direct synaptic contacts with the ganglion cell of the center. The bipolar cells of the inhibitory surround exert inhibitory effects upon the ganglion cells via the amacrine cell. The summation of the on-center excitatory activity with the off-surround inhibitory activity is resolved as the ganglion cell responses noted by Kuffler (1953).

The mosaic of the retinal receptor fields has an additional intricacy built into its organization. On the basis of responses to light stimulation, Granit (1955) described two types of retinal ganglion cells, which he called dominator cells and modulator cells. The dominator cells respond to any combination of wavelengths of the visual spectrum, and they have a broad spectral sensitivity curve resembling a photopic (scotopic) luminosity function. These cells monitor and signal the intensity of the light and the relative degree of brightness and darkness. These cells have a similar functional role as the broad-band cells (spectrally-nonopponent cells) of the lateral geniculate body, to be noted below (DeValois, 1965a, b). The modulator cells respond differentially to light of different wavelengths, and they may be said to be color coded. They resemble the spectrally-opponent cells of the lateral geniculate body (DeValois, 1965a; Wiesel and Hubel, 1966).

The concept of the center–surround receptor fields applies to color vision responses in the lateral geniculate body of the Rhesus monkey (Hubel and Wiesel, 1964; Wiesel and Hubel, 1966; DeValois, Abramov, and Mead, 1967). On the assumption that this organization applies to the retina of the color perceptive primates, the center of a receptor field would respond maximally to a narrow portion of the visual spectrum (e.g., red), whereas the antagonistic surround would respond maximally to another narrow portion of the spectrum (e.g., green). Applying the concept of retinal organization of Dowling and Boycott (1966), the following is postulated by these investigators. The linkage of red cones (those cones with the photopigment sensitive to the red portion of the spectrum) to bipolar cells to ganglion cell comprises the red center of the receptive field. The linkage of green cones to bipolar cells to amacrine cells comprises the green surround to the red center. The amacrine cells of the surround, in turn, interact with the ganglion cells of the red center.

The spectrally-opponent concept (e.g., red center green surround) is discussed below with the lateral geniculate body.

Retinogeniculate Pathway

INFRAGENICULATE PATHWAYS OF THE RETINOFUGAL FIBERS TO THE DORSAL LATERAL GENICULATE BODY

Until recently, the information concerning the retinotopic organization of the retinofugal fibers within the optic nerve, chiasma, and tract of the monkey and man has been based upon the researches of Parsons (1902), Brouwer and Zeeman (1926), and Polyak's researches in the 1930s (1957). In a modern study, Hoyt and Luis (1962, 1963) have analyzed these projections in the Java macaque monkey (Macaca irus) based on accurately placed retinal lesions produced by a retinal photocoagulator and fiber tracings observed on Nauta technique stained preparations. Their results are briefly summarized below (Fig. 4).

The nonmacular fibers from the retina maintain their retinal topography throughout the optic nerve. The fibers from the upper and lower temporal quadrants (those with uncrossed central projections) retain their relative superior-inferior temporal positions within the optic nerve and optic chiasma until the optic tract is reached. At this site a complex inward 90-degree rotation occurs so that (1) the fibers of the upper quadrant shift medially from their dorsolateral location in the optic nerve to an inferior medial location in the optic tract, and (2) the fibers of the lower quadrant pass from their ventrolateral location in the optic nerve to an inferior lateral location in the optic tract. The fibers of the nasal quadrants (those with crossed central projections) retain their superior-inferior nasal positions within the optic nerve. As they decussate within the optic chiasma, the fibers of the lower quadrant shift from their inferior medial location in the optic nerve by crossing through the lower anterior aspect of the optic chiasma to a location on the ventrolateral aspect of the optic tract. Many of these inferior nasal fibers loop into the opposite optic nerve (Wildbrand's loop) before re-entering the chiasma (Fig. 4). The fibers of the upper nasal quadrant shift from their superior medial location in the optic nerve by passing through the dorsal layer of the chiasma, crossing in its posterior chiasmal aspect, and finally becoming located in the medial aspect of the optic tract.

The macular fibers pass through the central and peripheral regions of the optic nerve (located even in the regions occupied by fibers projecting from the paracentral and peripheral retina) until they reach the chiasma, where (1) the decussating fibers rise until they reach the superior aspect of the chiasma and the contralateral optic

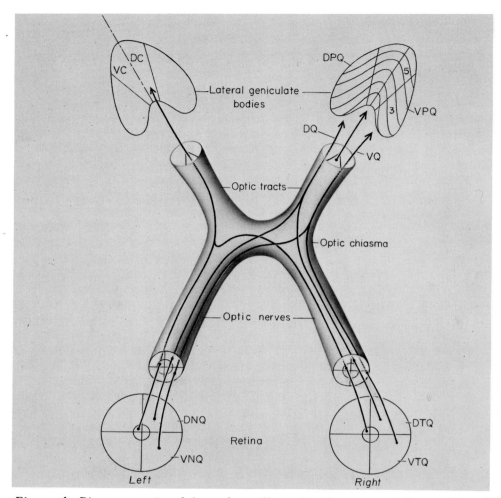

Figure 4. Diagram, as viewed from above, illustrating the course of the ganglion cell fibers projecting from the retina through the optic nerves, optic chiasma, and optic tracts to their terminations within the dorsal lateral geniculate bodies. The numbers 3 and 5 represent two of the six laminae of the lateral geniculate bodies. DC, region within the lateral geniculate body receiving projections from *dorsal central* regions of both retinas; DNQ, *dorsal nasal quadrant* of the retina; DPQ, region within the lateral geniculate body receiving projections from the *dorsal peripheral quadrants* of both retinas (DNQ of contralateral retina and DTQ of ipsilateral retina) ; DQ, fibers from the *dorsal peripheral quadrants* passing through the optic tract; DTQ, *dorsal temporal quadrant* of retina; VC, region within the lateral geniculate body receiving projections from *ventral central* regions of both retinas; VNQ, *ventral nasal quadrant* of retina; VPQ, region within lateral geniculate body receiving fibers from the *ventral peripheral quadrants* of both retinas (VNQ of contralateral retina and VTQ of ipsilateral retina) ; VQ, fibers from the *ventral peripheral quadrants* passing through the optic tract; VTQ *ventral temporal quadrant* of retina. Adapted from Hoyt, W., and O. Luis. 1962. Arch. Ophthal., 68:94-196.

tract, and (2) the nondecussating fibers rise and pass into the superior aspect of the ipsilateral optic tract. The total macular projection through the chiasma is so diffuse that Hoyt and Luis (1963) consider the chiasma to be basically a macular structure interspersed with and surrounded by extramacular fibers. The macular axons are mainly fine-calibered fibers, whereas the extramacular axons are primarily large-calibered fibers. The arrangement of the fibers in the optic tract is maintained throughout the optic tract to the lateral geniculate body.

OPTIC TRACT PROJECTIONS TO THE DORSAL LATERAL GENICULATE BODY

In the higher primates, the crossed fibers from the nasal hemiretina terminate in laminae 1, 4, and 6, and the uncrossed fibers from the temporal hemiretina terminate in laminae 2, 3, and 5 of the dorsal lateral geniculate body (LGB). The fibers of the upper nonmacular quadrants of the retina project to the medial aspect of the LGB, the fibers of the lower nonmacular quadrants project to the lateral aspect, and the fibers of the macular region project to the wedge-shaped sector of the upper posterior two-thirds region of the LGB (Fig. 4). This foveal projection is localized mainly in the parvocellular laminae 3, 4, 5, and 6 of the LGB and only slightly in the magnocellular laminae 1 and 2.

In man, the fibers from the temporal half of the macula project as uncrossed fibers to the ipsilateral LGB, and the fibers from the nasal half of the macula project as crossed fibers to the contralateral LGB (Kupfer, 1962). Glees, Hallerman, and Naeve (1964) contradict the view that corresponding quadrants of the retina terminate in a common half of the LGB.

Dorsal Lateral Geniculate Body

The dorsal lateral geniculate body of the primates and tupaiids is characteristically laminated into four to six layers (reviewed by Polyak, 1957; Noback and Moskowitz, 1963; Giolli and Tigges, 1970; Kanagasuntheram, Krishnamurti, and Wong, 1969). The retinal projections to the LGB are highly organized and have a sharply defined topographic representation. Minute lesions within the retina result in transneuronal degeneration changes limited to small, well-defined clusters of cells (Clark and Penman, 1934; Polyak, 1957). These transneuronal changes in the LGB of the Rhesus monkey are more rapid and of greater severity than are those in cat and rabbit (Matthews, Cowan, and Powell, 1960).

Each neuron of the LGB receives direct input from the retina and, in turn, projects directly to the striate cortex (area 17). Convergence and divergence are exhibited within this nucleus. Each retinofugal fiber synapses with several LGB neurons (divergence), and each LGB neuron receives input from several retinofugal fibers (convergence). The general mode of the termination of the retinofugal fibers within either the parvocellular layers or the magnocellular layers is essentially similar (demonstrated in the Rhesus monkey and the baboon by Glees, 1961). The relative sizes of the large cells in the magnocellular layers as compared to small cells in the parvocellular layers are probably differences related to the output projections rather than the differences in input (Glees, 1961). The evidence suggests that slight, if any, interactions occur between any two adjacent laminae (Granit, 1962).

At present, there is no experimentally substantiated reason for the number and arrangement of the laminae (laminar pattern) in the LGB in any mammal. Differences in the laminar patterns of the LGB and in color vision among the various taxonomic groupings of primates, namely the anthropoids, prosimians, tarsioids, and tupaiids, are probably the expression of the independent evolution of these features in these groups (Noback, Berger, Laemle, and Shriver, 1969).

Data concerning the number of neurons in the LGB of primates are sparse. The total number of neurons in the LGB of *Macaca mulatta* was reported to be 1,143,134 (Chow, Blum, and Blum, 1950) and of man to be 1,200,000 (Chacko, 1948) and 1,143,000 (Kupfer, Chumbley, and Downer, 1967). The latter authors noted 47,490 neurons in lamina 1; 15,010 in lamina 2; 426,890 in laminae 3 and 5; 553,610 in laminae 4 and 6; 601,100 in laminae 1, 4, and 6; and 441,100 in laminae 2, 3 and 5.

The LGB receives afferent input from sources other than the retina. The precise source of all these fibers remains to be determined. Multiple sensory projections to the LGB of the cat from nonvisual sources (e.g., auditory fibers) have been reported (Spinelli, Starr, and Barrett, 1968). Fibers projecting from the striate cortex to the LGB are demonstrable in the Rhesus monkey and galago (Beresford, 1962; Campos-Ortega, 1968). Until recently, the LGB was thought to receive its retinal input exclusively through axosomatic synapses (Glees, 1940; Glees and Clark, 1941). The electron microscopic studies of the normal and the deafferented LGB of the Rhesus monkey by Colonnier and Guillery (1964), Glees, Meller, and Eschner (1966), and Campos-Ortega, Glees, and Neuhoff (1968) have modified this view.

The fine structure of the LGB of the Rhesus monkey is summarized in Figure 5. The retinofugal fibers from the ganglion cells of the retina make four types of synaptic connections with the neurons of the LGB (Campos-Ortega, Glees, and Neuhoff, 1968; Colonnier and Guillery, 1964): (1) axosomatic synapses, (2) axodendritic synapses with both the primary stem dendrites (immediate extensions of the cell body) and secondary dendrites, (3) *boutons en passage*, and (4) complex glomerular endings (glomeruli).

The glomerulus is a synaptic complex of interlocking nerve processes of various origins. It consists of an enlarged axon terminal (retinofugal fiber) and other nerve processes located at the bifurcation of two stem dendrites of an LGB neuron. The glomerular complex includes (1) axodendritic synapses located (a) on the trunks of stem dendrites, secondary dendrites, and peripheral dendrites and (b) on the spines (thorns) of secondary dendrites and (2) axoaxonic synapses in which the presynaptic portion is contributed by the terminal of the retinofugal fiber.

Other terminal fibers are from unknown, probably nonretinal, sources. These include (1) small diameter axons that synapse with secondary dendrites (these may be striatogeniculate fibers; Guillery, 1967); (2) medium-sized axons that form axoaxonic synapses with the dendrites of the LGB neurons (Campos-Ortega, 1968)—the latter are the SD endings of Colonnier and Guillery (1964); (3) axons that form the postsynaptic element of an axoaxonic synapse; and (4) collateral axons of the efferent

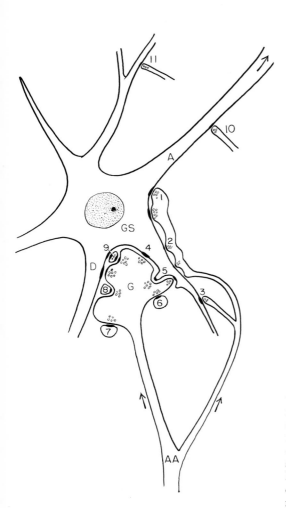

Figure 5. Schematic diagram of the ultrastructural organization of the lateral geniculate body in the rhesus monkey. The neuron (GS) is a geniculate neuron with an axon (A) projecting to the striate cortex. The axon (AA) is a terminal of a retinal ganglion cell. It is represented with one branch (to the right) forming several classical type synapses and another branch terminating as a bulbous ending (G). The bulbous ending is the central element of the glomerulus. The right axonal branch with its nonglomerular endings forms (1) an axosomatic synapse, (2) a synaptic *bouton en passage,* and (3) an axodendritic synapse. The glomerulus is a complex synaptic structure comprised of several types of synapses: (4) an axodendritic synapse, (5) an axodendritic synapse with the thorn of a dendrite, (6) an axodendritic synapse with an another neuron (possibly an interneuron), (7) an axoaxonic synapse with presynaptic element of synapse on bulbous ending, (8) an axodendritic synapse with dendrite of another geniculate neuron, and (9) an axonal thorn forming an axoaxonal synapse with the bulbous ending and axodendritic synapse with geniculate neuron. An axoaxonic synapse (10) is present on the axon (A) of the geniculostriate neuron. The axon of the axodendritic synapse (11) is the terminal of a neuron with its cell body in the striate cortex. The presynaptic element of a synapse contains presynaptic vesicles. D, dendrite; arrow indicates direction of nerve impulse. Adapted from Colonnier, M. L., and R. W. Guillery. 1964. Z. Zellforsch., 62:333-355; and Campos-Ortega, J. A., P. Glees, and V. Neuhoff. 1968. Z. Zellforsch., 87:82-100.

axon of an LGB neuron that projects to the visual cortex—this axon is the presynaptic element of an axoaxonic synapse. Golgi type II interneurons are present within the LGB (Szentágothai, 1967; Campos-Ortega, 1968). The precise manner in which the interconnections within the lateral geniculate body process the input from the receptive fields of the retina and, in turn, project the informational patterns to the striate cortex has yet to be determined.

NEUROPHYSIOLOGICAL ASPECTS

The neurons of the LGB and of the striate cortex are neurophysiologically different from the ganglion cells of the retina. The former exhibit greater irregularity in
their spontaneous activity (Spinelli, Starr, and Barrett, 1968). The neurons of the
LGB are similar to typical afferent neurons in that they are more excitable than motor
neurons (Bishop, 1964). In the light adapted state, the receptive field of an LGB
neuron is, like that of a retinal ganglion cell, circular in shape. Most receptive fields
are organized as on-center off-surround systems or as off-center on-surround systems.
Hubel and Wiesel (1966) noted an observable difference between the neurophysiological response of an LGB neuron and that of a retinal ganglion cell. The effectiveness of the surround of a receptive field in antagonizing the center is greater at the
geniculate level. As a consequence, the response of an LGB neuron is weaker than
that obtained from a retinal ganglion cell after the eye is exposed to a diffuse light.
Because the center and the surround are so closely antagonistically balanced, some
LGB neurons exhibit little, if any, response after exposure to diffuse light (Hubel and
Wiesel, 1966).

BROAD-BAND CELLS (SPECTRALLY-NONOPPONENT CELLS) AND
SPECTRALLY-OPPONENT CELLS

With respect to their response to different wavelengths, the neurons of the LGB
have been analyzed in the Rhesus monkey, an animal whose color vision is apparently
identical with that of man (DeValois, 1965a, b; Wiesel and Hubel, 1966; DeValois
and Jacobs, 1968), and in the catarrhine monkeys, *Saimiri* and *Cebus*, by Jacobs
(De Valois and Jacobs, 1968). On the basis of the responses evoked following the
diffuse stimulation of the retina with monochromatic light, two basic types of neurons
have been proposed: (1) broad-band cells (spectrally-nonopponent cells) and (2)
spectrally-opponent cells (DeValois, 1965a, b). The broad-band cells of the LGB
respond uniformly to all wavelengths and to white light. The spectrally-opponent
cells of the LGB are differentially sensitive to lights of different wavelengths. These
latter cells are presumed to be concerned with color vision. They are color coded.

Two types of broad-band cells have been described: excitatory neurons and inhibitory neurons. These neurons are responsive and sensitive to the luminosity of the
light stimuli (Jacobs, 1965a, b). They monitor whiteness and blackness. Some broad-
band neurons respond to stimulation of all wavelengths of light or white light by
increasing their firing rate (excitatory neurons), and others respond by decreasing
their firing rate (inhibitory neurons) relative to their normal spontaneous rate in a
dark environment. These neurons are links in the pathway monitoring the brightness
of light (DeValois and Jacobs, 1968). They are called spectrally-nonopponent cells
because they do not produce opposing responses to light at other regions of the light
spectrum.

The spectrally-opponent (color-coded) cells exhibit a differential sensitivity to
different wavelengths of light. The firing rate of a specific cell increases in response to
certain portions of the visual spectrum and decrease in response to other portions of
the spectrum. The spectrally-opponent cells exhibit excitatory responses to some wave-

lengths and inhibitory responses to other wavelengths. They are called spectrally-opponent cells because of the opposing responses to stimulation by light from opposite ends of the spectrum (DeValois and Jacobs, 1968). The peak sensitivities of these opponent systems in the LGB are similar to the peak absorption spectra for the three cone receptors of the Rhesus monkey's retina (Marks, Dobelle, and MacNichol, 1964; Wald, 1968).

Wiesel and Hubel (1966) characterized four types of spectrally-opponent cells in the LGB of the Rhesus monkey. Type I, type II, and type III are located in the parvocellular layers and type IV in the magnocellular layers. The type I neurons exhibit their responses in light adapted eyes to diffuse stimulation. In order of frequency, the five varieties of type I cells are (1) red on-center, green off-surround, (2) red off-center, green on-surround, (3) green on-center, red off-surround, (4) green off-center, red on-surround, and (5) blue on-center, green off-surround. It is postulated that the center is most directly connected with one of the three types of cones, and the surround is less directly connected with another of the three types of cones. The few type II neurons receive opponent inputs from two sets of cones with identical distributions. These are (1) green-on blue-off and (2) green-off and blue-on. The type III cells are organized with the center and the surround having identical spectral sensitivities. These neurons probably receive their input from several types of cones. Within the ventral magnocellular layers are two types of neurons including (1) cells similar to type III and (2) a type IV cell with a center-surround field with spectral sensitivity of the surround displaced to the red with respect to the center.

DeValois (1965a, b) and DeValois, Abramov, and Mead (1967) characterize four types of spectrally-opponent neurons. These include (1) red excitatory, green inhibitory cells, (2) yellow excitatory, blue inhibitory cells, (3) green excitatory, red inhibitory cells, and (4) blue excitatory, yellow inhibitory cells. This division represents the four basic ways in which the three cone types are linked together (DeValois and Jacobs, 1968). These authors conclude that the relative contribution of these opponent cells to the total LGB responses at a given wavelength approximates the human function for color appreciations across the spectrum.

COLOR VISION IN THE PRIMATES

The primates, including man, the anthropoid apes, the diurnal New World monkeys and the diurnal Old World monkeys, are presumed to possess color vision (Trendelenberg and Schmidt, 1930; Grether, 1939; Miles, 1958; DeValois, 1965a, b; Wiesel and Hubel, 1966; DeValois and Jacobs, 1968). In addition, the diurnal tree shrew, *Tupaia glis,* has color vision (Tigges, 1963; Shriver and Noback, 1967; Polson, unpublished). Many diurnal species of primates have not, as yet, been investigated.

On the basis of behavioral and physiological studies of the Rhesus monkey and the squirrel monkey, DeValois and Jacobs (1968) analyze the status of color vision in these species. The Rhesus monkeys (*Macaca irus* and *Macaca nemestrina*) and normal humans have essentially the same trichromatic vision. On the other hand, squirrel monkeys have poorer color vision that is qualitatively different from normal human trichromats but similar to protanomalous humans (weakness in the red system of trichromatic color vision). This difference in color vision of man and Old World monkeys (*Macaca*) from that of New World monkeys (*Saimiri* and *Cebus*) is the primary basis for the suggestion of DeValois and Jacobs (1968) that basic differences exist between these two major branches of primates. The weak color vision in *Saimiri* is attributed to the paucity of opponent cells, as compared to the number present in the Rhesus monkey.

Visual Cortex

STRIATE CORTEX AND VISUAL ASSOCIATION AREAS

The fibers of the optic radiations (geniculocalcarine fibers) project from the dorsal lateral geniculate body to the rentinotopically organized area 17 (striate cortex, visual area I). Other visual areas of the occipital lobe are visual association area 18 (parastriate area, visual area II) and visual association area 19 (peristriate area, visual III, preoccipital area). The general organization of the association fibers within and interconnecting cortical areas 17, 18, and 19 in the Rhesus monkey and the chimpanzee is outlined by Clark (1941), Crosby and Henderson (1948), McCulloch (1949), Bailey and von Bonin (1951), and Crosby, Humphrey, and Lauer (1962).

The longer association fibers project bilaterally from area 17 to area 18 of the same and opposite sides in the Rhesus monkey (Clark, 1941; Crosby and Henderson, 1948). Some fibers from area 17 may extend to area 19 and other noncortical areas (Crosby, Humphrey, and Lauer, 1962). In the Rhesus monkey, the regions of the striate cortex receiving input from the lower retinal quadrants are interconnected bilaterally through association fibers to area 18 and the dorsal aspect of area 19, while the regions of the striate cortex receiving input from the upper retinal quadrants are bilaterally interconnected to area 18 and the ventral aspect of area 19 (Crosby and Henderson, 1948). The possibility of independent and parellel projections from the lateral geniculate body to visual area I and visual area II must be considered (Glickstein, 1969).

Numerous fibers of the corpus callosum interconnect homologous regions of areas 18 and 19. No commissural interconnections between areas 17 of each side can be demonstrated in the chimpanzee and Rhesus monkey (von Bonin, Carol, and McCulloch, 1942; Bailey and von Bonin, 1951; Myers, 1962). In the chimpanzee, there are more commissural fibers of the corpus callosum interconnecting areas 19 than areas 18 (Bailey and von Bonin, 1951). The corpus callosum plays a role in synchronizing cortical activity (Chang, 1953). The homolateral and bilateral interconnections within areas 17, 18, and 19 are the matrices in which occur many of the complex processing prerequisites to visual perception and many visual reflexes. Visual experiences are exchanged between the occipital cortices of the two hemispheres (Myers, 1961; Glickstein, 1965; Gazzaniga and Sperry, 1967; Sperry, 1968). The interhemispheric transfer of learned visual experiences in the Rhesus monkey and the chimpanzee via the corpus callosum has been demonstrated by Myers (1960, 1961), Sperry (1962), and Downer (1959). The analysis of this functionally significant topic is beyond the scope of this presentation.

The geniculostriate fibers emerge from the white matter and pass into the striate cortex and terminate within laminae III and IV. These specific afferent fibers make direct synaptic connections with the spines along the central three fifths of the shafts of the apical dendrites of the pyramidal neurons of the striate cortex in laminae III and IV (in the rabbit by Globus and Scheibel, 1967; in the mouse by Valverde, 1967). In the primates it is probable that synaptic connections are made directly with the pyramidal cells and with the stellate cells of laminae III and IV of area 17. On the basis of a Golgi technique study of the striate cortex of the Rhesus monkey, Colonnier (1964) suggests two possible neuronal linkage patterns by which the precise specificity and retinotopic organization are relayed to and received by visual area I. (1) The axons from specific geniculate neurons make precise synaptic connections with specific cortical neurons, and (2) the axons terminate upon cortical neurons, both pyramidal cells and stellate cells, with dendritic fields organized with special geometrical shapes.

The striate cortex and the association visual cortex are organized into cylindrical columns (Fig. 6) extending from the cortical surface to the subcortical white matter (Hubel and Wiesel, 1965; Colonnier, 1966). Each of these columns is considered to be the functional unit in the postcentral gyrus (Powell and Mountcastle, 1959; Mountcastle and Powell, 1959) and in the striate cortex (Hubel and Wiesel, 1959) of the primates. This columnar organization is probably the fundamental pattern of the neocortex. In a way the cortex is arranged as a mosaic comprised of columns of neurons. Within each column, each neuron is linked in the vertical direction with the other neurons of the column and further tied in by such cortical neurons as the Martinotti cells throughout the entire depth of the cortex. Each column overlaps into

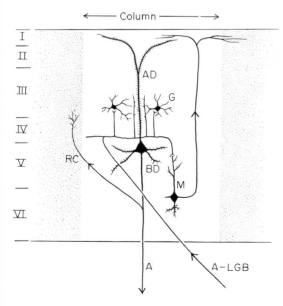

Figure 6. Schema of neuronal organization of column of visual area I (area 17, striate cortex). A, axon of pyramidal cell; AD, apical dendrite; A-LGB, axon of neuron in lateral geniculate body; BD, basilar dendrites; G, granule (stellate) cells; M, Martinotti cell; RC, recurrent collateral branch. Roman numerals indicate laminae of cerebral cortex.

adjacent columns. The interactions between adjacent columns utilize stellate inter-neurons which are oriented in a plane parallel to the cortical surface (at right angles to the vertical columns). There appear to be more stellate interneurons forming interconnections among the neurons within a column that interconnects with adjacent columns. The cortical column is a physiological concept which is not readily charac-terized anatomically (Hubel and Wiesel, 1969). The column is probably maintained, at least in part, by Golgi type II cells through collateral inhibition (Szentágothai, 1967).

The basic analyses of the neurophysiology of the visual cortex have been carried out in the cat by Hubel and Wiesel (1959, 1962, 1965) and in the Rhesus monkey and spider monkey by Hubel and Wiesel (1968, 1969). Each column in the visual cortex consists of neurons which have essentially the same receptive field organization. The neurons within each column are stimulated by neurons of the lateral geniculate bodies which, in turn, are stimulated by precise constellations of ganglion neurons (receptive fields) of the retina. The cells within area 17 respond optimally to patterns in the environment with a rectangular shape. The edge of the rectangle is a linear boundary. between a light field and a relatively dark field. Within the cortex the edge is repre-sented as a boundary between cortical neurons exhibiting inhibitory responses and those exhibiting excitatory responses. Thus each cortical neuron is integrated with other cortical neurons in its response (either excitatory or inhibitory) to the visual field stimulation. The border between the excitatory center and the inhibitory sur-round in the receptor fields of the retina and lateral geniculate body outline circles. In contrast, the borders between the excitatory regions and the inhibitory regions of the receptor field in the visual cortex outline more or less straight lines (line orienta-tion). The most effective patterns to stimulate cortical neurons are dark bars against light backgrounds and edges (borders) between light and dark areas (Hubel and Wiesel, 1959, 1965). In some as yet unknown way, the input from the circular fields of the lateral geniculate body is reorganized and transferred into the straight line fields of the cortex.

The neurons of the visual cortex have been subdivided into three physiologically defined groups in the cat (Hubel and Wiesel, 1965) and in the Rhesus monkey and spider monkey (Hubel and Wiesel, 1968): simple cells (fields), complex cells (fields), and hypercomplex cells (fields). The simple cells are detectors of stationary straight edges. They respond to stimuli from visual fields in which the borders between regions evoking excitatory responses and those evoking inhibitory responses are essentially straight lines in a specific spatial orientation and a fixed position. The complex cells are detectors of moving straight edges. They respond to stimuli from visual fields in which the borders are straight lines or slits in a particular orientation that can move slowly across the visual environment. The hypercomplex cells are the detectors of angles and curves. They respond to stimuli in which the borders are interrupted with angles, corners, and degrees of curvature. The simple and complex cells detect direc-tion of lines, while the hypercomplex cells detect interruptions of lines. The simple cells are presumed to be connected with complex cells and, in turn, the complex cells with hypercomplex cells. Within each column, the cells (fields) have essentially the same receptive field orientation.

In the striate cortex of the Rhesus monkey and the spider monkey, lamina IV and the deep portion of lamina III consist primarily of simple cells, lamina II and the superficial two thirds of lamina III of complex and hypercomplex cells, and laminae V and VI of complex and hypercomplex cells (Hubel and Wiesel, 1968). Most of the cells in lamina IV are driven by one eye only, with some responding to stimuli from the ipsilateral eye and others to the contralateral eye. The cells in laminae II, III, V, and VI are driven binocularly (Hubel and Wiesel, 1968). This indicates that the convergence from the fields of both eyes does not occur in the initial synaptic connections of the lateral geniculate body fiber projections to the striate cortex. The monocularly driven simple cells of the striate cortex interact with the neurons of the superficial laminae (II and III) and the deep laminae (V and VI). This implies that the act of fusion of the visual fields occurs in the laminae other than in lamina IV (Hubel and Wiesel, 1969).

The monkey has at least two types of independent columns: (1) columns with a common receptive field orientation as noted above and (2) columns according to eye preference. The latter are columns in which the projections from one eye predominate (Hubel and Wiesel, 1968, 1969). These columns are independent, but overlapping, systems of columns. There are probably other columns, such as color-coded columns.

In summary, the above observations indicate that the striate cortex of the monkey and presumably of all primates is organized (1) in vertical systems as superimposed, but independent, mosaics of physiologically defined columns and (2) in horizontal systems of hierarchically organized layers with cells of lamina IV driven monocularly and those of the other laminae binocularly.

ROLE OF ENVIRONMENTAL STIMULATION TO THE MAINTENANCE OF THE VISUAL PATHWAYS

From the time of the embryonic appearance of its neuroblasts until its structural and functional maturation in the infant and young animals, the developing primate visual system is subjected to at least two basic influences: genetic and environmental. The differentiation, growth, and precise synaptic connectivity of this system is primarily predetermined genetically (Jacobson, 1969; and others). Evidence supporting this thesis includes the observation that the visual pathways, including their exquisite synaptic connections, are well developed in newborn kittens before they open their eyes (Hubel and Wiesel, 1963). This neural connectivity is established before the eyes have received any photic stimulation. Stated otherwise, this stage is attained without the need of functional feedback (Jacobson, 1969; and others). Visual influences from the environment in the form of both diffuse and patterned light stimuli are essential for maintaining the normal structure and integrity of the visual pathways as well as the normal functional activity of the visual system.

Drastic reduction and complete deprivation of light stimulation results in morphologic, neurophysiologic, and behavioral deficits in the visual system of the chimpanzee (Chow, Riesen, and Newell, 1957; Rasch, Swift, Riesen, and Chow, 1961; Riesen, 1950, 1958, 1960, 1965, 1966) and of the cat (Wiesel and Hubel, 1963a). The researches of Riesen and his co-investigators are the classic pioneering studies in this area.

The degree to which the visual system is altered is related to the age of the animal and to the length of time the animal is subjected to visual deprivation. Short-term light deprivation produces chimpanzees that have difficulty in fixating objects and in following moving stimuli. Pattern discrimination is markedly altered. For example, the normal young chimpanzee reveals his visual recognition of a feeding bottle by a variety of anticipatory responses including vocalizations, whereas the light-deprived young chimpanzee responds to the bottle only after tactile contact is made. The longer the animal has been visually deprived or the earlier in infancy the deprivation is commenced, the more severe the effects to the visual system.

In turn, the degree to which the visual effects can be restored is related to the length of time a chimpanzee is subjected to light deprivation. Chimpanzees reared in total darkness from birth up to seven months of age may completely regain normal visual responses after being placed in a proper visual environment. Chimpanzees reared in total darkness from birth to more than sixteen months remain essentially blind even when subjected to normal visual environments. The severe effects are irreversible.

These blind animals did exhibit some visual reactions: startle responses to sudden presentation of light or the primitive pursuit of movements by the eyes in following gross visual stimuli. Degenerative histological changes can be demonstrated in the retina and lateral geniculate body of the young chimpanzee (Chow, Riesen, and Newell, 1957). The accompanying electrophysiologic changes reflecting these regressive changes can be recorded in the visual cortex of cats deprived of light from birth (Hubel and Wiesel, 1963a, b). The maintenance of the binocular inputs to the cortical visual neurons is dependent upon patterned visual stimulation. The functional role of visual stimulation upon the maturation of binocular connectivity to cortical neurons is dependent upon the kitten's receiving normal visual stimulation between the fourth and sixth weeks after birth (Hubel and Wiesel, 1963a, b). Depriving one eye of visual input before or after this critical period has slight, if any, effect on the binocular connectivity.

COLOR VISION AND THE VISUAL CORTEX

Some cells in the visual cortex are color coded (Hubel and Wiesel, 1968). The response of the neurons of the monkey's striate cortex to retinal stimulation by monochromatic light is essentially similar to that obtained from the neurons of the lateral geniculate body (Motokawa, Taira, and Okuda, 1962). These investigators noted the presence of cells yielding broad-band responses and others yielding spectrally-opponent responses.

In the mangabey monkey, *Cercocebus torquatus atys*, Lennox-Buchthal (1962) and Andersen, Buchmann, and Lennox-Buchthal (1962) demonstrate that spatial information and color are transmitted in different channels. In the macular area of the striate cortex are neurons which respond to narrow ranges of the blue, green, and red spectrum.

ENCEPHALIZATION AND THE "TWO VISUAL SYSTEMS"

The ascending sensory pathways consist of sequential levels of nuclear processing stations. The phylogenetic concept expressing this hierarchical organization with nuclei in the brain stem and cerebrum is called encephalization (Noback, 1959; and others). The subcortical levels have a significant role in the cruder discriminatory aspects of sensory perception, whereas the cerebral cortical level is crucial in the finer discriminatory aspects of sensory perception. In the visual system of primates, the superior colliculus of the tectum (midbrain level) is the subcortical nuclear level, and the geniculovisual cortex pathway complex is at the cerebral level. During mammalian evolution, the increasing dominance of the cortex (corticalization) has been assumed.

A modern version of encephalization is the concept of "two visual systems" (Schneider, 1969; Snyder and Diamond, 1968; Diamond and Hall, 1969). In this concept, the tectum and the cerebral cortex both have significant roles subserving different aspects of sensory perception. The precise formulation and full implications of this modern version await further studies of the neuroanatomy, neurophysiology, and physiological psychology of the mammalian visual system.

The relative functional contributions of the tectum and the cerebral cortex to vision have yet to be completely spelled out. The geniculocortical system may mask certain expressions of the phylogenetically older tectum (Schneider, 1969). According to Schneider, the optic tectum subserves the functional role by answering the question, "Where is it?" in terms of visiomotor responses (tectum may be the highest integrating center functioning to affect orienting movements), whereas the visual cortex fulfils its role by answering the question, "What is it?" in the form of learned responses.

After a bilateral occipital lobectomy, monkeys lost all ability to respond to visually presented spatial clues, but they did retain an ability to react to differences in total luminous flux (Klüver, 1942). This intensity discrimination is presumed to occur in the optic tectum. Rhesus monkeys with bilateral ablation of the entire striate cortex were able to localize moving objects (Denny-Brown and Chambers, 1955, 1958; Weiskrantz, 1963; Humphrey and Weiskrantz, 1967). A human patient with perimetrically blind fields perceived movements in a field which was entirely blind to stationary objects (Riddoch, 1917). Another patient with complete hemianopia was able to perceive small moving objects in the blind half of the eye, whereas he did not notice a stationary object following self-induced head movements (Denny-Brown and Chambers, 1955). Rhesus monkeys with bilaterally ablated superior colliculi had profound disturbances of their visual behavior. They explored for food when hungry, but otherwise they spent their awakened time staring aimlessly into space (Denny-Brown, 1962). Tree shrews with bilaterally ablated striate cortices retain some pattern discrimination habits (Snyder, Hall, and Diamond, 1966; Diamond, 1967). These observations indicate that the tectum has a role in visual recognition.

Some functional expressions of the tectum and the visual cortex are dependent upon direct and indirect interconnections between these two structures. The direct corticotectal tract originating from the occipital and preoccipital visual cortex is a major source of input to the superior colliculus (Crosby and Henderson, 1948; Crosby, Humphrey, and Lauer, 1962). The tectum may project influences to the cortex via circuits from the tectum to the thalamus (pulvinar and posterior thalamus) to the visual association cortex (outlined by Snyder and Diamond, 1968). These circuits have been utilized as being involved in the "two visual systems" concept by Schneider (1969) and in the dual visual projection circuits to the cortex in *Tupaia* by Snyder and Diamond (1968). In the former, the tectum is conceived as the focal processing site with two major sources of input from the eye: (1) the phylogenetically old direct retinotectal projections and (2) the phylogenetically new indirect corticotectal tract (part of the retinogeniculocorticotectal circuitry). In the latter, the phylogenetically new visual cortex in *Tupaia* and primates is conceived as being the focal processing area with two major sources of input from the eye: (1) the direct retinogeniculostriate pathway and (2) the indirect retinotectalpulvinar and posterior thalamic nuclei-association visual cortex circuitry (Diamond and Hall, 1969).

The question of the secondary visual areas of the monkey is reviewed by Zeki (1969).

REFERENCES

Anderson, V. O., B. Buchmann, and M. A. Lennox-Buchthal. 1962. Single cortical units with narrow spectral sensitivity in monkey (*Cercocebus torquatus atys*). Vision Res. 2:295-307.

Bailey, P., and G. von Bonin. 1951. The Isocortex of Man. Urbana, Ill., University of Illinois Press, 301 pp.

Beresford, W. A. 1962. A Nauta and gallocyanin study of the cortico-lateral geniculate projection in the cat and monkey. J. Hirnforsch., 5:210-228.

Bishop, P. O. 1964. Properties of afferent synapses and sensory neurons in the lateral geniculate nucleus. Int. Rev. Neurobiol., 6:191-255.

Bonin, G. von, H. W. Carol, and W. S. McCulloch. 1942. The functional organization of the occipital lobe. Biological Symposia, 1:165-192.

Brouwer, B., and W. P. C. Zeeman. 1926. The projection of the retina in the primary optic neuron in monkeys. Brain, 49:1-35.

Brown, P. K., and G. Wald. 1964. Visual pigments in single rods and cones of the human retina. Science, 144:45-52.

Boycott, B. B., and J. E. Dowling. 1969. Organization of the primate retina: Light microscopy. Phil. Trans. Roy. Soc. London, 255:109-176.

Campos-Ortega, J. A. 1968. Descending subcortical projections from the occipital lobe of *Galago crassicaudatus*. Exp. Neurol., 21:440-454.

——— P. Glees, and V. Neuhoff. 1968. Ultrastructural analysis of individual layers in the lateral geniculate body of the monkey. Z. Zellforsch, 87:82-100.

Chacko, L. W. 1948. The laminar pattern of the lateral geniculate body in the primates. J. Neurol. Neurosurg. Psychiat., 11:211-224.

Chang, H. T. 1953. Cortical response to activity of callosal neurons. J. Neurophysiol., 16:117-131.

Chow, K. L., J. S. Blum, and R. A. Blum. 1950. Cell ratios in the thalamocortical visual system of *Macaca mulatta*. J. Comp. Neurol., 92:227-239.

——— A. H. Riesen, and F. W. Newell. 1957. Degeneration of retinal ganglion cells in infant chimpanzees reared in darkness. J. Comp. Neurol., 107:27-42.

Clark, W. E. Le Gros 1941. Observations on the association fiber system of the visual cortex and the central representation of the retina. J. Anat., 75:225-235.

——— and G. G. Penman. 1934. The projection of the retina in the lateral geniculate body. Proc. Roy. Soc. (Biol.), 114:291-313.

Cohen, A. I. 1961a. Some preliminary electron microscopic observations of the outer receptor segments of the retina of the *Macaca rhesus*. *In* Smelser, G. K., ed. The Structure of the Eye, pp. 151-158. New York, Academic Press, Inc.

—— 1961b. The fine structure of the extrafoveal receptor of the Rhesus monkey. Exp. Eye Res., 1:128-136.

—— 1961c. Electron microscopic observations of the internal limiting membrane and optic fiber layer of the Rhesus monkey (*M. mulatta*). Amer. J. Anat., 108:179-198.

—— 1963. Vertebrate retinal cells and their organization. Biol. Rev., 38:427-459.

—— 1965. Some electron microscopic observations on inter-receptor contacts in the human and macaque retinae. J. Anat., 99:595-610.

Colonnier, M. L. 1964. The tangential organization of the visual cortex. J. Anat., 98:327-344.

—— 1966. The structural design of the neocortex. *In* Eccles, J. C. ed. Brain and Conscious Experience, pp. 1-23. New York, Pontificia Academia Scientiarum, Springer-Verlag.

—— and R. W. Guillery. 1964. Synaptic organization in the lateral geniculate nucleus of the monkey. Z. Zellforsch., 62:333-355.

Crosby, E. C., and J. W. Henderson. 1948. The mammalian midbrain and isthmus regions. II. Fiber connections of the superior colliculus. B. Pathways concerned in automatic eye movements. J. Comp. Neurol., 88:53-91.

—— T. Humphrey, and E. W. Lauer. 1962. Correlative Anatomy of the Nervous System. New York, The Macmillan Co. 731 pp.

Denny-Brown, D. 1962. The midbrain and motor integration. Proc. Roy. Soc. Med., 55:527-538.

—— and R. A. Chambers. 1955. Visuomotor function in the cerebral cortex. Arch. Neurol. Psychiat., 73:566-567.

—— and R. A. Chambers. 1958. Visual orientation of the macaque monkey. Trans. Amer. Neurol. Ass., 83:37-40.

DeValois, R. L. 1965a. Behavioral and electrophysiological studies of primate vision. *In* Neff, W. D., ed. Contrib. Sens. Physiol., 1:137-178.

—— 1965b. Analysis and coding of color vision in the primate visual system. Cold Spring Harbor Symposia on Quantitative Biology, 30:567-579.

—— I. Abramov, and W. R. Mead. 1967. Single cell analysis of wavelength discrimination at the lateral geniculate nucleus in the macaque. J. Neurophysiol., 30:415-433.

—— and G. H. Jacobs. 1968. Primate color vision. Science, 162:533-540.

Diamond, I. T. 1967. The sensory neocortex. *In* Neff, W.D., ed. Contrib. Sens. Physiol., 2:51-100.

—— and W. C. Hall. 1969. Evolution of neocortex. Science, 164:251-262.

Dowling, J. E. 1967. The site of visual adaptation. Science, 155:273-279.

—— 1968. Synaptic organization of the frog retina: An electron microscopic analysis comparing the retinas of frogs and primates. Proc. Roy. Soc. Biol., 170:205-228.

—— and B. B. Boycott. 1966. Organization of the primate retina: electron microscopy. Proc. Roy. Soc. Biol. 166:80-111.

Downer, J. L. de C. 1959. Changes in visually guided behavior following midsagittal division of optic chiasm and corpus callosum in monkey (*Macaca mulatta*). Brain, 82:251-259.

Gazzaniga, M. S., and R. W. Sperry. 1967. Language after section of the cerebral commissures. Brain, 90:131-148.

Giolli, R. A.. and J. Tigges. 1970. The primary optic pathways and nuclei of primates. *In* Noback, C. R., and W. Montagna, eds. Advances in Primatology. New York, Appleton-Century-Crofts, (Chapter 2).

Glees, P. 1940. Termination of optic fibers in the lateral geniculate body. Nature, 146:747.

—— 1961. Terminal degeneration and trans-synaptic atrophy in the lateral geniculate body of the monkey. *In* Jung, R., and H. Hornhuber, eds. The Visual System: Neurophysiology and Psychophysics, pp. 104-110. Berlin, Springer.

―――― and W. E. LeGros Clark. 1941. The termination of optic fibers in the lateral geniculate body of the monkey. J. Anat., 75:295-308.

―――― W. Hallermann, and H. Naeve. 1964. Die Repräsentation retinaler Sektoren im Corpus geniculatum lateralis in Affen. Graefe Arch. Ophthal., 167:367-376.

―――― K. Meller, and J. Eschner. 1966. Terminal degeneration in the lateral geniculate body of the monkey; an electron microscope study. Z. Zellforsch., 71:29-40.

Glickstein, M. 1965. Interhemispheric transfer, macular sparing and the central visual pathways. *In* Ettlinger, E. G., ed. Functions of the Corpus Callosum. Ciba Foundation Study Group No. 20, pp. 18-23. Boston, Little, Brown and Company.

―――― 1969. Organization of the visual pathways. Science, 164:917-926.

Globus, A., and A. B. Scheibel. 1967. The effect of visual deprivation on cortical neurons. A Golgi study. Exp. Neurol., 19:331-345.

Granit, R. 1955. Receptors and Sensory Perception. New Haven, Conn., Yale University Press.

―――― 1962. The visual pathway. *In* Davson, H., ed. The Eye, pp. 535-763. New York, Academic Press.

Grether, W. F. 1939. Color vision and color blindness. Comp. Psychol. Monograph 15. No. 4, pp. 1-38.

Guillery, R. W. 1967. Patterns of fiber degeneration in the dorsal lateral geniculate nucleus of the cat following lesions in the visual cortex. J. Comp. Neurol., 130:197-222.

Hall, M. O., D. Bok, and A. D. E. Bacharach. 1969. The incorporation of visual pigment (rhodopsin) into rod outer segment discs in the mature frog retina. Anat. Rec., 163: 303-304.

Hoyt, W., and O. Luis. 1962. Visual fiber anatomy in the infrageniculate pathway of the primate. Arch. Ophthal., 68:94-106.

―――― and O. Luis. 1963. The primate chiasm: details of visual fiber organization studied by silver impregnation techniques. Arch. Ophthal., 70:69-85.

Hubel, D. H., and T. N. Wiesel. 1959. Receptive fields of single neurons of the cat's striate cortex. J. Physiol. (London), 148:574-591.

―――― and T. N. Wiesel. 1960. Receptive fields of optic nerve fibers in the spider monkey. J. Physiol. (London), 154:572-580.

―――― and T. N. Wiesel. 1962. Receptive fields, binocular interaction and functional architecture in the cat's visual cortex. J. Physiol. (London), 160:106-154.

―――― and T. N. Wiesel. 1963. Receptive fields of cells in striate cortex of very young, visually inexperienced kitten. J. Neurophysiol., 26:994-1002.

―――― and T. N. Wiesel. 1964. Responses of monkey geniculate cells to monochromatic and white spots of light. Physiologist, 7:162.

―――― and T. N. Wiesel. 1965. Receptive fields and functional architecture in two nonstriate visual areas (18 and 19) of the cat. J. Neurophysiol., 28:229-289.

―――― and T. N. Wiesel. 1966. Spatial and chromatic interactions in the lateral geniculate body of the rhesus monkey. J. Neurophysiol., 29:1115-1155.

―――― and T. N. Wiesel. 1968. Receptive fields and functional architecture of monkey striate cortex. J. Physiol. (London), 195:215-243.

―――― and T. N. Wiesel. 1969. Anatomical demonstration of columns in the monkey striate cortex. Nature, 221:747-750.

Humphrey, N. K., and L. Weiskrantz. 1967. Vision in monkeys after removal of the striate cortex. Nature, 215:595-597.

Jacobs, G. H. 1965. Effects of adaptation on the lateral geniculate response to light increment and decrement. J. Opt. Soc. Amer., 55:1535-1540.

―――― 1969. Receptive fields in visual systems. Brain Res., 14:553-573.

Jacobson, M. 1969. Development of specific neuronal connections. Science, 163:543-547.

Kanagasuntheram, R., A. Krishnamurti, and W. C. Wong. 1969. Observations on the lamination of the lateral geniculate body in some primates. Brain Res., 14:623-631.

Klüver, H. 1942. Functional significance of the geniculo-striate system. Biological Symposia, 7:253-299.

Kuffler, S. W. 1953. Discharge patterns and functional organization of mammalian retina. J. Neurophysiol., 16:37-68.

Kupfer, C. 1962. The projection of the macula in the lateral geniculate nucleus of man. Amer. J. Ophthal., 54:599-609.

———— L. Chumbley, and J. de C. Downer. 1967. Quantitative histology of optic nerve, optic tract and lateral geniculate nucleus of man. J. Anat., 101:393-401.

Lennox-Buchthal, M. A. 1962. Single units in monkey, *Cercocebus torquatus atys*, cortex with narrow spectral responsiveness. Vision Res., 2:1-15.

Laemle, L. K. 1968. Retinal projections of *Tupia glis*. Brain, Behavior and Evolution. 1:473-499.

Marks, W. B., W. H. Dobelle, and F. F. MacNichol, Jr. 1964. Visual pigments of single primate cones. Science, 143:1181-1183.

Matthews, M. R., W. M. Cowan, and T. P. S. Powell. 1960. Transneuronal cell degeneration in the lateral geniculate nucleus of the macaque monkey. J. Anat., 94:145-169.

McCulloch, W. S. 1949. Cortico-cortical connections. *In* Bucy, P. C., ed. The Precentral Motor Cortex, pp. 211-242. Urbana, Ill., University of Illinois Press.

Miles, R. C. 1958. Color vision in the squirrel monkey. J. Comp. Physiol. Psychol., 51:328-331.

Missotten, L. 1960. Étude des synapses de la rétine humaine au microscope électronique. Proc. Europ. Reg. Conf. Electron Microscopy, Delft, 2:818-821.

———— 1965. The Ultrastructure of the Retina. Bruxelles, Editions Arscia; 180 pp.

———— M. Applelemans, and J. Michiels, 1963, L'ultrastructure des synapses des cellules visuelles de la rétine humaine. Bull. Soc. Franc. Ophthal., 76:59-82.

Motokawa, K., N. Taira, and J. Okuda. 1962. Spectral responses of single units in the primate visual cortex. Tohoku J. Exp. Med., 78:320-337.

Mountcastle, V. B., and T. P. S. Powell. 1959. Neural mechanisms subserving cutaneous sensibility, with special reference to the role of afferent inhibition in sensory perception and discrimination. Bull Hopkins Hosp., 105:201-232.

Moyer, F. 1961. Electron microscope observations on the origin, development, and genetic control of melanin granules in the mouse eye. *In* Smelser, G. K., ed. The Structure of the Eye, pp. 469-486. New York, Academic Press, Inc.

Myers, R. E. 1960. Failure of intermanual transfer in corpus callosum-sectioned chimpanzees. Anat. Rec., 136:358 (abs.).

———— 1961. Corpus callosum and visual gnosis. *In* Fessard, A., et al., eds. Brain Mechanisms and Learning, pp. 481-506. Oxford, Blackwell, and Springfield, Ill., Charles C Thomas, Publisher.

———— 1962. Commissural connections between occipital lobes of the monkey. J. Comp. Neurol., 118:1-16.

Noback, C. R. 1959. The Heritage of the Human Brain. New York, The American Museum of Natural History. 30 pp.

———— and N. Moskowitz. 1963. The primate nervous system: Functional and structural aspects in phylogeny. *In* Buettner-Janusch, J., ed. Evolutionary and Genetic Biology of Primates, 1:131-177. New York, Academic Press, Inc.

———— 1969. M. Berger, L. K. Laemle, and J. E. Shriver. Phylogenetic Aspects of the Visual Systems in Primates and *Tupaia*. Proc. 2nd Int. Congr. Primat., Atlanta, Ga. 1968 Vol. 3:49-54. Basel, New York, Karger.

Parsons, H. 1902. Degenerations following lesions of the retina in monkeys. Brain, 25:257-263.

Pedler, C., and R. Tilly. 1965. Ultrastructural variations in the photoreceptors of the Macaque. Exp. Eye Res., 4:370-373.

Polson, M. C. Unpublished data. Cited by R. L. DeValois, 1968.

Polyak, S. L. 1941. The Retina. Chicago, Ill., University of Chicago Press.

———— 1957. The Vertebrate Visual System. Chicago, Ill., University of Chicago Press.

Powell, T. P. S., and V. B. Mountcastle. 1959. Some aspects of the functional organization of the cortex of the postcentral gyrus of the monkey: A correlation of findings obtained in a single unit analysis with cytoarchitecture. Bull. Hopkins Hosp., 105:133-162.

Rasch, E., H. Swift, A. H. Riesen, and K. L. Chow. 1961. Altered structure and composition of retinal cells in dark-reared mammals. Exp. Cell Res., 25:348-363.

Riddoch, G. 1917. Dissociation of visual perceptions due to occipital injuries, with especial reference to appreciation of movement. Brain, 40:15-57.

Riesen, A. H. 1950. Arrested vision. Sci. Amer., 183:16-19.

——— 1958. Plasticity of behavior: Psychological aspects. *In* Harlow, H. F., and C. N. Woolsey, eds. Biological and Biochemical Bases of Behavior, pp. 425-450. Madison, University of Wisconsin Press.

——— 1960. Effects of stimulus deprivation on the development and atrophy of the visual sensory system. Amer. J. Orthopsychiat., 30:23-36.

——— 1965. Effects of early deprivation of photic stimulation. *In* Osler, S. F., and R. E. Cooke, eds. The Biosocial Basis of Mental Retardation, pp. 61-85. Baltimore, Md., The Johns Hopkins Press.

——— 1966. Sensory deprivation. *In* Stellar, E., and J. M. Sprague, eds. Progress in Physiological Psychology, pp. 117-148. New York, Academic Press, Inc.

Schneider, G. E. 1969. Two visual systems. Science, 163:895-902.

Shriver, J. E., and C. R. Noback. 1967. Color vision in the tree shrew (*Tupaia glis*). Folia primat., 6:161-169.

Snyder, M., and I. T. Diamond. 1968. The organization and function of the visual cortex in the tree shrew. Brain, Behavior and Evolution, 1:181-214.

——— W. C. Hall, and I. T. Diamond. 1966. Vision in tree shrews (*Tupaia glis*) after removal of striate cortex. Psychonomic Science, 6:243-244.

Sperry, R. W. 1962. Some general aspects of interhemispheric integration. In Mountcastle, V. B., ed. Interhemispheric Relations and Cerebral Dominance, pp. 43-49. Baltimore, Md., The Johns Hopkins Press.

——— 1968. Mental unity following surgical disconnections of the cerebral hemispheres. Harvey Lect., 62:293-323.

Spinelli, D. N., A. Starr, and T. W. Barrett. 1968. Auditory specificity in unit recordings from cats' visual cortex. Exp. Neurol., 22:75-84.

Szentágothai, J. 1967. The anatomy of complex integrative units in the nervous system. *In* Lissák, K., ed. Results in Neuroanatomy. Neurochemistry, Neuropharmacology and Neurophysiology (Recent Development of Neurobiology in Hungary), 1:9-45. Budapest, Akadémiai Kiadó.

Tigges, J. 1963. Untersuchungen über den Farbensinn von *Tupaia glis* Diard 1820. Z. Anthrop. Morph., 53:109-123.

Trendelenberg, W., and I. Schmidt. 1930. Untersuchungen über das Farbensystem der Affen. Z. Vergl. Physiol., 12:249-278.

Valverde, F. 1967. Apical dendritic spines of the visual cortex and light deprivation in the mouse. Exp. Brain Res., 3:337-352.

Wald, G. 1968. Molecular basis of visual excitation. Science, 162:230-239.

——— and P. K. Brown. 1958. Human rhodopsin. Science, 127:222-226.

——— P. K. Brown, and I. R. Gibbons. 1963. The problem of visual excitation. J. Opt. Soc. Amer., 53:20-35.

Weiskrantz, L. 1963. Contour discrimination in a young monkey with striate cortex ablation. Neuropsychologia, 1:145-164.

Wiesel, T. N., and D. H. Hubel. 1963a. Effects of visual deprivation on morphology and physiology of cells in the cat's lateral geniculate body. J. Neurophysiol., 26:978-993.

——— and D. H. Hubel. 1963b. Single-cell responses in striate cortex of kittens deprived of vision in one eye. J. Neurophysiol., 26:1003-1017.

———— and D. H. Hubel. 1966. Spatial and chromatic interactions in the lateral geniculate body of the rhesus monkey. J. Neurophysiol., 29:1115-1156.
Young, R. W.   1967.   The renewal of photoreceptor cell outer segments. J. Cell Biol.,
   33:61-72.
Zeki, S. M.   1969.   The secondary visual areas of the monkey. Brain Res., 13:197-226.

4

The Pyramidal Tract in the Primates

W. J. C. Verhaart

Laboratorium voor Neuro-anatomie
Wassenaarseweg 62
Leiden, The Netherlands

Introduction

The name "pyramidal tract," according to Nathan and Smith (1955), was derived from the medullary pyramids, which were originally described by Willis in 1664. The pyramidal fibers proper traverse the corona radiata, the di- and mesencephalon, and the pons before reaching the pyramid. In these levels they run together, accompanied by the corticopontine tracts and some fibers, presumably derived from the same cortical areas, terminating in supramedullary levels. Formerly when the pyramidal tract was assumed to be the entire upper motor pathway, it was believed that some pyramidal fibers terminated on the motor cranial nerve nuclei. This belief is no longer justified because the pyramidal fibers proper appear to terminate in a variety of nuclei of the grey matter of the medulla and spinal cord. Therefore, the only acceptable definition is that the pyramidal tract is the tract that contains the pyramidal fibers proper and, in addition, other fibers intermingled with the pyramidal bundle in the supramedullary levels of the central nervous system. In most primate genera this tract can be recognized by its large contingent of coarse fibers. In some primates the bundle has been actually demonstrated to contain all the pyramidal fibers proper and only a few fine fibers of Arnold's frontopontine tract. The latter joins the pyramidal tract in the low pons (Verhaart, 1948a, b).

The origin, course, decussation, and subsequent course in the spinal cord, the fiber content, and the termination of the pyramidal tract in a number of primate genera will be described in this paper. The genera studied include *Homo, Pan, Pongo, Hylobates, Symphalangus, Macaca, Papio, Presbytis, Saimiri, Lemur, Loris, Galago* and *Tupaia.*

As will be seen, the pyramidal tracts of all primates except *Tupaia* have much in common. *Tupaia* has been included in this study because, according to some taxonomists, *Tupaia* is a primate.

General Considerations

All of the fibers of the pyramidal tract were formerly assumed to originate from the Betz cells of the fifth layer of the central convolution. These cells showed chromatolytic changes following severance of a pyramid (Holmes and May, 1909). In many instances, however, degeneration in the pyramid has been observed following lesions of either the premotor cortex or the postcentral gyrus in a variety of mammals, including man (Kennard, 1935; Uchichima, 1936; Peele, 1942; Minckler, Klemme, and Minckler, 1944).

Häggqvist (1936) described the fiber content of the pyramidal tract in *Macaca* and found that it is chiefly composed of fine fibers. Ablation of the precentral convolution proved to be followed by degeneration of the coarse fibers and preservation of a large percentage of the fine fibers. On this basis, he concluded that these fibers are not of cortical origin.

Lassek (1940) and his co-workers found that in man there are over 20 times more pyramidal fibers than Betz cells. This apparently substantiated Häggqvist's opinion about the extracortcal origin of the fine pyramidal fibers. Following ablation of all the cerebral cortex frontal to the central sulcus in *Macaca*, Lassek (1952) noted that 30 percent of the pyramidal fibers, all of small size, were preserved, and Bucy (1957) concluded that in man only half of its fibers are of cortical origin. To the contrary, Lassek and Evans (1945) found that the pyramid lost all its fibers after a total right-sided decortication (the insula excepted).

At least the great majority of all pyramidal fibers in the dog arise in the cerebral cortex (Morin, Poursines, and Maffre, 1951; Maffre, 1953). These investigators found that after increasingly extensive cortical ablations the number of normal fibers preserved in the medullary pyramid decreased from 33 percent to 2 percent. The latter 2 percent were fine fibers. Because these fine fibers did not degenerate after a total unilateral decortication, these authors assumed that they arose in the basal ganglia. Maffre concluded that in the dog 80 to 85 percent of the pyramidal fibers originated in the posterior sigmoid gyrus, 5 percent in the anterior sigmoid gyrus, 3 percent in the gyrus proreus, and 5 percent in the retrosigmoid cortex.

The discrepancies between the preservation of 50 percent and 2 percent of the pyramidal fibers after large cortical ablations were explained by experimental observations in the cat by Van Crevel (1958) and in *Macaca* by Russell and DeMyer (1961). They demonstrated that fine fibers are much slower in showing signs of degeneration than are the coarse ones. It can, therefore, be considered as established that in the mammals studied at least 98 percent of the fibers in the pyramidal tract are derived from the ipsilateral cerebral cortex. This presumably applies to most mammals.

The coarse fibers of the pyramidal tract of man and *Macaca* originate predominantly, according to Mettler (1947), from the occipital part of area 4, the middle-sized ones from more frontal cortical areas, and the large numbers of fine ones from more occipital areas. In accordance with this, Woolsey and Chang (1948), by stimulating the pyramid in cats and monkeys, recorded evoked potentials in areas 6, 3, 2, 1, 5, and 7. Low-latency, low-threshold ones were especially recorded in area 4.

It is probable that in man and many other primates, all cortical fibers of the medulla pass through the pyramid. Some fibers leave the pyramids and terminate in the medulla, while other fibers ascend from the crossed pyramidal tract into the medulla. In many primates, the coarse pyramidal tract fibers in the corona radiata, the capsula interna, and the cerebral peduncle are distinctive in Häggqvist-stained sections cut perpendicular to the direction of the fibers (Mechelse, 1953).

The Pyramidal Tract in Man

In man the pyramidal tract is located in the intermediate third of the crus posterius of the capsula interna (Thurel, Nehlil, and O'Keefe, 1961; Hirayama, Tsubaki, Toyokura, and Okinaka, 1962; Bertrand, Blundell, and Musella, 1965). The cross-sectional area of the cerebral peduncle of the midbrain is subdivided as follows: the pyramidal tract comprises about one third of its area, the frontopontine (Arnold's) tract slightly more, and the parietotemperopontine (Türck's) tract slightly less of the remaining area (Verhaart, 1950; Lankamp, 1967). Within the pyramidal tract the fibers from the cortical leg area lie dorsolaterally and those from the face area ventromedially. In the low mesencephalon some fibers shift dorsally into the substantia nigra to form the stratum intermedium, the pedes lemnisci, and the nebulae of the medial lemniscus. The latter is at the junction of the mesencephalon and the pons.

PEDES LEMNISCI

The pedes lemnisci have been described by Dejerine (1901), Winkler (1926), Poppi (1927), Ronge (1928), Verhaart (1931, 1935), and recently by Lankamp (1967). Lankamp points out that the so-called pes lemnisci profundus consists of the lateral (pyramidal) part of the stratum intermedium, which shifts into the medial lemniscus to form the lateral group of nebulae. It is distinguished from the medial group derived from fine-fibered Arnold's tract by its coarse fibers. This pes lemnisci is regularly found in man and cannot be considered as an aberrant bundle.

The pes lemnisci superficialis is of macroscopic size only in a few cases. It detaches from the ventral side of the pyramidal area and runs medially along the ventral margin of the peduncle. It can be readily distinguished from the medial part of the peduncle by its coarse fibers. It has also been called the "Faisceau en echarpe" of Fere, because of its course around part of the peduncle. Most of its fibers as well as those of the nebulae either terminate in the basal pontine nuclei or shift ventrally to join the pyramidal bundles in the low pons. Some occasionally run with the lemniscus into the medulla. They were described by Winkler as the "Fibres aberrantes bulbo-protuberantielles" of Jumentiez.

The pes lemnisci medialis, which contains the fibers of the nebulae in the medial part of the medial lemniscus, does not contain pyramidal fibers but is derived from Arnold's frontopontine tract.

According to Dejerine (1901), Sand (1903), Riley (1960), and Humphrey

(1960), the nebulae consist of corticobulbar fibers and represent the tractus cortico-bulbaris motorius, innervating the motor cranial nerve nuclei. This has never been conclusively substantiated.

PONS AND MEDULLA

The pyramidal bundles diverge over the intermediate third of the basal pontine nuclei (pons proper). They intermingle minimally with the corticopontine tracts. In the caudal pontine level, the fibers assemble to form the compact medullary pyramid. The somatotopic dorsolateral to ventromedial arrangement of cortical leg, trunk, arm, and face areas is not found in each pyramid.

The pyramid decussates in the caudal bulb by traversing through the grey matter to the dorsolateral funiculus of the spinal cord. Some fibers descend uncrossed in the ventral funiculus. In addition, some small bundles shift into the ipsilateral dorso-lateral funiculus and join the crossed lateral tract (Mazras, Pansini, and Chodkiewicz, 1962).

The part of the pyramidal tract participating in the decussation varies greatly from man to man and similarly between both sides in the same specimen. These differences may be obvious throughout the cervical segments of the cord (Kamayana, Mannen, and Takahashi, 1963). A substantial crossing of pyramidal bundles in the cord has not been reported. As an exception, one pyramid may cross almost entirely and the other not at all (Mestrom, 1911; Luhan, 1959). In Luhan's case the right pyramidal tract had been totally severed at the junction of the pons and the medulla by a stab in the neck, the patient had suffered from a persistent left-sided spastic hemiplegia during a six-year survival period. At postmortem examination this right pyramidal tract was observed to be an uncrossed tract, a relatively large demyelinated area was noted at the ventromedial margin of the right ventral funiculus at Th 6 segment. Zenner (1898) described a man with a hemiplegia ipsilateral to a tumor of a cerebral hemisphere. He claimed that neither pyramidal tract crossed.

According to Mestrom (1911), Bidon in 1886 described a patient with a hemi-plegia ipsilateral to his cerebral lesion. Within the cord he noted ipsilateral degenera-tion of both the ventral and the lateral pyramidal tracts. Absence of a substantial crossing of both pyramids in an otherwise normally developed brain has been described by Verhaart and Kramer (1952). In this case both ventral funiculi were very wide, and the dorsolateral funiculi were small. Recently another such case was studied (Fig. 1). A survey of abnormal pyramidal bundles in the low medulla and the levels of decussation was made by Mestrom (1911), Sie Pek Giok (1956), and Nyberg-Hansen and Rinvik (1963). Some of the following data are derived from these reviews.

Rather frequently the so-called ventrolateral pyramidal tract can be seen to leave the pyramid in the low pons or the medulla and to shift laterally (usually located lateral to the inferior olive). It descends as uncrossed fibers into the cord at the periphery of the ventrolateral funiculus, near or within Helweg's tract area (Fig. 2; Barnes, 1901). In two cases, fibers could be followed into the lumbar intumescence. In the two other cases no fibers descended beyond the cervical levels. Inman (1917) observed this tract bilaterally in a neonatus, and Mizuno, Yoshida, and Okamoto

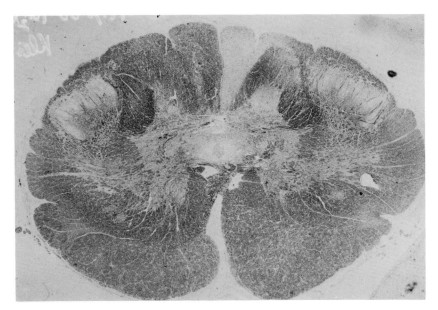

Figure 1. Junction of the medulla with the spinal cord in man in a case lacking a substantial pyramidal crossing. Both pyramidal tracts located at the ventral aspect, and there were no signs of crossing. Klüver-Barrera stain, x 10.

(1968) reported it to be rather common in Japanese. In one of my cases, part of it was noted in the low medulla as it projected dorsomedially to the central grey matter and ascended dorsal and dorsolateral to the hypoglossal nucleus and the nucleus prepositus. It appears to terminate in the rostral medulla (Figs. 3, 4).

Frequently Pick's bundle leaves one of the crossed pyramidal tracts caudal to the decussation and ascends into the medulla medial to the spinal trigeminal tract. Recurrent pyramidal fibers, as Pick's bundle, may be quite common in the low medulla, but they usually seem to run separately and therefore be invisible in normal material. Circumolivary bundles have been described by Dejerine (1901) as "Fibres pyramidales homolatérales superficielles," running at the outer side of the olive as superficial arcuate fibers. According to Mestrom (1911), Elliot Smith in 1904 reported seeing them in over 60 cases, with 55 restricted to the left side. Some may descend as the ventrolateral pyramidal tract, but, according to Schoen (1964), many fibers terminate in nuclei at the periphery of the lateral medulla and within the corpus restiforme or reach the floor of the fourth ventricle. In an old cortical lesion Marchi (1885) described a degenerated bundle crossing in the pons and recrossing in the medulla. Because there were several lesions, the tracing of this bundle was difficult.

Bumke (1907) saw a bundle project over a short distance in the dorsal funiculus caudal to the decussation. It joined the lateral tract within the dorsolateral funiculus at the second cervical segment. Hoche (1897) saw a degenerated pyramidal bundle cross and near the ventral horn descend to the first thoracic root, and Sträussler (1903) in a similar case could follow the bundle through the cervical intumescence. Ugolotti (1903), in a patient with a unilateral cerebral lesion, found some degenera-

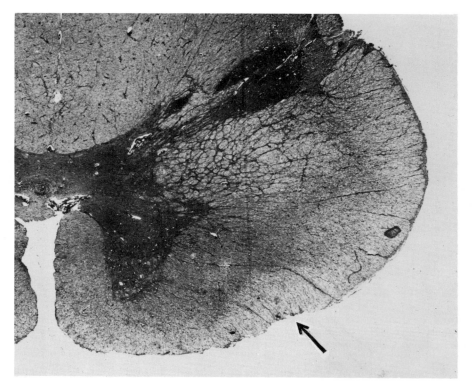

Figure 2. High cervical cord in man. Note the ventrolateral uncrossed pyramidal tract near Helweg's tract (arrow). Häggqvist stain, x 9.

tion in the contralateral cerebral peduncle. He ascribed this degeneration to fibers crossing in the corpus callosum.

SPINAL CORD

The crossed pyramidal tract enters the dorsolateral funiculus on its medial aspect to a position adjacent to the dorsal spinocerebellar tract. The situation in man is difficult to observe because the rubrospinal tract is indistinct. In the other primates it is obvious that the pyramidal tract displaces the rubrospinal tract ventrally and assumes a position at the lateral side of the dorsal born and dorsal to the rubrospinal tract. More caudally the dorsal spinocerebellar tract shifts ventrally. In the fourth cervical segment the lateral pyramidal tract lies near the peripheral surface. In the caudal half of the cervical cord (Marion C. Smith, 1957), the spinocerebellar tract shifts dorsally again, and the bulk of the pyramidal tract is displaced medially away from the periphery. A few separate bundles remain at the periphery between the fibers of the spinocerebellar tract. In the thoracic cord the spinocerebellar tract gradually terminates and disappears. In the lumbar intumescence, the lateral pyramidal tract lies at the periphery of the dorsolateral funiculus. The ventral uncrossed tract (Seki, Murakoshi, and Miyoshi, 1963) was followed for a few segments into

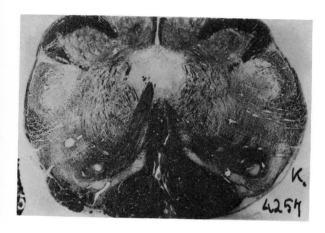

Figure 3. Ventrolateral pyramidal tract extending dorsomedially (left side) into the central grey matter. Weigert-Pal stain, x 10.

the lumbar intumescence along the wall of the median ventral fissure. In the low thoracic cord it consisted of separate bundles, somewhat spread between the others of the ventral funiculus. Schoen (1964), using the Nauta-Gygax method, could follow the tract into the lumbosacral segments.

Nicolesco and Hornet (1933) were of the opinion that the uncrossed ventral tract developed in apes and man because of their erect position and the increased dexterity of their hands. It can be followed through the cervical cord and the upper part of the thoracic cord only, innervating the motoneurons of the neck, the hands, and the upper part of the thorax. The suggestion that this tract innervates the upper thorax because the head is above the trunk instead of frontal to it in the quadrupeds is not tenable. This tract is present in the mole, the large rodents, the pinnipeds, *Procavia,* and the elephant (Verhaart, in press).

Figure 4. The pyramidal tract is located: (1) dorsomedially within the central grey matter; and (2) lateroventral to the olive where most of the tract is visible. Weigert-Pal stain, x 10

GENERAL COMMENTS

The pyramidal tract is presumed to be the principal central motor tract in man. This is suggested by a hemiplegia following its severance. Its fibers were presumed to terminate almost exclusively on motor neurons of the brain stem and the cord. In recent investigations, however, the fibers of the pyramidal tract have been proved to end in almost all nuclei of the brain stem and the cord, including the motor nuclei in man. Noorduyn (1959) calculated that of the pyramidal fibers just caudal to the pons in the ferret, about 25 percent leave the medulla. In man, with a shorter medulla and a wider pons, many more fibers enter the cord. It is estimated that there may be about 12 percent less fibers leaving than entering the medulla. The fibers terminate chiefly in the nuclei of the lateral funiculus, the nuclei of the dorsal funiculus except the lateral cuneate nucleus, the reticular formation, the arcuate nuclei, and the facial and hypoglossal nuclei, but not in the nucleus of the abducens nerve. Terminations are chiefly ipsilateral in the rostral and contralateral in the caudal half of the medulla (Kuypers, 1958).

The fibers of the lateral tract terminate chiefly in the intermediate grey matter and the lateral portion of the ventral horn of the cord. Those of the ventral tract terminate bilaterally in the medial part of the ventral horn and the lateral part of the intermediate grey (Schoen, 1964). In the lumbar intumescence the areas of degeneration shift somewhat dorsally, but otherwise they are identical to those in more rostral levels. No terminations of pyramidal fibers could be seen in Clarke's column. The human pyramidal tract, as determined by Lankamp (1967) and others, is composed of about 70 percent of fibers of 1 μ or less in diameter (the myelin sheath included), 14 percent of fibers about 2 μ, 8 percent 3 μ, 4.5 percent 4 to 6 μ, 1.5 percent 6 to 8 μ, 0.7 percent 8 to 10 μ, and 0.4 percent of larger fibers. It should be pointed out that in the technique used, Häggqvist's methyl blue-eosin staining, shrinkage amounts to about 25 percent (Fig. 5).

In the pyramidal area of the cerebral peduncle the fiber composition is less homogeneous than in the medullary pyramid, and the fibers are more closely packed, with fibers of 2 and 3 μ in diameter being more numerous. These may be the fibers which terminate in the pons. Fibers over 12 μ in diameter are relatively more numerous in the pyramid. Some increase in fiber size seems to occur between the mesencephalon and the medulla, or probably within the medulla, where the fibers are less closely packed. Total numbers of fibers of both pyramids in one specimen usually do not vary much, but those of different specimens may vary considerably. Variation in the fibers of all sizes occurs. The number of fibers ranges from about 500,000 to 1,000,000. Counting the very fine fibers is difficult, and the actual numbers may be somewhat higher (Lassek, 1942; Verhaart, 1947).

Unmyelinated fibers have been supposed to be very numerous. In Häggqvist-stained preparations it is obvious that they only can be small and scarce, since no space between the fibers is visible for fibers over 1 μ in diameter. Moreover, in such preparations fibers of that size show a distinct myelin sheath. A sheath is visible in fibers of not more than about 0.95 μ. In the pyramid of the coypu rat, Goldby and Kacker (1963) did not see unmyelinated fibers in electron micrographs. The smallest myelinated fibers they found were about 0.5 μ in diameter. The range of fiber sizes

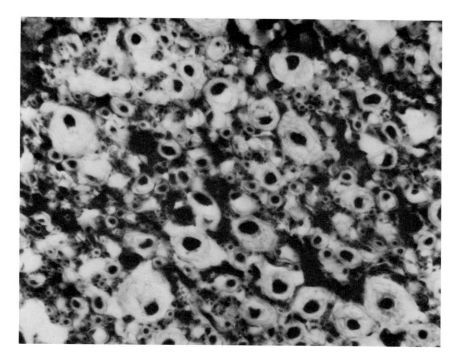

Figure 5. Human pyramid. Häggqvist stain, x 1,000.

in the human pyramid and other levels of the pyramidal tract is as large as in any other tract of the central nervous system. The fiber pattern is characteristic because in other tracts either the small or the very large fibers are rarer.

In man, the coarse fibers arise from Betz cells in the occipital part of the motor area (Mettler, 1947). Fine fibers seem to be derived, in part, from the frontal portions of the cortical area of origin of the pyramidal tract. These fibers diminish in number in lesions of the frontal part of the internal capsule and in frontal cortical degeneration of Pick's disease (Verhaart, 1947; Schenk, 1961).

The fiber content of the pyramidal tract may be compared with that of the other large fiber systems descending into the cord. In man, the pyramid is much larger than the medial longitudinal fasciculus. The coarsest fibers in these bundles are of the same size, and there is no striking difference in their fiber patterns. The rubrospinal tract and the lateral vestibulospinal tract are small. Their coarse fibers are not larger in caliber than are those of the pyramid. A high cervical level of the cord clearly demonstrates that in man the pyramidal tract is by far the largest tract projecting fibers from the encephalon to the spinal cord (Fig. 6).

The Pyramidal Tract in the Pongidae

The pyramidal tract of the chimpanzee within the internal capsule and the cerebral peduncle occupies the intermediate third as in man, but the extent of the frontopontine

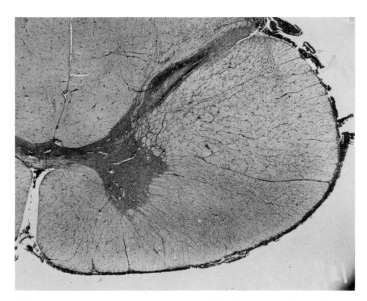

Figure 6. High cervical segment in man, with the large lateral pyramidal tract. Häggqvist stain, x 12½.

tract is somewhat smaller. The pyramidal area is located somewhat more rostrally in the capsule and somewhat more medially in the peduncle than in man. Its large fibers are characteristic. The stratum intermedium and the pes lemnisci profundus are as marked as in man. A pes superficialis could not be found in the few specimens available, but this does not establish its nonexistence in *Pan*.

The tracts in both *Pan* and *Pongo* split up into separate bundles, which spread within the basal pontine nuclei (pons proper) as in man. The pyramidal bundles can be similarly traced caudally. They intermingle only slightly with those of the corticopontine tracts. In the medulla the pyramid is large (Fig. 7), and its massive crossing assumes a large proportion of the medulla (Fig. 8). The lateral pyramidal tract can be seen to displace the rubrospinal tract ventrally within the dorsolateral funiculus of the spinal cord. Besides crossed fibers, each tract in the cord contains a small number of uncrossed fibers in *Pan* (Fulton and Sheehan, 1935).

The lateral pyramidal tract in the first cervical segment is large (Fig. 9). It lies medial to the dorsal spinocerebellar tract. In the second segment of both *Pan* and *Pongo*, the spinocerebellar tract shifts somewhat medially so that the pyramidal tract bundles form an uninterrupted layer along the lateral periphery of the funiculus. More caudally the spinocerebellar tract shifts back laterally, and only a few small pyramidal bundles remain at the lateral periphery. The ventral pyramidal tract just caudal to the crossing is fairly large. In the material available, it could not be followed caudally. In the chimpanzee of Fulton and Sheehan (1935), this tract was traced to the tenth thoracic segment.

Few aberrant pyramidal bundles have been observed in the limited material discussed in the literature. A tiny Pick's bundle in a *Pongo* was noted in the collec-

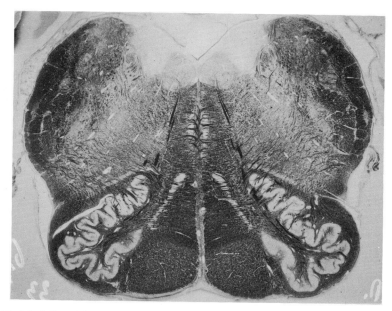

Figure 7. Medulla of *Pongo*. The large pyramid abuts against the darker-stained medial lemniscus. Weigert-Pal stain, x 6.

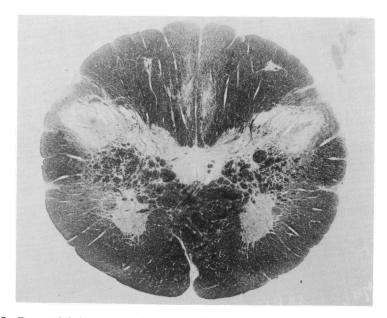

Figure 8. Pyramidal decussation in *Pongo*. Note its large size. Weigert-Pal stain, x 10.

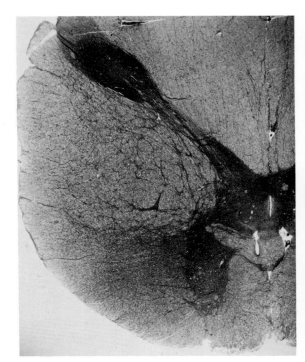

Figure 9. High cervical level in *Pan*. Note the large lateral pyramidal tract. Häggqvist stain, x 13.

tion. The pyramidal fibers in the chimpanzee terminate in the facial, trigeminal, and hypoglossal motor nuclei, in the supraspinal nucleus, and in the ventral horn of the spinal cord (Kuypers, 1958). Some fibers end in the nucleus of the trigeminal tract, the nuclei of the dorsal funiculus, the lateral reticular formation, the intermediate grey matter, and the base of the dorsal horn of the cord. Kuypers emphasizes the exclusive termination of the fibers from the caudal zone of area 4 on the motoneurons of the anterior horn of spinal cord.

The fiber content and the fiber size range of the pyramids of *Pan* and *Pongo* are about the same as in man. According to Lassek and Wheatley (1945), the fiber content represents an intermediate stage between that of the monkey and that of man. Of significance to this writer is that the pyramids, as in those of man, contain a fairly large number of very coarse fibers as well as large numbers of middle-sized and small ones. The latter may be less numerous than in man, possibly because of the less well-developed frontal lobe of the apes. As they enter the cord, the pyramidal tracts of these apes and man are much larger than the other distinct motor tracts, and the large fibers are large in numbers. As already indicated, the rubrospinal tract in these apes can be recognized in normal material. However, this tract still is small when compared to the pyramidal tracts of the high cervical cord.

The Pyramidal Tract in the Hylobatidae

The subfamily Hylobatidae consists of the genera *Hylobates* and *Symphalangus*, that resemble each other. The latter are somewhat larger. In my material, no difference between their pyramidal tracts could be discerned. *Hylobates*, the gibbon, is much smaller than the large apes. Its brain is much smaller, and the pattern of its sulci is much simpler. The central convolutions, as in *Macaca*, are very distinct because there are no accessory sulci. Otherwise, its lobes are somewhat larger and have a few more sulci than those of *Macaca*.

The pyramidal tract within the internal capsule and the cerebral peduncle can readily be distinguished as in man, *Pan*, and *Pongo* by its coarse fibers. It, however, occupies a greater part of both the crus posterius of the capsule and the cerebral peduncle. The surface area of the peduncle occupied by Arnold's tract is smaller. The cross-sectional area of the pyramidal tract in one case amounted to 5.8 mm², that of Turck's tract 3.5 mm², and that of Arnold's tract 2.5 mm². This demonstrates that the pyramidal tract is almost as large as the two corticopontine tracts combined (Verhaart, 1948b).

In the low mesencephalon a small stratum intermedium is visible, and pyramidal bundles shift dorsally to form nebulae within the medial lemniscus. These nebulae are not very numerous. The pes lemnisci profundus also can be seen, but other such bundles have not been noticed in the material available. In the pes pontis the pyramidal tract is split up into bundles which spread over the central part of the basal pontine nuclei. In the medulla, the tract takes its usual course. It is rather large relative to the size of the medulla (Fig. 10). Abnormal bundles are not seen. As in

Figure 10. Medulla of *Hylobates*. Note large pyramid. Häggqvist stain, x 12.

the other primates described, the decussation traverses through the center of the grey matter to the dorsolateral funiculus of the cord.

The lateral pyramidal tract is large in the high cervical segments. It does not traverse the dorsal spinocerebellar tract, which is located along the lateral periphery of the funiculus. A ventral pyramidal tract could not be distinguished. Because the fiber pattern of the pyramidal tract resembles that of the sulcomarginal fascicle, this ventral tract may not be characterized in normal material. Abnormalities in the decussation have not been noticed, but this may be because of the limited material available. The pyramidal tract can be followed throughout all lumbar segments. Petras (1968), in cortical ablation experiments, found the pyramidal fibers to terminate on motoneurons as in *Pan* and man.

The number of fibers in the medullary pyramid in *Hylobates* is smaller than in *Pan*. Its coarse fibers are numerous and as large, but the fine fibers are fewer. The total number of fibers can be estimated at about 300,000, of which 230,000 are 1 μ in diameter, 13,000 are 6 to 8 μ, and 11,000 are up to 12 μ in diameter (Fig. 11). The coarse fibers of this tract are as large as those of the medial longitudinal fasciculus, the rubrospinal tract, and the lateral vestibulospinal tract. The pyramidal tract is definitely much larger than all these fiber systems together.

The Pyramidal Tract in the Cercopithecidea

The following description is based upon the pyramidal tract of *Macaca*. It is assumed that this tract is basically similar in such genera as *Papio* and *Presbytis*.

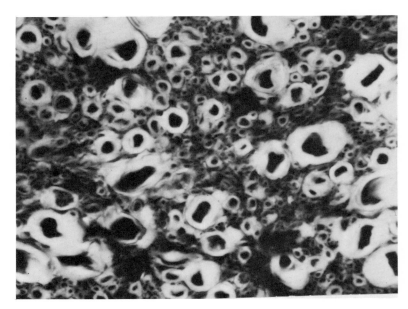

Figure 11. Pyramid of *Hylobates*. Häggqvist stain, x 1,000.

In *Macaca* the pyramidal tract is located in the intermediate part of the capsula interna crus posterius and the cerebral peduncle (Glees, Cole, Liddel, and Phillips, 1950; Mechelse, 1953). It occupies about half the cross-sectional area of the cerebral peduncle. The other half is shared by Türck's tract and the smaller Arnold's tract. A stratum intermedium within the substantia nigra cannot be distinguished. Both the pes lemnisci profundus and the nebulae within the medial lemniscus are scanty. In the pons the pyramidal tract splits up into bundles which spread through the central part of the basal pontine nuclei. The pyramids are not large (Fig. 12). An occasional small Pick's bundle is present. The decussation is similar to that reported in the other primates. The absence of abnormalities is significant, considering the large number of specimens examined.

The somatotopic organization of the fibers from the face, arm, and leg cortical areas as seen in man is maintained throughout the internal capsule, the cerebral peduncle of the midbrain, and the rostral pons (Barnard and Woolsey, 1956). Caudal to this level this organization is not preserved.

After decussating, the lateral pyramidal tract joins the dorsolateral funiculus and displaces the distinct rubrospinal tract ventrally (Verhaart, 1954). A narrow ventral pyramidal tract sometimes can be followed well into the thoracic cord.

Liu and Chambers (1964) observed a small uncrossed lateral and a smaller ventral corticospinal tract in the cord, the former descending throughout the cord and the latter not extending beyond L 7 segment. In a unilateral hand area cortical ablation, the uncrossed lateral tract degenerated down to the Th 4 segment, the ventral tract to the C 6 segment, and the crossed lateral tract throughout the length of the cord. From the cortical foot area, fibers could be followed in the ventral tract to the

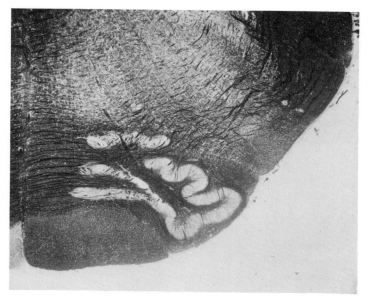

Figure 12. Medulla of *Macaca.* Note that the pyramid is smaller than in *Hylobates* and *Pongo.* Weigert-Pal stain, x 14.

L 4 segment, and in the other tracts throughout the cord. Following postcentral gyrus ablations, the ventral tract showed no signs of degeneration, whereas degeneration was pronounced in the contralateral tract and slight in the uncrossed lateral tract.

In the second cervical segment, a large part of the lateral pyramidal tract is located at the periphery of the cord lateral to the dorsal spinocerebellar tract. In the third segment, however, the latter tract shifts laterally, and except for a few separate bundles, the pyramidal tract lies medial to the dorsal spinocerebellar tract. This shift has been observed in many specimens and moreover was described in 1889 by Sherrington.

Many details of the cortical origin of pyramidal fibers were determined by Woolsey and Chang (1948) by antidromic stimulation of the pyramid, and by Russell and DeMyer (1961) by cortical ablations. The latter investigators found that 29 percent originated in area 6, 31 percent in area 4, and 40 percent in the parietal lobe. Following total decortication and after severance of the cerebral peduncle in the midbrain, 1.3 percent of axons do not degenerate. These fibers are almost exclusively grouped at the margins of the pyramid. These authors assume that these fibers are derived from surrounding fiber systems. These observations are consistent with those of Woolsey and Chang (1948).

The pyramidal fibers terminate in the intermediate grey matter and the ventral horn (Hoff and Hoff, 1934; Hoff, 1935). These projections were bilateral, although chiefly contralateral, and that to the ventral horn, greater in adult than young animals. Kuypers (1962) confirmed the latter point.

The number of fibers in the pyramid of *Macaca* was less than in the chimpanzee (Lassek et al., 1945b). Of about 260,000 fibers of the pyramid, about 2,200 are 8 μ and somewhat larger in size, and 200,000 are fine fibers (Fig. 13). The total numbers of fibers varied considerably, but the size of the largest fibers and the relative numbers of fibers of the successive sizes were similar in different specimens.

The Pyramidal Tract of the Cebidea

The information about the pyramidal tract in the ceboids, except *Saimiri*, is scanty. In *Saimiri sciureus* the pyramidal area of the cerebral peduncle is much larger than that of Arnold's tract, but only somewhat larger than the Türck's tract area. As in the other Anthropoidea, the pyramidal tract can be distinguished by its coarse fibers, which are lacking in the rest of the cerebral peduncle. A stratum intermedium is not visible in the substantia nigra, a pes lemnisci is not distinct, and a few nebulae are found within the medial lemniscus. In the pes pontis the peduncle splits up into bundles, and the pyramidal bundles spread over the center of the basal pontine nuclei. In the medulla the pyramid is relatively large (Fig. 14) and runs its usual course in the medioventral corner. The pyramidal decussation to the dorsolateral funiculus of the cord is as usual, and an uncrossed ventral pyramidal tract at the wall of the fissura mediana ventralis can be followed over the rostral half of the cervical cord. The large rubrospinal tract is displaced ventrally by the lateral pyramidal tract (Verhaart, 1966, Fig. 2). In the thoracic cord the spinocerebellar tract shifts ventrally, and the pyramidal tract reaches the lateral periphery of the dorso-

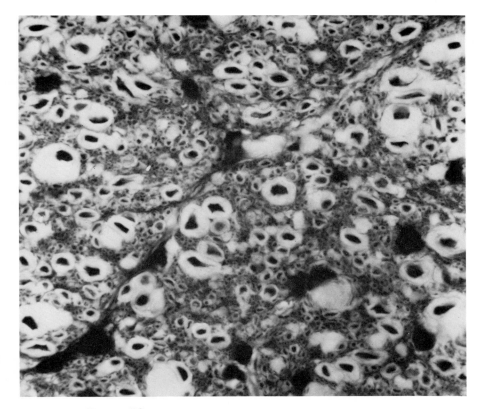

Figure 13. Pyramid of *Macaca.* Häggqvist stain, x 1,000.

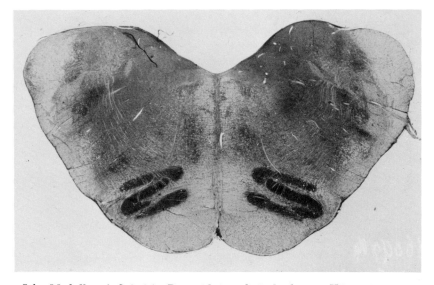

Figure 14. Medulla of *Saimiri.* Pyramid is relatively large. Häggqvist stain, x 11.

lateral funiculus (Fig. 15). Experimental studies indicate that pyramidal fibers terminate mainly in the dorsolateral part of the ventral horn, the lateral part of the intermediate grey matter, the nucleus proprius of the dorsal horn, and slightly in the ventral and medial parts of the ventral horn.

Following precentral cortical ablations in a number of ceboids, cercopithecoids, *Hylobates*, and *Pan*, Petras (1968) demonstrated degenerated fibers throughout the cord in a massive plexus in the lateral parts of the dorsal horn base, in the zona intermedia, and in the ventral horn. In the prehensile tailed ceboids, the spider monkey and the woolly monkey, the coccygeal segments receive many cortical projections. This is in contrast to the absence of such projections in prehensile tailed carnivores. The origin of the pyramidal fibers in *Saimiri*, as determined by the neurphysiological data of Welker, Benjamin, Miles, and Woolsey (1957), is consistent with results observed in other primates. The fiber size within the pyramid ranges from fine fibers to coarse ones up to 8 μ in diameter. The coarse fibers, up to 11 μ, of the other systems entering the cord are much more numerous (Fig. 16). Although the pyramid contains fairly coarse fibers, they are less prominent than in *Macaca* (Verhaart, 1966).

Lassek (1943) found that the pyramid of *Ateles* contains about 505,000 fibers between 1 and 12 μ in diameter. Most are small and a few are of middle size. The

Figure 15. Rostral thoracic segment of *Saimiri*. The dorsal spinocerebellar tract has shifted ventrally. The lateral pyramidal tract is located at the periphery of the dorsal half of the dorsolateral funiculus. Häggqvist stain, x 100.

Figure 16. Cervical segment of the cord of *Saimiri*. Note the relatively fine fibers of the pyramidal tract in upper half of figure as contrasted to the coarse fibers of the rubrospinal tract in lower half of figure. Häggqvist stain, x 100.

number is high, but *Ateles* is large compared to *Saimiri*, and the coarse fibers within its pyramid are rare. The largest fibers of 12 μ diameter may be correlated with the animal's large size.

The Pyramidal Tract of the Callitrichidae

According to Shriver and Matzke (1965), the marmoset, *Oedipomidas*, has a large crossed lateral corticospinal tract and a small uncrossed corticospinal tract within the dorsolateral funiculus. The former tract extends throughout the spinal cord, whereas the latter projects to cervical levels. These pyramidal fibers terminate in the base of the dorsal horn and zona intermedia of the spinal cord.

The Pyramidal Tract in the Prosimii

The pyramidal tract in the slow loris (*Nycticebus coucang Boddaert*) arises chiefly, according to Campbell, Yashon, and Jane (1966), in the precentral cortex apparently in much the same way as in *Macaca*. In loris and lemur the tract can be recognized in the peduncle, because the other peduncular areas are composed of smaller fibers. The area medial to it consists of a few small bundles and that lateral to it amounts to less than a quarter of the cross-sectional area of the peduncle. Therefore, the portion of the peduncle occupied by the pyramidal tract is much larger than in the higher primates. This is related to the reduction in the size of the corticopontine tracts. A stratum intermedium consisting entirely of pyramidal fibers is visible.

The peduncle splits up into bundles within the pes pontis. The pyramidal fibers spread over the dorsal three fifths of the basal pontine nuclei. Within the medulla, the fairly large pyramid is located at its usual ventromedial site. At the transition with the cord the tract crosses to the dorsolateral funiculus, displacing the rubrospinal tract ventrally. Tilney and Riley (1928) depict a similar decussation in *Lemur mongoz* and *Tarsius spectrum*.

Within the cervical segments the lateral pyramidal tract occupies about half of the cross-sectional area of the dorsolateral funiculus (Verhaart, 1966, Fig. 5). Its lack of coarse fibers (Fig. 17) adjacent to the spinocerebellar and the rubrospinal tracts (Fig. 18) is marked. The pyramidal tract can be followed throughout the cord in the dorsolateral funiculus. Campbell, Yashon, and Jane (1966) found in the loris *Nycticebus* a few uncrossed fibers in the dorsolateral funiculus which could be traced to the lumbar intumescence. These fibers terminate primarily in the dorsal horn and the intermediate grey. A few fibers terminate in the ventral horn. This latter sparse termination was considered almost equal to that in *Saimiri* (Schoen, 1966). The fiber content in loris and lemur differs from that in the Anthropoidea by the lack of fibers over 4.5 μ in diameter. The pyramidal tract in the medulla and the cord is conspicuous in prosimians because of its rather homogeneous fine-fiber pattern. In the cerebral peduncle, the corticopontine tracts can be distinguished from the pyramidal tract because they lack fibers of 4 μ in diameter. In the high cord and the very low medulla the pyramidal tract is medium in size. Its coarse fibers are about half the size of those in the sulcomarginal fascicle (Verhaart, 1966, Fig. 6).

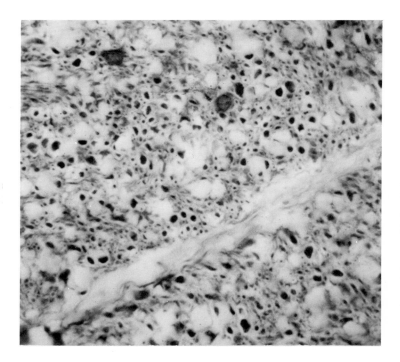

Figure 17. Pyramid of *Lemur*. Häggqvist stain, x 1,000

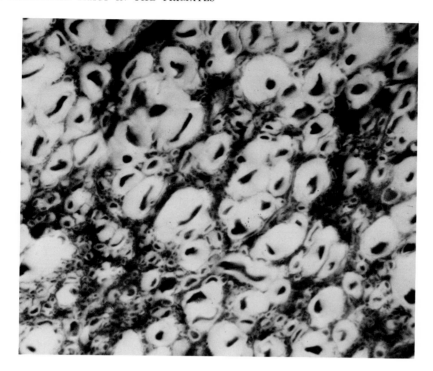

Figure 18. Rubrospinal tract of *Lemur*. Häggqvist stain, x 1,000.

The fibers of the pyramid in *Galago* do not surpass 4 μ in diameter, but otherwise the pyramidal tract does not differ from those of the larger prosimii (lemur and loris).

The Pyramidal Tract in Tupaia

The pyramidal tract in *Tupaia* differs from that of the prosimii. In the cerebral peduncle, the tract can be distinguished from the lateral third (Türck's bundle), in which fibers are smaller, but not from the medial aspect (Arnold's bundle). In the pes pontis the pyramidal tract splits up into separate bundles within the basal pontine nuclei. In the medulla, it lies at its usual medioventral site, where it is flat and small (Fig. 19). At the junction of the medulla and the cord the pyramidal tract crosses to the dorsal funiculus, where it is located along the medial margin of the dorsal horn (Verhaart, 1966, Fig. 8). It consists of a small number of discrete bundles, which comprise one fifth of the cross-sectional area of the funiculus. Caudal to the cervical intumescence it is reduced to a few tiny bundles in the most ventral part of the dorsal funiculus. It terminates at midthoracic levels (Verhaart, 1966). This description is consistent with those of Jane, Campbell, and Yashon (1965) and Shriver and Noback (1967). All these authors were able to trace, in specimens with ablated cortices,

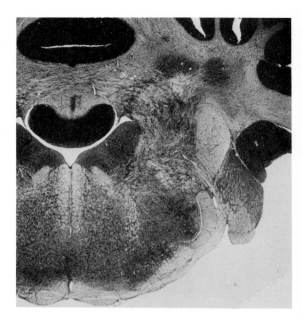

Figure 19. High medulla of *Tupaia*. Note the small pyramid located ventrally and the medial lemniscus located dorsomedial to the pyramid. Häggqvist stain, x 12.

crossed fibers through thoracic segments and uncrossed fibers through cervical segments. These fibers terminated in the dorsal horn and the intermediate grey matter, but not in the ventral horn.

The fiber pattern of the pyramid is homogeneous, with most fibers measuring 1 μ in diameter. A few fibers may reach 2 μ (Verhaart, 1966, Fig. 7). In the high cervical cord the pyramidal tract is, because of its small size and its fine fibers, not conspicuous.

Comment

The pyramidal tract of all primates has an identical course through the brain stem and the spinal cord. The level of decussation is always at the junction of the medulla and spinal cord. This course and level of decussation are similar in the carnivora, but in the other orders of mammals they may vary in several respects.

The crossing to the dorsolateral funiculus is apparently not related to the tract's position near the intermediate grey matter (site of termination of many fibers) because the ventral part of the dorsal funiculus (location of the tract in *Tupaia* and other mammals) does not lie further away from the nuclei of termination in the cord.

The wide fiber size range within the pyramid tract in man, Pongidae, and Hylobatidae is not found in any other group of mammals. The differences between the fine-fibered pyramidal tract in the prosimii and the multifiber size spectrum in the tract of *Homo* comprise a wider range than found in any other order of mammals. An increase in the number of fine fibers in the Pongidae and man is attributed to the enlargement of the frontal lobe and its projection, Arnold's frontopontine tract. A number of fine fibers of this tract join the pyramid in the low pons (Verhaart, 1948a, b).

The pyramidal fibers in most mammals end in the dorsal horn and the intermediate grey of the cord, but in primates they also terminate in large numbers within the motoneuronal cell groups of the ventral horn in all intumescential segments (Petras and Lehman, 1966). They could demonstrate this ventral horn invasion in *Ateles*, *Macaca*, *Hylobates*, and *Pan*. Jane, Campbell, and Yashon (1965) found a few terminal fibers in the ventral horn of *Nycticebus coucang*. The former authors also found a few such fibers in the raccoon, a carnivore. It is probable that the ventral horn may be the terminal site for pyramidal fibers in the pinnipeds, with their large pyramids and fiber size range (Verhaart, in press). Whether this motoneuronal projection is confined to fibers of a certain relatively large critical size is not known.

On the assumption that greater fiber size and further caudal extent of the pyramidal tract into the spinal cord are indicative of a higher "rank," the following is proposed. The pyramidal tracts of *Homo, Pan, Pongo* (presumably the gorilla also), and *Hylobates* rank above all others, and those of *Macaca* and *Saimiri* rank below them and equal to those of the pinnipedia. Those of the prosimii, ranking lower again, equal that of the bear but surpass that of the cat. In the bear the fiber size range is larger but the tract is smaller than in the prosimii, and in the cat both are somewhat smaller than in the bear (Verhaart, in press).

The proposition of Nathan and Smith (1955) to substitute the name "cerebrospinal tract" for that of "pyramidal tract" because it indicates its origin and end, is acceptable because it is the only tract carrying fibers from the cerebrum to the spinal cord. However, this term overlooks the fact that this tract projects fibers to all levels of the brain stem.

The pyramidal tract of *Tupaia* has no special feature in common with that of the other primates. It does resemble these tracts in the marsupials, *Didelphis* and *Trichosurus*. In *Tupaia* and these mammals the pyramidal tracts are small, cross to the dorsal funiculus, and end within the thoracic cord. This resemblance is superficial. The marsupials are not phylogenetically related to the primates.

REFERENCES

Barnard, J. W., and C. N. Woolsey. 1956. A study of localization in the corticospinal tracts of monkey and rat. J. Comp. Neurol., 105:25-50.

Barnes, S. 1901. Degeneration in hemiplegia: with special reference to a ventrolateral pyramidal tract, the accessory fillet and Pick's bundle. Brain, 24:463-501.

Bertrand, G., J. Blundell, and R. Musella. 1965. Electrical exploration of the internal capsule and neighbouring structures during stereotaxic procedures. J. Neurosurg., 22:333-343.

Bucy, P. C. 1957. Is there a pyramidal tract? Brain, 80:376-392.

Bumke, O. C. E. 1907. Ueber Variationen im Verlauf der Pyramidenbahn. Arch. Psych., 42:1-18.

Campbell, C. B. G., D. Yashon, and J. A. Jane. 1966. The origin, source and termination of corticospinal fibers in the slow loris, *Nycticebus coucang* (Boddaert). J. Comp. Neurol., 127:101-112.

Dejerine, J. 1901. Anatomie des centres nerveux. Tome 2, Paris, J. Rueff.

Fulton, J. F., and D. Sheehan. 1935. Uncrossed lateral pyramidal tract in higher primates. J. Anat., 69:181-187.

Glees, P., J. Cole, E. G. T. Liddel, and C. G. Phillips. 1950. Beobachtungen über die motorische Rinde des Affen. Arch. Psychiat. Z. Neurol., 185:675-689.

Goldby, F., and G. N. Kacker. 1963. A survey of the pyramidal system on the coypu rat, *Myocastor coypus*. J. Anat., 97:517-531.

Häggqvist, G. 1936. Analyse der Faserverteilung in einem Rückenmarksquerschnitt. Z. Anat. Forsch., 39:1-34.

Hirayama, K., T. Tsubaki, Y. Toyokura, and S. Okinaka. 1962. The presentation of the pyramidal tract in the internal capsule and basis pedunculi. Neurology, 12:337-342.

Hoche, A. 1897. Ueber Variationen im Verlauf der Pyramidenbahn. Neur. Centr., 16: 993-997.

Hoff, E. C. 1935. Corticospinal fibers arising in the premotor area of the monkey. Arch. Neurol. Psychiat., 33:687-697.

——— and H. E. Hoff. 1934. Spinal terminations of the projection fibers from the motor cortex of primates. Brain, 57:454-474.

Holmes, G., and W. P. May. 1909. On the exact origin of the pyramidal tract in man and other mammals. Brain, 32:1-44.

Humphrey, T. 1960. The development of the pyramidal tracts in human fetuses, correlated with cortical differentiation. *In* Tower, D. B., and J. P. Schadee, eds. Structures and Function of the Cerebral Cortex, 93-103. Amsterdam, Elsevier Publ. Comp.

Inman, T. G. 1917. An anomaly in the pyramidal decussation with remarks on Helweg's bundle. J. Nerv. Ment. Dis., 45:214-219.

Jane, J. A., C. B. G. Campbell, and D. Yashon. 1965. Pyramidal tract: A comparison of two prosimian primates. Science, 147:153-155.

Kamayana, M., T. Mannen, and K. Takahashi. 1963. Variations of the pyramidal decussation. A clinicopathological study. Tokyo Clin. Neurol., 3:444-452.

Kennard, M. A. 1935. Corticospinal fibers arising in premotor area of monkey, as demonstrated by Marchi method. Arch. Neurol. Psychiat., 33:698-711.

Kuypers, H. G. J. M. 1958. Corticobulbar connections to the pons and lower brain stem in man. Brain, 81:364-388.

——— 1958. Some projections from the peri-central cortex to the pons and lower brain stem in monkey and chimpanzee. J. Comp. Neurol., 110:221-256.

——— 1962. Corticospinal connections. Postnatal development in the Rhesus monkey. Science, 138:678-680.

Lankamp, D. J. 1967. The fibre composition of the pedunculus cerebri (crus cerebri) in man. Thesis, Leiden, Luctor et Emergo.

Lassek, A. M. 1940. Human pyramidal tract. II. A numerical investigation of the Betz cells of the motor area. Arch. Neurol. Psychiat., 44:718-724.

——— 1942. The human pyramidal tract. IV. A study of the mature, myelinated fibers of the pyramid. J. Comp. Neurol., 76:217-225.

——— 1943. The pyramidal tract. A study of the large motor cells of area 4 and the fiber components of the pyramid in the spider monkey (*Ateles ater*). J. Comp. Neurol., 79:407-413.

——— 1952. A study of the effect of complete frontal lobe extirpations on the fiber components of the pyramidal tract. J. Comp. Neurol., 96:121-125.

——— and J. P. Evans. 1945a. Human pyramidal tract. Effect of hemispherectomies on fiber components of pyramids. J. Comp. Neurol., 83:113-119.

——— and M. D. Wheatley. 1945b. The pyramidal tract. An enumeration of the large motor cells of area 4 and the axons in the pyramid of the chimpanzee. J. Comp. Neurol., 82:299-302.

Luhan, J. A. 1959. Long survival after unilateral stab wound of medulla with unilateral distribution. Arch. Neurol., 1:427-434.

Lui, C. N., and W. W. Chambers. 1964. An experimental study of the corticospinal system in the monkey (*Macaca mulatta*). J. Comp. Neurol., 123:257-284.

Maffre, S. 1953. Étude physiologique et morphologique du faisceau pyramidal chez le chien d'après les conséquences de son exclusion "chronique." Thesis, Marseille, M. Leconte.

Marchi, V. 1885. Sopra un caso di doppio incruciamento dei fascei piramidali. Arch. Ital. Mal. Nerv., 22:255.

Mazras, G., A. Pansini, and J. Chodkiewicz. 1962. Traject cortico-capsulare de la voie motrice homolatérale. Rev. Neurol., 107:76-80.

Mechelse, K. 1953. De vezelstructuur van de capsula interna en pedunculus cerebri bij Macaca ira. Thesis, Leiden, "De Sleutelstad."

Mestrom, J. H. J. 1911. Variaties der pyramidebaankruising. Thesis, Amsterdam, C. L. van Langenhuysen.

Mettler, F. A. 1947. Extra cortical connections of the primate cortex. J. Comp. Neurol., 86:119-166.

Minckler, J., R. M. Klemme, and D. Minkler. 1944. Course of efferent fibers from human premotor cortex. J. Comp. Neurol., 81:259-277.

Mizuno, N., M. Yoshida, and M. Okamoto. 1968. Helweg's triangular fasciculus in anencephalic fetuses. J. Comp. Neurol., 132:167-188.

Morin, G., Y. Poursines, and S. Maffre. 1951. Sur l'origin de la voie pyramidale. Documents obtenues par la methode des dégénérescences descendantes chez le chien. J. Physiol., 43:75-96.

Nathan, P., and M. C. Smith. 1955. Long descending tracts in man. Brain, 78:248-303.

Nicolesco, J., and T. Hornet. 1933. Contribution a l'etude du faisceau de Türck. L'Encephale, 28:10-33.

Noorduyn, N. J. A. 1959. Quantitative aspects of the pyramidal tract. Thesis, Gorinchem, J. Noorduyn en Zn.

Nyberg-Hansen, R., and E. Rinvik. 1963. Some comments on the pyramidal tract with special reference to its individual variations in man. Acta Neurol. Scand., 39:2-30.

Peele, T. L. 1942. Cytoarchitecture of individual parietal areas in monkey (Macaca mulatta) in distribution of efferent fibers. J. Comp. Neurol., 77:693-737.

Petras, J. M. 1968. Corticospinal fibers in New World and Old World simians. Brain Res., 8:206-208.

—— and R. A. W. Lehman. 1966. Corticospinal fibers in the raccoon. Brain Res., 3:195-197.

Poppi, U. 1927. Ueber die Fasersysteme der Substantia nigra. Arb. Neurol. Inst. Wiener Univ., 29:8-49.

Riley, H. A. 1960. An Atlas of the Basal Ganglia, Brain Stem and Spinal Cord. New York, Hafner Publ. Comp.

Ronge, P. H. 1928. Over de pedunculo-tegmentale vezelbundel. Nederl. T. Geneesk., 72:1528-1531.

Russell, J. R., and W. DeMyer. 1961. The quantitative cortical origin of pyramidal axons of Macaca rhesus. Neurology, 11:96-109.

Sand, R. 1903. Beitrage zur Kenntnis der cortico-bulbären und cortico-pontinen Pyramidenfasern beim Menschen. Arb. Neurol. Inst. Wiener Univ., 10:185-222.

Schenk, V. W. D. 1961. The fibre pattern in pyramidal tract in Pick's lobar atrophy. Psychiat. Neurol. Neurochir., 64:176-187.

Schoen, J. H. R. 1964. Comparative aspects of the descending fibre systems in the spinal cord. In Eccles, J. C., and J. P. Schadé, eds. Progress in Brain Research. Amsterdam, Elsevier Publ. Comp., 203-222.

—— 1966. Corticospinal projections in some primates. Acta Morph. Neerl. Scand., 6:408-409.

Seki, Yasushi, Fujiya Murakoshi, and Minoru Miyoshi. 1963. Comparative anatomical and experimental studies on the anterior pyramidal tract. Nihon Univ. J. Med., 5/2: 1-32.

Sherrington, C. S. 1889. On nerve-tracts degenerating secondary to lesions of the cortex cerebri (preliminary). J. Physiol., 10:429-432.

Shriver, J. E., and H. A. Matzke. 1965. Corticobulbar and corticospinal tracts in the marmoset monkey (Oedipomidas oedipus). Anat. Rec., 151:416.

—— and C. R. Noback. 1967. Cortical projections to the lower brain stem and spinal cord in the tree shrew (Tupaia glis). J. Comp. Neurol., 130:25-54.

Sie, P. G. 1956. Localization of fibre systems within the white matter of the medulla oblongata and the cervical cord in man. Thesis, Leiden, Eduard IJdo.

Simpson, G. G. 1945. The principles of classification of mammals. Bull. Am. Museum Nat. Hist., 85:i-xvi, 1-350.

Smith, M. C. 1957. Observations on the topography of the lateral column of the human cervical spinal cord. Brain, 80:263-272.

Sträussler, E. 1903. Zur Morphologie des normalen und pathologischen Rückenmarkes und der Pyramidenseitenstrangbahn. Jahrb. Psych. Neurol., 23:260-298.

Thurel, R., J. Nehlil, and P. O'Keefe. 1961. Traitement stéréotaxique des mouvements involontaires. Role de la lésion du faisceau pyramidal dans la capsule interne. Rev. Neurol., 104:327-329.

Tilney, F., and H. A. Riley. 1928. The Brain from Ape to Man. London, H. K. Lewis Company.

Uchichima, S. 1936. Ueber die corticalen extrapyramidalen Fasern aus der Area 8 der Grosshirnrinde der Katze. Z. Mikr. Anat. Forsch., 40:541-557.

Ugolotti, F. 1903. Nuove richerche sulle vie piramidali nell'uomo. Riv. Pat. Nerv. Ment., 8:145-154.

Van Crevel, H. 1958. The rate of secondary degeneration in the central nervous system. Thesis, Leiden, Eduard IJdo.

Verhaart, W. J. C. 1931. On the fibersystems in the midbrain which pass from the pedunculus cerebri to the lemniscus medialis. J. Nerv. Ment. Dis., 73:241-257.

——— 1935. Die aberrierenden Pyramidenfasern bei Menschen und Affen. Schweiz. Arch. Neurol. Psychiat., 36:170-190.

——— 1947. On thick and thin fibers in the pyramidal tract. Acta Psychiat. Neurol., 22:271-281.

——— 1948a. The pes pedunculi and pyramid. J. Comp. Neurol., 88:139-155.

——— 1948b. The pes pedunculi and pyramid in *Hylobates*. J. Comp. Neurol., 89: 71-78.

——— 1950. Hypertrophy of the pes pedunculi and pyramid as result of degeneration of contralateral corticofugal fiber tracts. J. Comp. Neurol., 92:1-16.

——— 1954. Fiber tracts and fiber patterns in the anterior and the lateral funiculus of the cord in *Macaca ira*. Acta Anat. London, 20:330-373.

——— 1966. The pyramidal tract of *Tupaia*, compared to that in other primates. J. Comp. Neurol., 126:43-50.

——— 1967. The non-crossing of the pyramidal tract in *Procavia capensis* (Storr) and other instances of absence of the pyramidal crossing. J. Comp. Neurol., 131:387-392.

——— Comparative anatomical aspects of the mammalian brain stem. In Press.

——— and W. Kramer. 1952. The uncrossed pyramidal tract. Acta Psychiat. Neurol. Scand., 27:181-200.

Welker, W. I., R. M. Benjamin, R. C. Miles, and C. N. Woolsey. 1957. Motor effects of stimulation of cerebral cortex of squirrel monkey (*Saimira sciureus*). J. Neurophysiol., 20:347-363.

Winkler, C. 1926. De bouw van het zenuwstelsel. Vol. 3, Haarlem, Erven F. Bohn.

Woolsey, C. N., and H. T. Chang. 1948. Activation of the cerebral cortex by antidromic volleys in the pyramidal tract Res. Publ. Ass. Res. Nerv. Ment. Dis., 27:146-159.

Zenner, Philip. 1898. Ein Fall von Hirngeschwülst in der linker motorische Sphäre, linksseitiger Lähmung, Abwesenheit der Pyramidenkreuzung. Neurol. Centralbl., 17:202-203.

5

The Allocortex in Primates

Heinz Stephan *and* Orlando J. Andy

Max-Planck-Institut für Hirnforschung, Neuroanatomische Abteilung, Frankfurt/Main-Niederrad, Germany and Department of Neurosurgery, University of Mississippi Medical Center, Jackson, Mississippi 39216

Introduction: Classification and Definition

The surface of the telencephalon can be subdivided on a macromorphological level into the more dorsal and lateral iso- or neocortical mantle (pallium) and the more ventral and medial rhinencephalon. The allocortex represents the surface of the rhinencephalon. We will discuss macromorphology, size, and structural differentiation of several representative structures of the allocortex.

The terms "isocortex" and "allocortex" were introduced by Vogt (1910). The word "allocortex" (the other cortex) functioned from the beginning as a collective term specifying the entire region of the "nonisocortex." This term is applied to all cortical areas, which are definitely less developed than and/or very different from the typical 6-layered isocortex. The whole group is very heterogeneous and heteromorphic. The various areas originate phylogenetically and ontogenetically at different times and in different manners, and they are, in their final state, of very different basic structures. Therefore, the allocortex has become more and more subdivided:

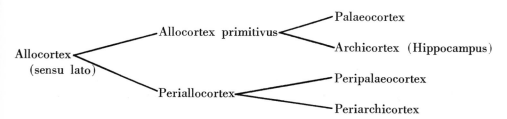

This basic subdivision goes back to Filimonoff (1947), who classified the transitional structures between allocortex and isocortex as "cortex intermedius" or "periallocortex". The subdivision has its roots, however, in the studies of many older scientific disciplines and such investigators as Elliot Smith, C.U. Ariens Kappers, K. Brodmann, O. Vogt, M. Rose, and Brockhaus.

The allocortex in the proper sense, or *allocortex primitivus* of our nomenclature, is a thin cortex with very few clearly defined cell layers, and/or its cortical structure is in general very poorly developed.* The two types, *palaeocortex* and *archicortex* (the latter corresponding to the hippocampus), must be separated from one another on the basis of their very distinct ontogenetic development. In contrast to all other cortical formations, including the archicortex, the typical palaeocortex does not develop through a cortical plate.

According to Filimonoff (1947) the *periallocortex* completely covers the allocortex primitivus and separates it everywhere from the isocortex. Filimonoff subdivides the periallocortex into transitional areas between palaeocortex and isocortex (=*peripalaeocortex*) and between archicortex and isocortex (=*periarchicortex*). The peri*palaeo*cortex consists of intermediate insular formations; the peri*archi*cortex consists of the entorhinal and praesubicular fields as well as of the retrosplenial, supracallosal, and subgenual areas.

The periallocortex clearly has more layers than has the allocortex primitivus, but it is always immediately adjacent to it. It differs from the isocortex in possessing a variety of specific characteristics for each of its parts. Important and fairly frequent in this regard is the existence of a homogeneous superficial layer of myelinated fibers, which led Meynert (1868, 1872) to distinguish a white and a gray cortex. Additional characteristics can be: one or several almost cell-free layers (e.g., lamina dissecans in the regio entorhinalis), strong granulation of the external layers (regio praesubicularis, regio retrosplenialis), very short myelinated fibers and/or almost complete absence of stratification (regio infraradiata ventralis, regio subgenualis posterior). The periallocortex can be defined simply as that cortex which is adjacent to the allocortex primitivus and which differs very clearly from the typical 6-layered isocortex. (For a detailed classification see Fig. 4.)

A further transitional formation between the allocortex and the true isocortex may be separated, the structure of which more nearly resembles the typical isocortex and is therefore regarded by us as a part of the isocortex. For that reason, we prefer to designate this formation, with Vogt (1956) and Sanides (1962), as *proisocortex* in contrast to Bailey and Bonin (1951) and Gastaut and Lammers (1961), who termed it *juxtallocortex*. The proisocortex is placed between periallocortex and true isocortex.

Material and Methods

The investigations were carried out on serial sections from a total of 63 species in our collection—22 insectivores, 20 prosimians, and 21 simians. For the species used, see legend of Figure 3.

The vast majority of the specimens were collected during several expeditions in the Congo and in Madagascar. The monkeys from Southeast Asia were obtained through

---

* This definition is, however, not applicable to the primary olfactory centers (bulbus olfactorius and bulbus olfactorius accessorius), which have a completely different structure, with a number of definite layers. Nevertheless, we include them with the allocortex primitivus.

animal dealers. A few species were sent to us alive by friends. We would like to thank particularly Dr. Virgil L. Jacobs (Manila and Kansas City) for the valuable specimens of *Urogale* and *Tarsius*.

Most of the brains were fixed by perfusion with Bouin's fluid and, occasionally, with formalin immediately after death and, as soon as possible, removed and weighed. The weight so obtained tallies fairly well with fresh brain weight (Stephan, 1960). The brains were embedded in paraffin and sectioned serially. The sections, 10, 15, or 20 μ thick, were stained alternately with cresylviolet for nerve cells and by the Heidenhain-Woelcke technique for myelinated nerve fibers.

Methods for estimating and comparing the brain volumes have been described in previous publications (Stephan, 1967a, b). To facilitate the understanding of the quantitative results, we would like, however, to repeat here the main points of those methods. 1. Volume estimation from enlarged photographs of serial sections at equal intervals (Fig. 1). 2. Comparison of the absolute values by the allometric method, i.e., taking into account the differences in body size. 3. Reference to the size of the corresponding structures in the basal insectivores, which are the most primitive living placentals according to characteristics of the brain (Fig. 2). 4. "Progression indices" allow a direct numerical estimate of how many times a given brain structure of a certain species is larger than the corresponding structure in a typical basal insectivore of the same body weight (Fig. 3). The progression indices are indicative values, which, although not precise, are certainly sufficient for the type of comparison made here. 5. The various progression indices were arranged in scales and compared (Figs.

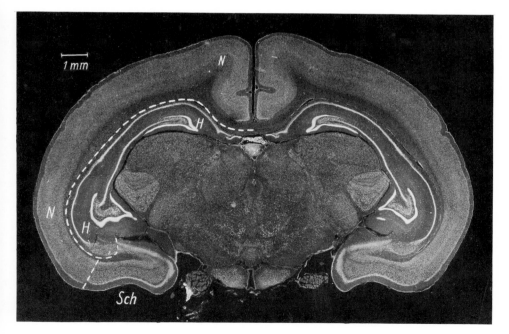

Figure 1. Projection of a histological section. *Galago demidovii* A 102, frontal section 636, cresylviolet stain, 20 μ thick. H Hippocampus, N Neocortex, Sch Schizocortex.

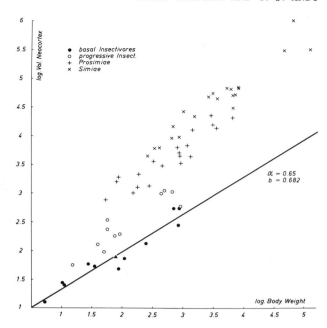

Figure 2. Volumes of neocortex in relation to body weight plotted on a double logarithmic scale. Reference base is the line through the point of the mean values for the basal insectivores with the most probable gradient for the neocortex, 0.65. This value was obtained by comparing as many related groups as possible. It expresses the most typical size relation between volume of the neocortex and body weight.

3, 5, and 7). Further comments about the methods used are contained in the figure legends.

The neocortex and the following divisions and structures of the allocortex were studied: bulbus olfactorius, paleocortex + amygdaloid complex, septum, schizocortex (= regio entorhinalis + praesubicularis), and hippocampus. Many of these parts are composed of several partial structures. A further subdivision of cerebral regions and the measurement of smaller and more circumscribed structural units are in progress.

The Ascending Primate Scale

All primates, as well as many, if not all, recent orders of placental mammals, have their phylogenetic origin in insectivore-like ancestors. This information has been derived from paleontological studies on fossils. Thus the results of the scientific approach, known as *comparative neuroanatomy*, can to a certain degree be used in the interpretation of phylogenetic evolution, if the comparisons are based on the insectivores.

The *recent* representatives of the insectivores (to which comparative neuroanatomical investigations are necessarily restricted) are not uniform with regard to brain development. With the aid of quantitative methods, we have tried (since 1956 together with Bauchot and Spatz) to identify the species with the most primitive cerebral pattern.

We have grouped together these primitive forms as *basal insectivores*.* To this group belong representatives of the tenrecs (Tenrecidae), hedgehogs (Erinaceidae), and shrews (Soricidae). Of all placental mammals the basal insectivores may be expected to show the least degree of change since their first appearance (permanent types). Hence, they can be expected to have remained comparatively similar to the early forerunners of the placental mammals and therefore to represent a good base of reference for evaluating evolutionary progress. The evolutionary progress is expected to be best indicated by that structure, the size of which most greatly increases in the course of evolution.

For each of the measured brain structures we have determined the average index of progression in the 20 prosimians, 21 simians, and the total of these 41 primates so far investigated. It was expected that the neocortex, which contains the most highly developed structures of the central nervous system, would show the strongest progression. Its extraordinary supremacy in comparison to all other measured structures is, however, surprising. In the prosimians the neocortex is, on the average, 14½ times and in the simians 45½ times as large as in the basal insectivores. Its size represents the best cerebral criterion presently available for the classification of a given species in a scale of increasing evolutionary stages. The graph based on the indices of neocortical progression (Fig. 3) shows that within the primates many different evolutionary stages are preserved in recent material.

This scale of increasing neocorticalization represents a quantitatively well founded *ascending primate scale*. It represents no direct evolutionary line, in which the respective higher forms have passed through the individual lower stages. However, it is very possible, and even likely, that one or the other of the lower forms is similar to those stages, through which the higher forms have evolved during phylogenesis.

The lowest position in the ascending primate scale (Fig. 3) is occupied by the tree shrews (Tupaiidae), the systematic classification of which is still debated,† and the Lepilemurini, including the genera *Lepilemur* and *Hapalemur* from Madagascar. The latter stand only slightly higher than the Tupaiidae (Index of Progression of the Neocortex: IPN=8.3 against 7.7). Comparatively low neocorticalization is shown by the mouse and dwarf lemurs (Cheirogaleinae): IPN=9.0 to 12.0. The highest indices of neocorticalization within the prosimians are found in the true lemurs (Lemurini): IPN=17.5 to 23.3; in the tarsier (*Tarsius*): IPN=21.5; and in the aye-aye (*Daubentonia*): IPN=26.5. The position of *Daubentonia* is uncommonly high and exceeds that of all other prosimians and advances into the province of the

---

* *Basal, basic form, basic group* is to be understood in the sense of "occupying within the *recent* placental mammals the lowest place in the characteristics of the brain." In the course of phylogenetic development the fossil relatives of these recent basal insectivores, which may have played a role in the evolution of the placental mammals, evidently represented stages of passage. For these fossils the term *layer* or *level* would be more appropriate.

† By some investigators they are classified as insectivores, whereas others consider them as primates. It is, however, almost generally admitted that they have to be placed in a transitional area between insectivores and primates. Regarding their indices of neocorticalization they are definitely more closely related to the prosimians. This fact supports the opinion accepted by the majority of investigators that they should be classified as subprimates, along with the prosimians. Recent suggestions that they should be separated entirely from both insectivores and primates are not well founded.

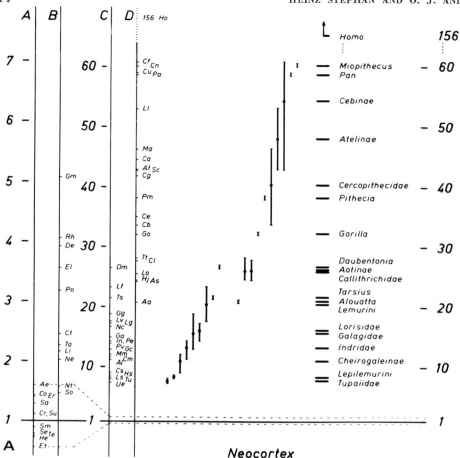

Figure 3. A Progression indices of the neocortex. They express the number of times the neocortex is larger than that of a typical basal insectivore of equal body weight. (a) On the left side (vertical columns) the species are listed: (A) basal insectivores, (B) progressive insectivores, (C) prosimians, (D) simians; in the middle (vertical bars) the systematic groups of primates are listed according to their respective variabilities; on the right side (horizontal bars) the averages of the indices within these systematic groups are listed. Order of the vertical bars (middle) from left to right according to increasing neocortical progressions (=ascending primate scale). Broken line=variability within the basal insectivores.

simians. The uncommonly low positions of the howler (*Alouatta*): IPN=20.8, and of the Gorilla (*Gorilla*): IPN=32.1, among the simians are surprising. Both genera are obviously more primitive in their brain development than hitherto assumed. The very high position of the talapoin (*Miopithecus*): IPN=60.1, is probably related to secondary "dwarfing" (Bauchot and Stephan, in press). Also unexpected is the very great distance of the human (*Homo*) from all other primates (Fig. 3b). This distance is quantitatively larger than is the step from the basal insectivores up to the chimpanzee. The uncommonly large neocortex of the human evidently represents the

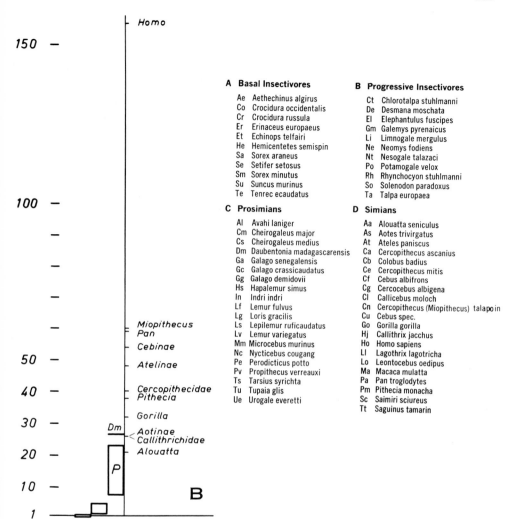

A Basal Insectivores

Ae	Aethechinus algirus
Co	Crocidura occidentalis
Cr	Crocidura russula
Er	Erinaceus europaeus
Et	Echinops telfairi
He	Hemicentetes semispin
Sa	Sorex araneus
Se	Setifer setosus
Sm	Sorex minutus
Su	Suncus murinus
Te	Tenrec ecaudatus

B Progressive Insectivores

Ct	Chlorotalpa stuhlmanni
De	Desmana moschata
El	Elephantulus fuscipes
Gm	Galemys pyrenaicus
Li	Limnogale mergulus
Ne	Neomys fodiens
Nt	Nesogale talazaci
Po	Potamogale velox
Rh	Rhynchocyon stuhlmanni
So	Solenodon paradoxus
Ta	Talpa europaea

C Prosimians

Al	Avahi laniger
Cm	Cheirogaleus major
Cs	Cheirogaleus medius
Dm	Daubentonia madagascarensis
Ga	Galago senegalensis
Gc	Galago crassicaudatus
Gg	Galago demidovii
Hs	Hapalemur simus
In	Indri indri
Lf	Lemur fulvus
Lg	Loris gracilis
Ls	Lepilemur ruficaudatus
Lv	Lemur variegatus
Mm	Microcebus murinus
Nc	Nycticebus cougang
Pe	Perodicticus potto
Pv	Propithecus verreauxi
Ts	Tarsius syrichta
Tu	Tupaia glis
Ue	Urogale everetti

D Simians

Aa	Alouatta seniculus
As	Aotes trivirgatus
At	Ateles paniscus
Ca	Cercopithecus ascanius
Cb	Colobus badius
Ce	Cercopithecus mitis
Cf	Cebus albifrons
Cg	Cercocebus albigena
Cl	Callicebus moloch
Cn	Cercopithecus (Miopithecus) talapoin
Cu	Cebus spec.
Go	Gorilla gorilla
Hj	Callithrix jacchus
Ho	Homo sapiens
Ll	Lagothrix lagotricha
Lo	Leontocebus oedipus
Ma	Macaca mulatta
Pa	Pan troglodytes
Pm	Pithecia monacha
Sc	Saimiri sciureus
Tt	Saguinus tamarin

Figure 3 (cont.) B A reduced scale to demonstrate the actual position of the human.

morphological basis for the very high and complex functional capacity of his central nervous system.

Macromorphology and Its Changes in the Ascending Primate Scale

We will discuss a few representatives of different evolutionary levels, namely, hedgehog (*Erinaceus*), galago (*Galago*), guenon (*Cercopithecus*), and human (*Homo*). The surface pattern of the various allocortical structures, which in the lower macrosmatic mammals shows a simple and clear arrangement, becomes rather complex

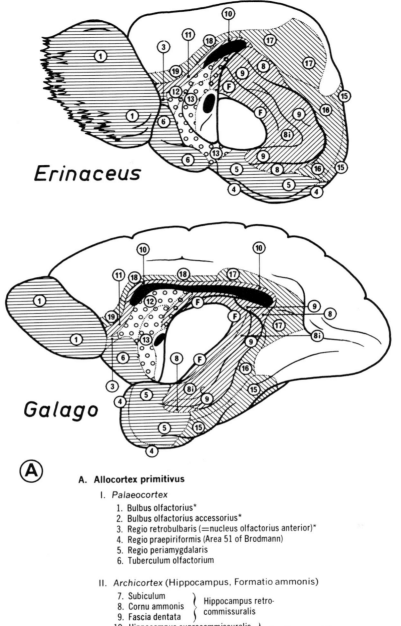

Erinaceus

Galago

A.

A. Allocortex primitivus

    I. *Palaeocortex*

        1. Bulbus olfactorius*
        2. Bulbus olfactorius accessorius*
        3. Regio retrobulbaris (=nucleus olfactorius anterior)*
        4. Regio praepiriformis (Area 51 of Brodmann)
        5. Regio periamygdalaris
        6. Tuberculum olfactorium

    II. *Archicortex* (Hippocampus, Formatio ammonis)

        7. Subiculum
        8. Cornu ammonis   Hippocampus retro-
        9. Fascia dentata   commissuralis
       10. Hippocampus supracommissuralis   Taenia tecta of Rose
       11. Hippocampus praecommissuralis

    Structures with uncertain affiliation

       12. Septum*
       13. Diagonal band of Broca (Regio diagonalis)*

Figure 4. Medial views of the telencephalon in *Erinaceus, Galago, Cercopithecus,* and *Homo*, showing the position and shape of the various allocortical regions in representatives of the ascending primate scale. Commissures are in black. F Fornix, 8 i Cornu ammonis inversus

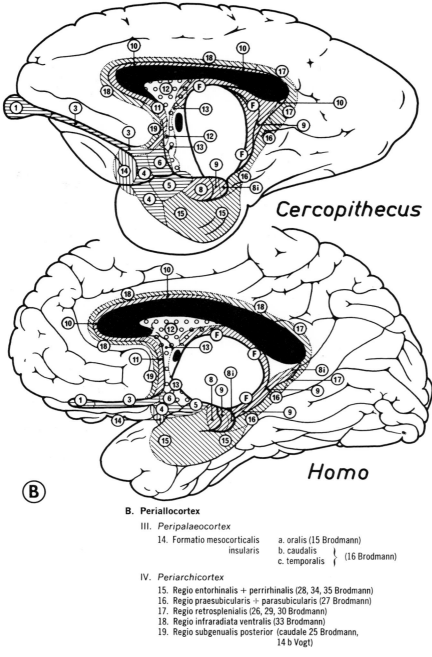

Cercopithecus

Homo

B

B. Periallocortex

    III. *Peripalaeocortex*

        14. Formatio mesocorticalis   a. oralis (15 Brodmann)
                          insularis   b. caudalis   (16 Brodmann)
                                      c. temporalis

    IV. *Periarchicortex*

        15. Regio entorhinalis + perrirhinalis (28, 34, 35 Brodmann)
        16. Regio praesubicularis + parasubicularis (27 Brodmann)
        17. Regio retrosplenialis (26, 29, 30 Brodmann)
        18. Regio infraradiata ventralis (33 Brodmann)
        19. Regio subgenualis posterior (caudale 25 Brodmann,
                                     14 b Vogt)

*These structures are not generally accepted as being cortical.

Figure 4. Medial views of the telencephalon in *Erinaceus, Galago, Cercopithecus,* and *Homo,* showing the position and shape of the various allocortical regions in representatives of the ascending primate scale. Commissures are in black. F Fornix, 8 i Cornu ammonis inversus

in the higher primates. The changes can be traced only in a few regions with the aid of macromorphological landmarks. In most of the cortical areas such landmarks are absent, and their location can only be determined by means of surface reconstructions. Figure 4 results from such reconstructions based on histological serial sections.

The changes in the position and shape of the allocortical structures in the ascending primate scale are primarily passive. They can be, directly or indirectly, related to the very pronounced expansion of the isocortex (neocortex).

The ventral section of the rhinencephalon, the *piriform lobe,* is separated from the pallium by the sulcus rhinalis lateralis. Its originally very wide, longitudinally oriented pars anterior becomes more and more narrow, is gradually displaced ventralward, and eventually assumes a position which is almost transversed to the longitudinal axis of the brain. As a consequence of the development of a true temporal lobe the pars posterior forms an increasingly larger angle with the pars anterior. The frontal surface of the pars posterior is shifted dorsalward and finally, in the human, becomes attached to the ventral surface of the pars anterior. In addition, the pars posterior is more and more displaced medialward by the ventrally expanding neocortex and is increasingly occupied by the periarchicortex, which advances from its caudal region. In the higher primates the pars posterior of the lobus piriformis is named gyrus parahippocampalis.

The *tuberculum olfactorium* is located caudal and medial to the pars anterior of the piriform lobe. This structure is practically not involved in the changes of shape and position of the remaining palaeocortex but represents, so to speak, a fixed landmark, which may serve as a reference point for determination of the aforementioned changes. Its relatively stable position is probably due to its close contact with parts of the basal ganglia (nucleus accumbens, complex of basal nucleus). The olfactory tubercle becomes more and more flattened and covered by the dorsal surface of the temporal lobe. In the higher primates it is only poorly developed.

The *bulbus olfactorius* is relatively large in the insectivores and lies entirely in front of the hemispheres. In the ascending scale it becomes relatively smaller and increasingly overgrown by the isocortical frontal lobe. However, even in the highest forms it retains its position below the tip of the frontal lobe. This is evidently due to its fixation to the lamina cribrosa, which moves forward as a part of the frontal bone when the frontal lobe undergoes its strong expansion. Since, as a part of the caudally adjoining structures, the olfactory tubercle is fixed in its position also, the process in higher primates results in a marked stretching of the intermediate structures (*pedunculus olfactorius*). At the same time the cortical structures of the olfactory peduncle (regio retrobulbaris) become more and more reduced. As a result, the fibers predominate in higher primates, and the peduncle is then frequently described as tractus olfactorius. In lower forms, the olfactory tract constitutes only a small part of the whole olfactory peduncle.

The changes in macromorphology of the *hippocampus* are mainly caused by the corpus callosum. The less differentiated *hippocampus praecommissuralis,* which in the primitive insectivores runs in a straight line from rostroventral caudodorsalward, becomes bent in primates, so that its dorsal aspect runs rostralward due to the strong expansion of the corpus callosum. Finally, it circles around the genu corporis callosi (Fig. 4).

Correspondingly, the *hippocampus retrocommissuralis* in its dorsal region is gradually displaced caudalward in concert with the strong extension of the corpus callosum caudally. Simultaneously, the ventral region is being displaced forward through the rotation of the temporal lobe (Spatz, 1966). The hippocampus thus rotates approximately 90° clockwise (Fig. 4). The ventral area is progressively enlarged in comparison with the dorsal one and becomes more and more folded into the depth of the temporal lobe. Essentially, in the simians, only the *uncus* remains on the surface.

Macromorphological changes in the periarchicortical surface are present mainly in the ventral part, i.e., in the schizocortex.

In the insectivores the *schizocortex* covers the caudal pole of the piriform lobe, which in these forms also represents the caudal pole of the total hemisphere. In the primates the lobus piriformis is progressively displaced in a ventral and finally a medial direction. The caudal pole now consists completely of the isocortical occipital lobe. The expansion of the temporal isocortex in a rostral and ventral-medial direction also carries with it the bordering schizocortex, so that this cortical region, which was originally behind the prepiriform and periamygdaloid formations, now comes to lie in the vicinity (*Cercopithecus*) and even partly in front (*Homo*) of the praepiriform and periamygdalar structures.

The *periamygdalar structures* cannot participate in these displacements because they are fixed to the subcortical parts of the amygdaloid complex. Thus the result is a rotation around this fixed region.

The changes in position and size of the *septum* must likewise be related to the strong expansion of the corpus callosum. In the lower forms the septum is wide and compact in transverse sections, and the well-developed septal nuclei extend immediately up to the corpus callosum. In the higher primates the corpus callosum moves away from these nuclei, and a true septum pellucidum is formed. For a more detailed analysis see Andy and Stephan (1966, 1968).

Volume Comparison of Various Allocortical Structures in the Ascending Primate Scale

COMPARISON OF THE PROPORTIONAL COMPOSITION OF THE ENDBRAIN

As Figure 4 and the macromorphological investigation have shown, the relative volume occupied by the allocortical centers in the total telencephalon becomes gradually smaller. This is also evident from Table 1. The relative decrease may be a result of a reduction of the allocortical centers themselves, but it could also be the consequence of a pronounced increase of other brain structures, for example of the neocortex. This question will be investigated by using the allometric method in the various allocortical regions.

ALLOMETRIC COMPARISON

In the same manner as the progression indices of the neocortex (Fig. 3), those of allocortical structures have also been arranged in scales (Figs. 5 and 7). These

TABLE 1

Percentages of the Various Parts of the Hemispheres in the Total Endbrain
(averaged within the systematic groups)

	Bulbus olfactorius	Palaeocortex + Amygdaloid Complex	Septum	Striatum	Schizocortex	Hippocampus	Neocortex
Basal Insectivores	17.6	30.2	2.9	7.6	5.3	14.3	22.0
Prosimians	2.9	6.6	1.2	7.7	3.3	7.0	71.5
Simians	0.2	2.4	0.5	5.7	1.1	2.6	87.6

scales give information about the comparative size of these structures in the individual species and in the systematic groups. To determine whether there are definite tendencies in the size alteration of the various structures in the ascending primate scale and which species show an especially strong deviation from a given trend, we have compared the progression indices of the individual structures directly with those of the neocortex (Figs. 6a and b). The progression indices of the neocortex are used as the quantitative expression for the position of the various species in the ascending primate scale.

Bulbus olfactorius (Figs. 5 and 6a). In most prosimians the olfactory bulb is more or less clearly reduced, although there exist some forms in which the size of the olfactory bulb is still insectivore-like. This is the case in the tree shrews, in the dwarf galago, and in the aye-aye (Indices of Progression: IP=1.3, 1.3 and 1.1, respectively). The remainder of the prosimians have smaller olfactory bulbs than does the average basal insectivore. A still rather large olfactory bulb is found in the potto (*Perodicticus*) and in the dwarf and mouse lemurs (Cheirogaleinae), the indices of which are 0.8 to 0.9. A more marked reduction, down to half the size of the olfactory bulb in the typical basal insectivore, is found in the galagos (with the exception of *Galago demidovii*), in the lorises, and in the true lemurs (IP=0.5 to 0.7). Still stronger is the reduction in the sportive and gentle lemurs (*Lepilemur* and *Hapalemur*), in the tarsier (*Tarsius*), and in the predominantly vegetarian indris (*Avahi, Propithecus*: IP=0.2 to 0.4). The indri (genus *Indri*) shows the strongest reduction of the olfactory bulb of all prosimians (IP=0.13). In this genus the size of the olfactory bulb is only one-eighth of that in a basal insectivore of the same body size.

In the simians the olfactory bulb is always strongly reduced. It is largest in the night monkey (*Aotes*), but even here its size is only one-fifth of that in the average basal insectivore (IP=0.20). In descending order follow the marmosets (*Callithricidae*: IP=0.1 to 0.2) and the Old World and New World monkeys, with indices between 0.06 and 0.13. There is a still greater reduction in the leaf-eating guerezas (*Colobus*) and howlers (*Alouatta*) and in the Gorilla (IP=0.04). A somewhat larger olfactory bulb is found in the chimpanzee (IP=0.07), whereas the human shows by far the greatest reduction of the olfactory bulb among all primates investigated (IP = 0.023). Thus, the size of the human olfactory bulb is less than one-fortieth that of basal insectivores.

Figure 6a shows a clear trend of olfactory bulb diminution correlated with increasing neocorticalization among the primates. One can note from this figure that in recent primates the decrease is very strong in the prosimian phase. In the beginning of the simian phase (having a general index of neocorticalization of 25) the olfactory bulb is already reduced by four fifths. The values approach asymptotically the zero line without reaching it. There exists no primate without an olfactory bulb.

Deviating from this general tendency, the olfactory bulbs of the dwarf galago (Gg) and the aye-aye (Dm) are by far less reduced than in other prosimians with the same degree of neocorticalization. Conversely, in all indrises and in the sportive and gentle lemurs the olfactory bulb is clearly more strongly reduced (Fig. 6a).

Accordingly, there exists no necessity that the neocortex can only develop when the centers of the olfactory system are simultaneously reduced. This is very well demonstrated by the situation in the elephant, which has a very well developed neocortex and, at the same time, a rather large olfactory system. The reduction of the olfactory centers appears as a functional adaptation, which is vastly paralleled in the primates with a progressive neocorticalization.

Paleocortex. The paleocortex, including the amygdaloid complex, shows no quantitative deviations from the basal insectivores up to the simians. The indubitably existing reduction of the olfactory structures of the paleocortical complex (demonstrated by surface measurements; Stephan, 1961) seems to be equalized by an enlargement of the higher centers of the amygdaloid complex. A further subdivision of the whole complex is planned.

Hippocampus. Figures 6b and 7 show a clear trend of hippocampal enlargement, correlated with increasing neocorticalization, among the prosimians. This trend, however, does not continue in the simians. The mean values remain unchanged, with an average progression index of 2.3. Comparatively low values are found among the prosimians in *Loris* and among the simians in *Gorilla*. Comparatively high values are found among the prosimians in *Lemur* and *Daubentonia*, and among the simians in *Homo*. The human has a progression index of 4.2; i.e., his hippocampus is more than 4 times as large as that of a hypothetical basal insectivore of the same body weight.

The wide scattering of the hippocampal indices for similar neocorticalization (Fig. 6b) indicates further that there is no close size relation between hippocampus and neocortex. Very high indices, up to 3.8, are reached in the Macroscelididae, which are progressive insectivores with a still poorly developed neocortex. The Macroscelididae are in this respect clearly separated from all other insectivores. Physiological and behavioral studies on this highly specialized group can perhaps throw some light upon the function of the hippocampus.

Schizocortex. Proportions similar to those observed in the hippocampus are also found in the schizocortex. Here again a clear progression is observed in the primates, in contrast to the basal insectivores. The mean progression index is somewhat higher than for the hippocampus. Within the prosimians a clearly progressive trend appears once more. This trend is not carried in the simians, but, as was the case in the hippocampus, there is stagnation or even a slight regression.

Alouatta and *Gorilla* show particularly low values. Comparatively high values

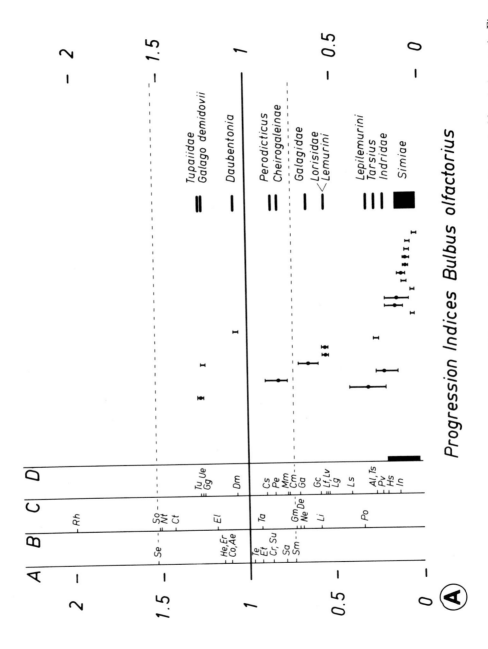

Figure 5. A Progression indices of the bulbus olfactorius. All species investigated. Explanation and abbreviations as in Figure 3.

122

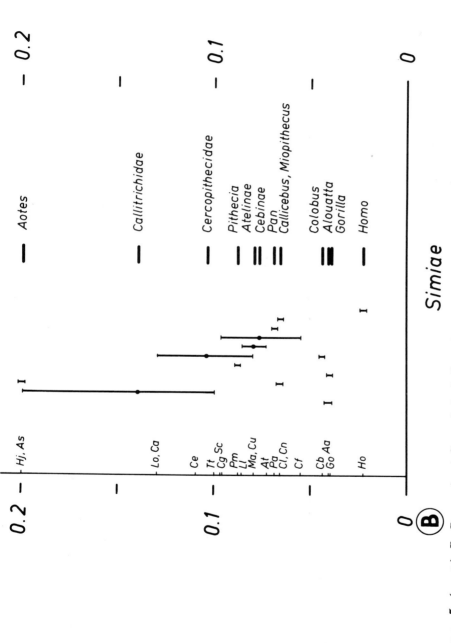

Figure 5. (*cont.*) **B** Progression indices of the bulbus olfactorius. Simiae plotted to an enlarged scale. Explanation and abbreviations as in Figure 3.

123

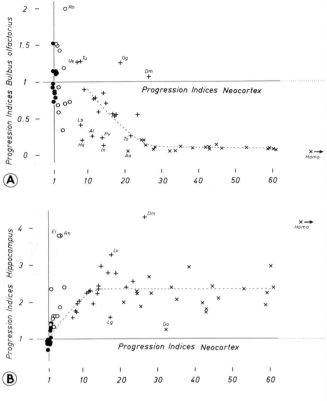

Figure 6. Progression indices of the bulbus olfactorius (a) and hippocampus (b) in relation to those of the neocortex. The broken lines represent the general course of size development of the olfactory bulb and hippocampus in the ascending primate scale.

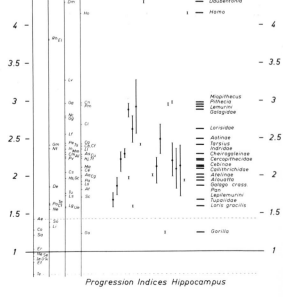

Figure 7. Progression indices of the hippocampus. Explanation and abbreviations as in Figure 3.

are present among the prosimians once more in *Daubentonia* (6.2), and among the simians, again in *Homo* (5.3).

The comparative neuroanatomical results resemble very strikingly those obtained for the hippocampus.

Septum. The proportions for the septum are also remarkably similar, although the progression indices are in general a little lower. The prosimians show a mean progression index of 1.9 at a fairly constant level; i.e., this value is reached very soon in low prosimians and does not change later. The same value is also retained in the simians. In this group, one finds a mean index of 2.1 when *Homo* is included and of 2.0 when he is excluded.

Very low values are found among the prosimians in *Lepilemur* and *Hapalemur* and among the simians, as before, in *Alouatta* and *Gorilla*, whereas high values are observed again in the prosimians for *Daubentonia* and in the simians for *Homo*. These results parallel perfectly those already reported for the hippocampus and the schizocortex.

Man has by far, for hippocampus, schizocortex, and septum, the highest *absolute* volume size among all the primates so far investigated. The volumes of these structures are in all cases more than twice as large for *Homo* as for *Gorilla*, the body size of which is much greater.

Intracerebral Volume Comparison and Its Functional Interpretation

From the results of the forgoing size comparisons in the ascending primate scale we can expect that hippocampus, schizocortex, and septum do not vary independently of one another.

This dependence becomes very clear when the volumes are correlated directly with one another (Fig. 8a). The exceptionally good correlation is entirely independent of the very distinct evolutionary levels of the various species. It holds true from the primitive insectivores up to man. When hippocampus and septum are compared, the slope of the regression line is almost exactly 1; i.e., when one of the structures doubles, so does the other one. On the other hand, the schizocortex, which represents more highly differentiated cortex, shows a somewhat more pronounced enlargement (Fig. 8a), and the slope of the regression line stays close to 1.1.

The well-known and very close functional interrelations between these three limbic structures are thus clearly reflected in their size interdependence. Correspondingly, surface measurements of the olfactory system structures have established that the secondary olfactory centers are reduced in exactly the same proportion as the primary olfactory bulb (Stephan, 1961). Here again very clear size relationships can be observed between structures which are functionally interdependent. One could expect to find equivalent size correlations between olfactory and limbic structures if both systems were in close functional interdependence.

However, the direct correlation of any limbic structure with the primary olfactory center makes it evident that this is not so. It is clear from Figure 8b, that a given size of the olfactory bulb may be correlated in different species to a very different

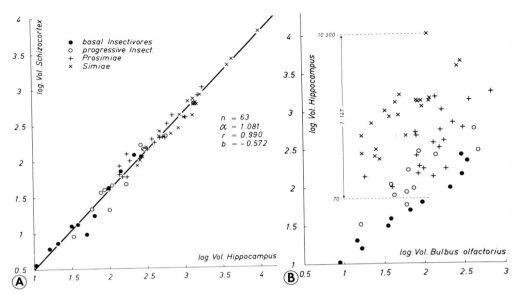

Figure 8. Size correlation between hippocampus and schizocortex (a) and bulbus olfactorius and hippocampus (b) in double logarithmic scales. In (a) the points are close to the regression line. In (b) the points are scattered over the whole scale. As an example, we see that the ratio of the volume of the human hippocampus to that of a basal insectivore (with the same olfactory bulb volume) is 10.300 to 70 cu mm or 147:1. The sizes of the two structures are obviously independent of one another.

size of the hippocampus. It is therefore indicated that the limbic structures develop independent of the olfactory structures.

This independence may also be expected from the above mentioned very distinct tendencies of the size developments in the ascending primate scale (compare Fig. 6a with Fig. 6b). The clear reduction of the olfactory structures stands in contrast to the progression of the limbic centers. In view of the comparative neuroanatomical investigations which established these highly diversified developmental trends, we believe that convincing reasons for the separation of the olfactory and limbic systems exist.

Although the function of the limbic system is not yet accurately known, it is obviously not dependent on a specific sense organ, as are for instance the visual, auditory, and gustatory systems. In contrast to these sense-dependent systems, such systems as the limbic system were described by Hassler (1964) as "sense-independent" systems.

The Functional Systems in Their Relationship to the Classification of the Allocortex

If we compare the distribution of the various allocortical subdivisions (Figs. 4 and 9b) with the position and extension of the limbic and olfactory structures (Fig. 9a), it becomes evident that the olfactory system is purely palaeocortical while the limbic system is predominantly archicortical and periarchicortical.

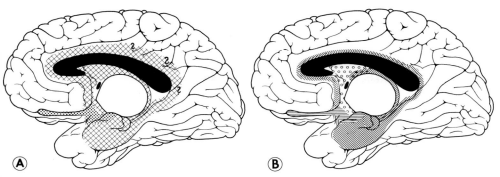

Figure 9. Position and extension of the olfactory (stippled area) and limbic (loosely crossed area) systems (a) and of the main regions of the allocortex (b) in man. Horizontal stripes = palaeocortex; vertical stripes = peripalaeocortex; oblique stripes up to right = archicortex; oblique stripes up left = periarchicortex; open circles correspond to septum and diagonal band, the architectonical attribution of which is uncertain.

Possibly the limbic system is entirely restricted to these latter types of cortex, so that it can more or less be described as the "system of archicortex" in a wider sense. In this case it would thus be more clearly definable from an anatomical point of view. But there are still some questions: (1) Septum and diagonal band, two structures which are undoubtedly limbic, have been assigned to the palaeocortex by many researchers. However, these two regions are so atypical in their cortical structure that their classification as palaeocortex is truly questionable. According to older results, such as those of Johnston (1913), they possess a closer developmental and morphological relationship to the archicortex. We are at present inclined to support this interpretation. (2) In the cingulate gyrus, one can distinguish several strips of cortical structures running parallel to the corpus callosum. It is uncertain if and to what degree the different strips truly belong to the limbic system and in which type of cortex they must be classified. Future research will determine whether or not the limbic system in this sphere goes beyond the border of the periarchicortex.

Attempt at a Phylogenetic Interpretation

In all probability the preceding size comparisons allow conclusions about the prevailing trends in the phylogenetic development of the parts of the allocortex, i.e., whether a progressive or a regressive development has taken place. This direction can reliably be determined also for certain structures, the size of which changes only little and in which an evolutionary trend is not recognizable without quantitative analysis. One such structure is the septum, which on the basis of simple macromorphological studies is generally believed to undergo strong reduction in the ascending primate scale, especially in the human. However, allometric investigations demonstrate just the opposite, i.e., a clearly progressive development (Andy and Stephan, 1966, 1968). The apparent reduction is suggested by the very strong enlargement of other parts of the brain, especially that of the neocortex.

Quantitative analysis has shown that of the allocortical structures under investigation, only the olfactory centers have undergone a regression, whereas all other structures have become larger during phylogeny. The by far strongest progression is found in the neocortex, and the indices of progression of the neocortex are therefore used to establish a quantitatively founded primate scale.

It is not possible, however, to make detailed statements concerning the specific ways in which the sizes of the structures of the recent species (which represent the end points of the individual evolutionary lines) have been reached. A continuous enlargement seems unlikely in such structures, as for example, the hippocampus, the size of which varies very strongly in the ascending primate scale (Fig. 6b). So many species and systematical groups deviate from the general trend of the hippocampus in the ascending scale (progressive phase from insectivores to prosimians; stagnation from prosimians to simians) that it seems more likely that during the development of this structure in the various species, strongly progressive phases have alternated with less strong or even with regressive ones. In addition it can be assumed that after splitting into the various phylogenetic lines, the further evolution of the given structures has become independent within these lines, regarding both the intensity of size alterations and the lapse of time. This is strongly suggested by the marked scattering of the indices of progression.

Thus it is possible that forms similar to recent prosimians may have played a role during the phylogenetic development of the simians, even if certain characteristics set them apart and outside the general trend in the ascending scale. For example, the observation of a very strong development of the olfactory bulb in the tree shrews (Fig. 6a; Ue, Tu) does not argue against the possible importance of tree shrew-like forms in primate phylogeny. It is theoretically possible that in a first evolutionary phase (from insectivores to tree shrew-like forms) the olfactory bulb became enlarged and, subsequently in a second phase, was strongly reduced. Comparative neuroanatomical results must be interpreted with great reserve when considering the exact way in which the recent end points of evolution may have been reached.

Histological Changes of Allocortical Structures in the Ascending Primate Scale

Are the reduction in size of the olfactory centers and the enlargement of the limbic centers accompanied by structural changes proceeding in specific directions?

Bulbus olfactorius (Fig. 10). Along with the distinct reduction in volume of the olfactory bulb, its histological pattern undergoes specific alterations, the most outstanding of which is a progressive dissolution of its layers. Whereas in the prosimians clearly defined laminae still exist, their distinctive structure is gradually lost in the progression from the monkeys up to man.

In the chimpanzee the layers seem to have completely disappeared in some places, whereas in others they are rather well preserved. In addition, the regular course of the layers is disturbed so that the laminae assume a tortuous course and bulge. These alterations, which in the chimpanzee are confined mainly to the rostral part of the bulb, involve the whole bulb in man.

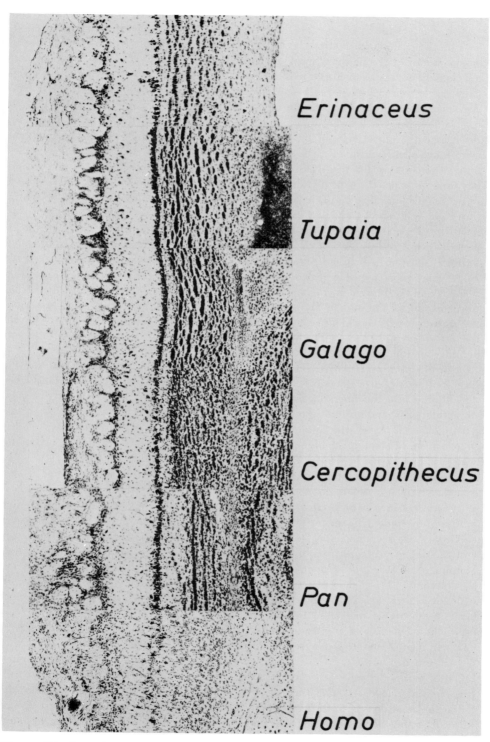

Erinaceus

Tupaia

Galago

Cercopithecus

Pan

Homo

Figure 10. Frontal sections through olfactory bulbs. Cresylviolet stain. All sections 20 μ thick, except for *Erinaceus* (10 μ).

In all species with a strongly reduced bulb the glomeruli (second layer) are no longer arranged in one or at most two strata, as is generally the case. Instead, they are densely packed, sometimes in three, four, or more strata. The size of the originally rather uniform glomeruli becomes more and more variable. The mitral (fourth) cell layer, well developed up to the higher primates, shows foci of beginning dissolution in the apes. It appears that in man the plexiform (third and fifth) layers are fused, and the mitral cells of the fourth layer are more widely scattered throughout a uniform plexiform layer. The mitral cell layer remains compact in a few places only. The width of the inner plexiform (fifth) layer increases strongly in the ascending primate scale. In contrast, the inner granular (sixth) layer is distinctly reduced in the higher primates, and in man it appears to be almost obliterated. The concentration of the granular cells in clodlike clusters becomes increasingly broken up.

Regio retrobulbaris (=*nucleus olfactorius anterior*). This region is located in the rostral part of the olfactory peduncle. It is characterized by a rather uniform, more or less broad pyramidal cell layer covered by a wide molecular layer. In the macrosmatic species it encircles the central olfactory ventricle or its remaining vestiges and becomes almost completely reduced in the ascending scale. In the higher primates and in the human the structure no longer exists as a continuous layer, but the remains of the retrobulbar cortex are scattered in the form of cell groups within the olfactory bulb and peduncle. The originally strongly dominating cell regions become quantitatively superseded by the fibers of the olfactory tract.

Regio praepiriformis. The praepiriform region is the most important and the largest olfactory cortical area. It is composed histologically of an outer plexiform layer (containing also the fibers of the lateral olfactory tract), a layer of darkly stained pyramidal cells, and an inner polymorphic layer. It is superficial to part of the claustrum. The cell layer, which is especially well developed in the prosimians, becomes increasingly broken up in higher primates. The general tendency in the ascending scale is characterized by dispersal of the cells and widening of the cell layers.

Similar tendencies are found in the *regio periamygdalaris*, which is not always easy to delimit from the regio praepiriformis.

Tuberculum olfactorium. The stratification of the olfactory tubercle is similar to that of the praepiriform cortex. In the ascending scale several distinct and directed alterations are recognizable. The deep polymorphic layer becomes gradually smaller and in higher primates does not exist, except as a few cell-poor and pale zones. Simultaneous with this reduction of the third layer, an increasing dissolution of the cell (second) layer takes place. In contrast to the insectivores and prosimians, in which it is always clear, this layer increasingly loses its character as a distinct cortical layer in the higher primates. In man the cortical character is entirely lost in places, especially in the caudal and medial regions. In the rostral and especially in the lateral parts, an identifiable second layer still exists.

Regio diagonalis. The diagonal band of Broca is a band of fibers, accompanied by large pyramidal cells. The ventral area is provided with a superficial, almost cell-free molecular layer (lamina zonalis), the appearance of which may suggest that the region be regarded as a cortical structure. Apart from an increase of the cell size with increasing body size structural alterations in the ascending primate scale could not be observed.

Septum. Structural alterations proceeding in a specific direction could not be detected in the septum. The nuclei retain their proper characteristics, by which they are identifiable through the whole ascending primate scale, from the basal insectivores up to man. As in the diagonal band, the cells become larger and more loosely arranged with increasing body size.

Hippocampus. The less differentiated rostral parts of the hippocampus (prae- and supracommissural hippocampus; see Fig. 4) become increasingly reduced in the ascending primate scale. In the praecommissural hippocampus a continuous cortical layer is scarcely recognizable in the higher primates and in man. It may thus be indicated that if a projection from the olfactory bulb to the hippocampus exists, it is probably directed to this rostral subdivision of the hippocampus.

The subiculum and field H_1 within the retrocommissural hippocampus (Fig. 4) are comparatively broad hippocampal areas with loosely arranged cells. They show a relative increase toward the higher primates (from 10 percent in *Setifer* to 13 to 14 percent in *Crocidura* and *Galemys*, 15 percent in *Galago*, and 44 percent in *Cercopithecus*). The main increase is thus between prosimians and simians. Inversely, fields H_2 and H_3, characterized by a narrow band of densely crowded cells, clearly show a relative decrease. The proportion of the fascia dentata shows a slight relative decrease with respect to the total hippocampus (from 22 percent to 15 percent). The measurements available are not sufficient for a strictly allometric comparison.

Schizocortex. Progressive trends are more pronounced in the schizocortex, which represents a more highly differentiated cortical structure. The schizocortex is characterized by the presence of one or several almost cell-free zones between the various layers (Rose, 1927). The schizocortex is made up of the regio entorhinalis, regio perirhinalis, and regio prae- and parasubicularis. The regio entorhinalis is by far the most extensively developed of these.

In the hedgehog the *regio entorhinalis* is still undifferentiated (Fig. 11). A wide lamina dissecans is intercalated between an external and an internal cell layer. In *Lepilemur* (a primitive prosimian) the external zone is already clearly differentiated into two cell layers. The lamina dissecans is narrow and sharply defined. In *Cercopithecus* and *Homo* the internal zone is differentiated and can be subdivided into at least two clear sublayers. In man the lamina dissecans is not so distinct in that part of the regio entorhinalis here represented, but in the rostromedial region close to the amygdala two very distinct laminae dissecantes can be observed. His entorhinal area can be subdivided into a series of well-defined subareas (Rose described 23). In the hedgehog on the other hand its whole extension appears almost uniform. As a whole, the size increase of the entorhinalis in the primates keeps pace with a very clear structural differentiation.

A similar trend is observed in the *regio praesubicularis*, which is very well developed in the primates and can hardly be recognized as such in the primitive insectivores.

Summary

A comparative investigation on macromorphology, volume, and structural differentiation of various representative structures of the allocortex [bulbus olfactorius, palaecortex+amygdaloid complex, septum, schizocortex (=regio entorhinalis+

Lepilemur

Homo

Erinaceus

Cercopithecus

praesubicularis), and hippocampus] was made in 20 prosimian and 21 simian species and in primitive basal insectivores (related extinct species of which are generally considered to be forerunners of the primates). A classification of the allocortex and a definition of its main subdivisions are given.

The volume comparisons are expressed with the aid of the allometric method. From insectivores to primates and within the series of primate brains, the by far highest progression is found in the neocortex. Its allometric size (expressed by indices of progression, IP) represents the best cerebral criterion at present available for the evolutionary level of a given species. A scale based on the indices of neocortical progression represents a quantitatively well founded *ascending primate scale*.

The *changes in position and shape* of the allocortical structures in the ascending primate scale are primarily passive. They may, directly or indirectly, be related to the very pronounced expansion of the isocortex (neocortex). The allocortex, still dominating in the telencephalon of the basal insectivores, becomes increasingly displaced back onto a ring surrounding the corpus callosum and the hilus of the hemispheres. In the primates it becomes definitely smaller (i.e., relative to the total telencephalon).

The *allometric volume comparisons* show, however, that a true size reduction is found only in the olfactory centers (to a lesser degree in the prosimians than in the simians), whereas the centers of the limbic system (septum, hippocampus and schizocortex) increase in size. This progression is greatest in prosimians, whereas in simians the further increase is only small. The relative diminution (related to the total telencephalon) is the consequence of a pronounced increase of other brain structures, for example, of the neocortex in the ascending primate scale.

There exists a clear interdependence between functional and quantitative interrelationships. Within both limbic and olfactory systems, the structures have very impressive size correlations with one another which suggest a close functional relationship. In contrast, the size of the limbic structures is completely independent of that of the primary olfactory center (olfactory bulb). This independence is also obvious from the above mentioned distinct tendencies of size development in the ascending primate scale. The clear reduction of the olfactory structures stands in contrast to the progression of the limbic centers.

The trends in the ascending primate scale may in all probability reflect the prevailing phylogenetic trends. The results must, however, be interpreted with all reserve when considering the exact and specific way in which the brain structure volumes of the recent species (which represent the end points of evolution) have been reached.

The changes in size are paralleled by structural changes. The reduction of the olfactory bulb is accompanied by directed alterations, the most outstanding being an increasing effacement of the layers and a diminution of the inner granular cells. An

Figure 11. Frontal sections through the rostral regio entorhinalis. Cresylviolet stain.

a. *Erinaceus europaeus* 939, section 1340, 10 µ thick, x 32.
b. *Lepilemur ruficaudatus* M 73, section 1022, 15 µ thick, x 34.
c. *Cercopithecus ascanius* A 219, section 1270, 20 µ thick, x 10.5.
d. *Homo sapiens* 1044, section 3210, 20 µ thick, x 6.7.

effacement of the layers is also found in the secondary olfactory cortices. No essential histological alterations are determinable in the diagonal band and in the septum, whereas in the schizocortex a distinct progress in structural differentiation is present. The entorhinal cortex is especially large and well differentiated in man.

As far as is possible with metrical and comparative histological methods, we were able to show that the limbic system structures do not undergo any regression in phylogeny but show evidence progress in volume increase and structural differentiation. This is in clear opposition to the olfactory system structures, which become reduced both in size and differentiation. In view of the comparative neuroanatomical investigations which established these highly diversified developmental trends, we believe that convincing reasons for the separation of the olfactory and limbic systems exist.

The functional separation of the allocortical structures into olfactory and limbic systems corresponds adequately with the recent subdivisions (based primarily on ontogenesis; as suggested by Filimonoff) into palaeocortex, peripalaeocortex, archicortex, and periarchicortex. The archicortex and periarchicortex contain the limbic structures (archicortical limbic system), and the palaeocortex (and probably the peripalaeocortex as well) contain the olfactory structures (palaeocortical olfactory system).

REFERENCES

Andy, O. J., and H. Stephan. 1966. Phylogeny of the primate septum telencephali. *In* Hassler, R., and H. Stephan, eds. Evolution of the Forebrain, 389-399. Stuttgart, Thieme.
——— and H. Stephan. 1968. The septum in the human brain. J. Comp. Neurol., 133: 383-409.
Bailey, P., and G. Bonin. 1951. The Isocortex of Man. Urbana, University of Illinois Press.
Bauchot, R., and H. Stephan. 1966. Données nouvelles sur l'encéphalisation des Insectivores et des Prosimiens. Mammalia, 30:160-196.
——— and H. Stephan. 1968. Etude des modifications encéphaliques observées chez les Insectivores adaptés à la recherche de nourriture en milieu aquatique. Mammalia, 32:228-275.
Brodmann, K. 1909. Vergleichende Lokalisationslehre. Leipzig, J. A. Barth.
Filimonoff, I. N. 1947. A rational subdivision of the cerebral cortex. Arch. Neurol. Psychiat. 58:296-311.
Gastaut, H., and H. J. Lammers. 1961. Anatomie du Rhinencéphale. *In* Alajounanine, T. ed. Les Grandes Activités du Rhinencéphale. Paris, Masson et Cie.
Hassler, R. 1964. Zur funktionellen Anatomie des limbischen Systems. Nervenarzt, 35: 386-396.
Johnston, J. B. 1913. The morphology of the septum, hippocampus, and pallial commissures in reptiles and mammals. J. Comp. Neurol., 23:371-478.
Meynert, Th. 1868. Der Bau der Großhirnrinde und seine örtlichen Verschiedenheiten nebst einem pathologisch-anatomischen Corollarium. Leipzig.
——— 1872. Vom Gehirne der Säugetiere. *In* Stricker's Handb. d. Lehre v. d. Gewebe, 694-808.
Rose, M. 1927. Die sog. Riechrinde beim Menschen und beim Affen. J. Psychol. Neurol., 34:261-401.
Sanides, F. 1962. Die Architektonik des menschlichen Stirnhirns. Zugleich eine Darstellung der Prinzipien seiner Gestaltung als Spiegel der stammesgeschichtlichen

Differenzierung der Großhirnrinde. Monographien aus dem Gesamtgebiet der Neurologie und Psychiatrie, 98. Berlin, Göttingen, Heidelberg, Springer.

Spatz, H. 1966. Gehirnentwicklung (Introversion-Promination) and Endocranialausguß. *In* Hassler, R., and H. Stephan, eds. Evolution of the Forebrain, 136-152. Stuttgart, Thieme.

Stephan, H. 1960. Methodische Studien über den quantitativen Vergleich architektonischer Struktureinheiten des Gehirns. Z. Wiss. Zool., 164:143-172.

———— 1961. Vergleichend-anatomische Untersuchungen an Insektivorengehirnen. V. Die quantitative Zusammensetzung der Oberflächen des Allocortex. Acta Anat., 44: 12-59.

———— 1966. Größenänderungen im olfaktorischen und limbischen System während der phylogenetischen Entwicklung der Primaten. *In* Hassler, R., and H. Stephan, eds. Evolution of the Forebrain, 377-388. Stuttgart, Thieme.

———— 1967a. Quantitative Vergleiche zur phylognetischen Entwicklung des Gehirns der Primaten mit Hilfe von Progressionsindices. Mitt. Max-Planck-Ges., 2:63-86.

———— 1967b. Zur Entwicklungshöhe der Insektivoren nach Merkmalen des Gehirns und die Definition der "Basalen Insektivoren." Zool. Anz., 179:177-199.

———— and O. J. Andy. 1964. Quantitative comparisons of brain structures from Insectivores to Primates. Amer. Zool., 4:59-74.

———— and H. Spatz. 1962. Vergleichend-anatomische Untersuchungen an Insektivorengehirnen. IV. Gehirne afrikanischer Insektivoren. Versuch einer Zuordnung von Hirnbau und Lebensweise. Morph. Jb., 103:108-174.

Vogt, C., and O. Vogt. 1956. Weitere Ausführungen zum Arbeitsprogramm des Hirnforschungsinstitutes. J. Hirnforsch., 2:403-427.

Vogt, O. 1910. Nouvelle contribution à l'étude de la myéloarchitecture de l'écorce cérébrale. Congrès des neurologistes et aliénistes de langue francaise à Bruxelles.

6

Functional Architecture of Motor and Sensory Cortices in Primates in the Light of a New Concept of Neocortex Evolution*

FRIEDRICH SANIDES

Department of Anatomy,
University of Ottawa, Canada.

The Concept of Duality of the Neocortex

The dual structure of the neopallium—a parapiriform moiety and a parahippocampal moiety—was first conceived by Dart (1934) as a result of painstaking architectonic and stimulation studies on various South African reptiles. These studies were an outgrowth of the principal investigations of Johnston (1915), Crosby (1917), and Elliot Smith (1919) on the forebrain of reptiles. Dart already anticipated the principle of duality to be valid for the mammalian neocortex. Actually, it was Abbie who succeeded in presenting architectonic evidence of the duality of the neocortex, first in monotremes (1940) and later in marsupials (1942). In cytoarchitectonic terms Abbie subdivided the entire neocortex of echidna and platypus into two major components, one related to and adjacent to the hippocampus (archicortex), the other one to the piriform cortex (paleocortex). Both moieties show a differentiation into several stages. Within the parahippocampal neocortex Abbie distinguished four successive stages of differentiation and within the parapiriform neocortex three stages. This progressive differentiation takes place in both major components by thickening of the cortex, accentuation of the lamination, and eventually appearance of granular cells (granularization). In the marsupial *Perameles*, Abbie (1942) found the principle of the "dual nature of the neopallium" fully sustained. He concluded that the different architectonic fields represent successive waves of circumferential differentiation in evolution, commencing from the hippocampus and from the piriform cortex, respectively.

These important works of Abbie did not receive the attention they merit. Thus,

* This work was supported by grants from the Medical Research Council of Canada.
The author wishes to thank Dr. W. Hendelman for proofreading the manuscript and for his helpful comments on English usage, and Mrs. E. Baranyak for the preparation of the histological material.

20 years later, in 1962, on the basis of cytoarchitectonic and myeloarchitectonic data in the extensive human frontal lobe, we independently proposed the same principle: the dual origin of the neocortex. The combination of the cytoarchitectonic and myelo-architectonic methods proved to be particularly valuable, not only in outlining the coinciding areas more reliably but also in tracing differential trends in several successive areas. The myeloarchitectonic method is advantageous because, operating at lower magnification, a series of architectonic areas can be surveyed simultaneously (Fig. 5).

Since our initial findings in the frontal lobe of man (1962a, b, 1964) we found the principle of a dual origin of neocortical differentiation confirmed in a series of primates (*Nycticebus, Saimiri, Macaca, Pan*), in Carnivora (cat, raccoon), in Rodentia (rat), in Insectivora (*Erinaceus*), and in Chiroptera (*Myotis lucifugus*).

A diagrammatic presentation of this principle is illustrated in the frontal lobes of man and monkey (Fig. 1). It is important to recall that the greatly expanded neocortical lobes of higher mammals still are bordered ventromedially and ventrolaterally by the old protocortices, the archicortex and the paleocortex. In the coronal sections of primates' frontal lobes (Fig. 1) the archicortex is represented by the supracallosal hyppocampus (vH, the vestigia hippocampi of Elliot Smith, 1919),

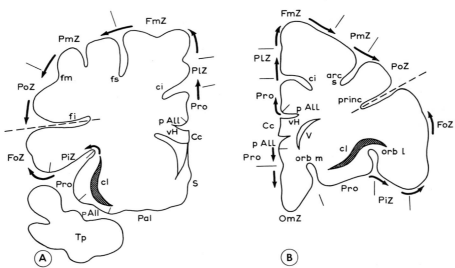

Figure 1. Coronal diagrams of frontal lobe of man (a) and monkey (b). The arrows indicate the differential trends from the cingular proisocortex (Pro) medially and the insular proisocortex laterally. Because of the lesser vault of the frontal lobe of the monkey the plane at the level of the sulcus principalis does not pass through the paleo-cortex (Pal)—the last source of insulolimbic differentiation—but only through the caudo-orbital claustrocortex (Pro). The paleocortex is present in the section through the human brain. The dashed line through sulcus frontalis inferior (fi) in man and sulcus principalis (princ) in monkey marks the basic medio/limbic borderline of the two pre-frontal spheres. Sulci: arc, arcuatus superior; ci, cinguli; fm, frontalis medius; fs, frontalis superior; orbm, orbitalis medialis; orbl, orbitalis lateralis; Cc, corpus callosum; cl, claustrum; S, septum; V, ventricle; for further abbreviations see Table 1.

whereas the bulk of the primate hippocampus is displaced by a sagittal rotation into the depth of the temporal lobe. The paleocortex, although reduced in the microsmatic simian primates, retains its original ventral position (Pal, Fig. 1a). Because the vault of the frontal lobe of the monkey is less than in man, a coronal section through the equivalent frontal regions of the convexity in the former does not include the paleocortex but rather the neocortical proisocortex, caudo-orbitally (Pro, Fig. 1b). (See Table 1 for abbreviations.)

It appears necessary to insert some remarks on the nomenclature of the cortical architecture. Most of the terms which we use were originally coined by Brodmann (1909) and C. and O. Vogt (1919). The neocortex, insofar as it passes through a six-laminated period during fetal life, is referred to as isogenetic cortex (isocortex). The older cortices—the medial archicortex (hippocampal formation of mammals) and the lateral paleocortex (olfactory cortex proper) which exhibit peculiar characteristics in addition to very limited lamination—are called the allogenetic cortex (allocortex). However, as we will see, two successive intermediate structural steps (Filimonoff, 1947; Sanides, 1962b; Stephan, 1963) are intercalated between the primitive allocortex and the mature isocortex, namely, the periallocortex (which is adjacent to the primitive allocortex) and the proisocortex (which is adjacent to the mature isocortex). The most primitive types of allocortex are also referred to as allocortex primitivus (Fig. 1).

The characteristic periallocortex and proisocortex show different regional and areal architectonic elaborations, in relationship to the bordering isocortical lobes. Medially, adjacent to the archicortex, they are bound to the limbic lobe, and ventrolaterally, adjacent to the paleocortex, they are bound to the insula Reilii, which was formerly called the stem lobe. Both these "lobes" are phylogenetically old structures. The insular cortex should be designated as part of the limbic cortex for ontogenetic and phylogenetic reasons (Yakovlev, 1959). The anterior cingulate gyrus and the anterior insular cortex exhibit basic architectonic resemblances.

It was Meynert (1872) who made the basic observation that looking at the freshly exposed brain we can distinguish two major components of cortex, that with a whitish surface and that with a greyish surface. The latter corresponds to the entire isocor-

TABLE 1. *Explanation of Abbreviations*

A I	primary auditory area	Pal	paleocortex
A II	secondary auditory area	pAll	periallocortex
All	allocortex primitivus	parK	parakoniocortex
FmZ	frontomotor zone	parM	paramotor area
FoZ	frontopercular zone	PiZ	parinsular zone
FpZ	frontopolar zone	PlZ	paralimbic zone
G	gustatory area	PmZ	paramotor zone
Gig	area gigantopyramidalis	PoZ	paropercular zone
H	hippocampus	pre Fr	prefrontal cortex
Ism	intermediate sensorimotor area	preM	premotor area
Ka	auditory koniocortex	proM	promotor area
Ks	somatic koniocortex	proK	prokoniocortex
lam. diss.	lamina dissecans	Prt	parietal cortex
Mpl	supplementary motor area	SmI	primary somatic area
MsI	primary motor area	SmII	secondary somatic area
OmZ	orbitomedial zone		

tex, and the former corresponds to the allocortex, including periallocortex. The whitish color reflects the fact that the cell-poor molecular or zonal layer possesses here particularly strong tangential fiber plexuses of which the striae olfactorii fibers are one example. This condition corresponds to the primitivity of the allocortex which does not yet depend exclusively on thalamic afferents.

In cytoarchitectonics we can disregard the first cell-poor layer. For example the so-called second layer of the isocortex forms the first real cellular layer. The periallocortex (the first architectonic step away from allocortex primitivus) is composed of two real cell strata, with emphasis on the inner one, and with a more or less discernible narrow layer devoid of cells in between. This blank layer is referred to as lamina dissecans (Figs. 3 and 16), since it cuts the cortical plate into the two cell strata. These strata are not comparable with the laminae of the isocortex. However, we will consider how the latter emerge from the former in the differential process of evolution.

The next step, *proisocortex*, is more laminated in that the inner stratum is differentiated into a pyramidal-celled layer V and spindle-celled layer VI. At the same time the outer stratum further differentiates into pyramidal-celled layer III adjacent to the relatively small-celled dense layer II. Actually there is a relative increase in emphasis of the outer stratum. In addition a fourth granular layer can make its first appearance in the level of the former lamina dissecans. Lamina IV belongs, in our classification as derived from comparative architectonic studies (Sanides and Krishnamurti, 1967), to the outer stratum. The proisocortex of the anterior cingulate gyrus is distinguishable from that of the anterior insula in that it is devoid of a lamina IV; i.e., it is agranular. The insular proisocortex has an incipiently granular to well-developed granular layer.

The limbic and insular proisocortices are adjacent to the paralimbic zone (PIZ) and a parinsular zone (PiZ), respectively (Fig. 1). By zones we mean belts of fields, each at a similar differential stage. Thus the numerous individual human architectonic areas of the frontal lobe can be organized into an array of consecutive zones. Commencing with the archicortical supracallosal hippocampus and its periarchicortex (pAll) is the sequence of proisocortex (Pro), paralimbic zone (PlZ), frontomotor zone (FmZ), paramotor zone (PmZ), and paropercular zone (PoZ). Commencing with the basal paleocortex and its ventroinsular peripaleocortex (pAll) is the sequence of the insular proisocortex (Pro), the parinsular zone, (PiZ), and the frontopercular zone (FoZ), which occupies the inferior frontal gyrus.

Thus the dividing line between predominantly archicortical limbic influences and predominantly paleocortical insular influences in the prefrontal cortex appears to be the inferior frontal sulcus (Fig. 1a). Moreover, in the dorsal part of the pars triangularis on the inferior frontal gyrus (corresponding to Vogt's area 58) and in the center of the orbital cortex [corresponding to Vogt's area 60, (Fig. 4)] bound to the transverse orbital sulcus are maximally differentiated areas within the prefrontal cortex of man which appear to be the product of an integration of medial limbic and insulolimbic influence (Sanides, 1962b, 1964, and Fig. 26).

As Figure 1b shows, essentially the same zonal array is valid for the frontal lobe of rhesus monkey. On the basis of combined cytoarchitectonic and myeloarchitectonic studies, the less elaborated frontal granular cortex can be shown to exhibit the same differential zones. The dividing line here between the medial limbic zone of influence and the insulolimbic zone of influence is the sulcus principalis, which is the equivalent to the inferior frontal sulcus of man (Sanides and Schiltz, 1967).

Concerning the sulcus principalis as being the limit between the medial limbic influenced moiety and the lateral insulolimbic influenced moiety of the rhesus monkey's frontal granular cortex, Nauta (1964) arrived at a remarkably similar conclusion, using quite another approach. He traced prefrontolimbic connections with his experimental silver technique. He refers to "a certain dualism in the prefrontolimbic associations" in that the dorsomedial part of the prefrontal cortex is projecting mainly on the cingulum bundle in the cingulate gyrus and from there backward to retrosplenial and parahippocampal regions. On the other hand, the ventrolateral part of the prefrontal cortex, including the orbital cortex, projects mainly, by the uncinate fascicle, onto the rostral temporal lobe, from where connections to the amygdala are projected. In addition, collaterals leave the uncinate fascicle, as it passes through the capsula extrema, and terminate in the claustrum. Such collaterals, according to the concept of Bishop (1959), may possibly be the evolutionarily older fiber connections. In this way Nauta also found the principal sulcus to be a fundamental borderline between both spheres of prefrontolimbic connections.

To demonstrate the main features of the differential trends from both limbic bordering regions, which we will refer to as "ur-trends," * we begin with the cytoarchitectonics of the proisocortex of the anterior cingulate gyrus (Fig. 2). It exhibits as the most striking characteristic a bandlike fifth layer of dense medium-sized pyramidal cells, which was also described by Bailey and von Bonin (1951) as a "juxtallocortical" feature. Another conspicuous limbic feature of the anterior cingulate gyrus in man is the presence of large, extremely slender pyramidal and spindle cells, called rod cells, in its deep sublayer Vb. The latter are not present in the insular proisocortex, but the bandlike lamina V is the same there as in the cingulate gyrus. The limbic features undergo a diminution in the adjacent paralimbic (Fig. 1) and parinsular (PiZ) belts, respectively. At the same time new progressive characteristics emerge, for example, increase in overall cell size, and especially a relative increase of lamina III, which is still weak in Pro, particularly in the anterior cingular one. These are the two main cytoarchitectonic trends. It must be added that on the way to FmZ with its large efferent lamina V pyramidal cells, the PIZ is intermediate with regard to lamina V pyramidal cells which are larger and much less dense than in Pro with its band of smaller lamina V pyramidal cells, and on the other hand smaller and denser than those of FmZ.

After passing FmZ in the lateral direction a granular lamina IV makes its initial appearance in PmZ, marking the beginning of a stepwise granularization. At the same time the large efferent V pyramidal cells begin to decrease in size, step by step, and the pronounced increase in size of the lamina IIIc pyramidal cells bordering lamina IV continues. The differential trend from the insular Pro is basically similar. One main difference, however, is that the anterior insular Pro is, as mentioned above, not agranu-

---

* In our German monograph on the frontal lobe we referred to the differential "trends" issuing from the archicortex medially and from the paleocortex laterally as "Ur-gradations," meaning, primeval or protogradations. We prefer now to speak of trends instead of gradations and propose the term "ur-trends" for both primeval trends. The old Germanic stem "ur" is preserved in the English in "ordeal."

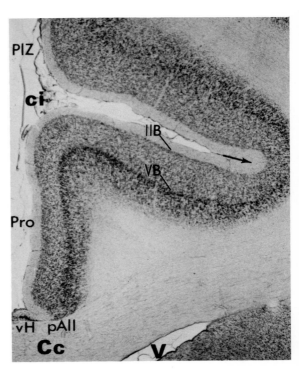

Figure 2. Proisocortex (Pro) of anterior cingulate gyrus of *Macaca*. PlZ, paralimbic zone. VB, bandlike V of dense pyramidal cells, which are larger and less dense in PlZ. IIB, accentuated II of Proisocortex. Cc, corpus callosum; ci, cingulate sulcus.

lar as is the anterior cingular Pro, but is dysgranular where it borders the precentral motor cortex. This means that there is a weak lamina IV which is still intermingled with lamina IIIc pyramidal cells. More rostrally the insular cortex has an even better demarcated lamina IV. In consequence the granularization proceeds faster from the insular cortex and culminates in the inferior frontal gyrus. The most remarkable fact is that even with the fundamental structural contrasts between the archicortex and paleocortex, there exists a striking similarity of the medial and lateral differential trends.

The cytoarchitectonic sequence of zones in man is illustrated in our frontal lobe monograph (Sanides, 1962b). As the frontal diagram (Fig. 1a) shows, the sequence occurs over a series of gyri. The fundamental relationships of architectonic areas to the sulcogyral configuration will be considered on page 149. We have, however, the unique possibility of demonstrating the main stages of the differential trend in an unconvoluted stretch of cortex without interference of surface indentations. This opportunity is offered by the Simian primates' gyrus rectus alongside the olfactory sulcus. The horizontal section through the gyrus rectus of the squirrel monkey (Fig. 3) demonstrates the range of differentiation from allocortex (All, precommissural hippocampus) successively through periallocortex (pAll), proisocortex (Pro), orbitomedial zone (OmZ) to the granular frontopolar zone (FpZ).

Before we discuss this differential trend in the squirrel monkey, it is necessary to clarify some aspects of comparative cytoarchitectonics. The major source of the difficulty encountered in comparing cortical areas and in examining homologies in mam-

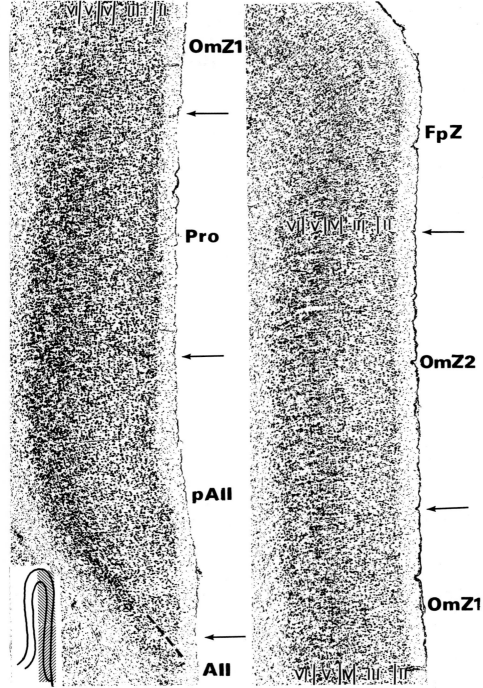

Figure 3. Horizontal section through gyrus rectus of *Saimari*; b is rostral to and continuous with a x 36 (See table 1 for abbreviations)

mals of different organization levels is the greater density of nerve cell bodies in lower mammals. The best characterization of this phenomenon is given by the grey-cell coefficient (von Economo and Koskinas, 1925), which is the ratio of the total volume of a nucleus or cortical area to the sum of the volumes of the perikarya (cell bodies) of the nerve cells contained within. Thus, it is virtually a measure of the interperikaryal space of an area. Ascending the scale of primates, this ratio increases markedly and is highest for man. Computed with modern methods in different series of mammals, the grey-cell coefficient is generally considered to be an indication of the level of organization of the cerebral cortex (Shariff, 1953; Haug, 1956). Moreover, there is also a correlation with brain size and weight (Cragg, 1967).

Thus, the cerebral cortex of the squirrel monkey has a cell density more than twice that of man, as does the cortex of the prosimian Nycticebus. This is expressed by the tendency of cell layers to fuse, at low magnification, a prerequisite for the evaluation of cell populations. In spite of this changing average cytoarchitectonic picture we can recognize and pursue the differential trends, first described in man, without difficulty.

As the insert of Figure 3 shows, we deal with a horizontal section through the whole length of the median cortex of the gyrus rectus representing the posterior half (left) and anterior half (right). Immediately caudal to the primitive cortex (All) is the nucleus of the diagonal band (DB). Irregular groupings of middle-sized dark staining cells without any lamination are found in this wedge-shaped cortical formation (All). This is the small remnant of allocortex primitivus of the precommissural hippocampus at this level. At its surface All becomes superposed by less darkly staining smaller pyramidal and multiform cells of the outer stratum. An indication of a lamina dissecans (dashed line) is present at the edge of the darker and denser celled inner stratum and the lighter and looser celled outer stratum. This is the two-strata-periallocortex (pAll). At the outer rim of the outer stratum is a condensation of darker, somewhat larger cells. These are forerunners of a layer II. Without any sharp edge the transition occurs into the better laminated Pro. The inner stratum exhibits an incipient differentiation in laminae V and VI, with the darker staining pyramidal cells in lamina V. At the same time within the outer stratum a third layer (III) with larger pyramidal cells in the deeper part emerges. Layer II is accentuated, continuing the cell condensations of pAll.

The transition to the next area, the first orbitomedial area (OmZ1), again without a sharp boundary, shows a further progress in lamination by the emergence of an incipient inner granular layer (IV). This is the dysgranular stage with granule cells still intermingled with small pyramidal cells. At the same time the inner stratum is less pronounced, and the narrow lamina V of rather dense middle-sized pyramidal cells is distinguishable from the looser lamina VI. The accentuation of lamina II tapers off 1 to 2 cm beyond the transition from the Pro. Lamina II is now composed of somewhat smaller cells.

The next area (OmZ2) is characterized by an increase in granularization; i.e., it has a clear-cut granular lamina IV. At the same time lamina II with denser, smaller pseudogranular cells is more demarcated from lamina III, which has a rim of larger pyramidal cells next to lamina IV. The inner stratum further is less pronounced, and a rather light lamina Vb is striking.

The final step to FpZ is characterized by a further enlargement of the granular lamina IV and by a decrease of the size of the lamina V pyramidal cells, which are now approximately matched by the deeper lamina III pyramidal cells. Lamina VI is now composed of smaller lighter-staining cells, so that the inner stratum has lost its predominance.

Much higher degrees of differentiation, with very large lamina IIIc pyramidal cells prevailing over lamina V pyramidal cells and with a high degree of granulariza-tion, are reached in the two differential maxima of the inferior frontal gyrus of man: Vogt's area 58 in the upper part of the pars triangularis, and Vogt's area 60 in the center of the orbital cortex, bound to the sulcus orbitalis transversus (Fig. 4). Both appear to be the product of a final integration of the medial and lateral ur-trends.

The differential trend in myeloarchitectonics is best demonstrated by the stepwise increase in myelin content.* Another factor concerns the appearance of the stripes of Baillarger and their increase in intensity. Particularly the inner stripe of Baillarger, which is composed of intracortical association fibers, shows a stepwise increase with the differential trends in the integration cortices. The most readily demonstrable trend of increase of the myelin content is seen in a coronal section through the midline cortex and paramotor zone of man's frontal lobe (Fig. 5) and in a coronal section through Saimiri's whole hemisphere at the level of the sensorimotor region (Fig. 6).

It is a general rule in myeloarchitectonics of the isocortex that the diameters of the projection fibers of an area are directly related to the average myelin content of that area (Hopf, 1956). Highly myelinated area (as the primary sensory and motor ones) also have the thickest projection fibers. This allows the application of the vast experience of Bishop in comparative neurology of the fiber tracts. After a "life among the axons" (Bishop, 1965) with systematic comparative studies of electrophysiological properties and diameter spectra of the axons of peripheral nerves, of ascending tracts of the spinal cord and brainstem, and of the immediately subcortical thalamic projec-tion fibers, Bishop came to the conclusion that the finer myelinated fibers of related systems are basically older in evolution that the heavier myelinated ones. "Myeliniza-tion of small fibers and addition of successively larger fibers in the course of mam-malian central nervous system evolution applies not only to *one* function structure, but relates to the acquisition, at the higher and more recently developed central struc-tures, of a fiber spectrum similar to that prevalent in the periphery long before this central development in mammals" (Bishop and Smith, 1964). Thus, we may refer to a *"myelination trend in evolution."*

Figure 5 shows the example of this trend in man, particularly of the medial differential trend of limbic origin. On both sides of the interhemispheric fissure the very finely myelinated Pro of the cingulate gyri is seen. Two intermediate steps of the paralimbic zone on the left (47l and 47z) and one on the right (47l) grade to the maximum myelination of the convexity (areas 47) in the paramotor zone (nomenclature after Vogt, 1910, and Sanides, 1962b).

Concerning the myelination trend in *Saimiri* (Fig. 6), the overall myelination

---

* The myeloarchitectonics of the cerebral cortex were developed by the Vogts (1919) as a useful method of cortical partitioning. They were particularly applied to the human isocortex by the Vogts and their disciples. Hopf (1966) recently developed a method of objective registration of the myeloarchitectonics of the isocortex by the use of an extinction writer. This method allowed Hopf (1968) to confirm the former qualitative results of the partitioning of the human cerebral cortex by a quantitative method.

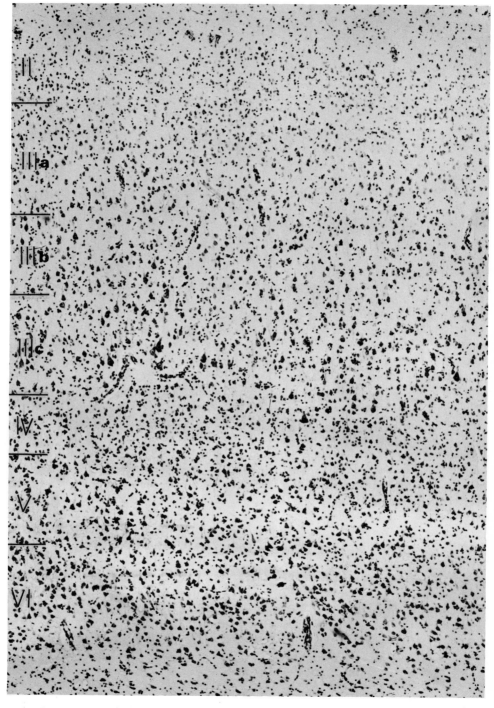

Figure 4. Central field of man's orbital cortex with maximum differentation x 80 (See max Fig. 26c). From Sanides. 1962b Monogr. Neurol. Psychiat., 98.

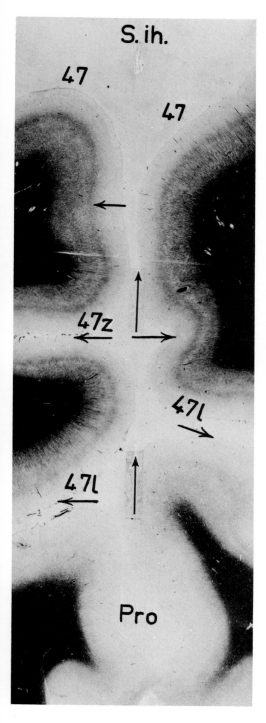

Figure 5. Coronal section through the interhemispheric fissure (S.ih.) of man's frontal lobe, demonstrating the myelination trend, x 5. From Sanides. 1962b. Monogr. Neurol. Psychiat., 98.

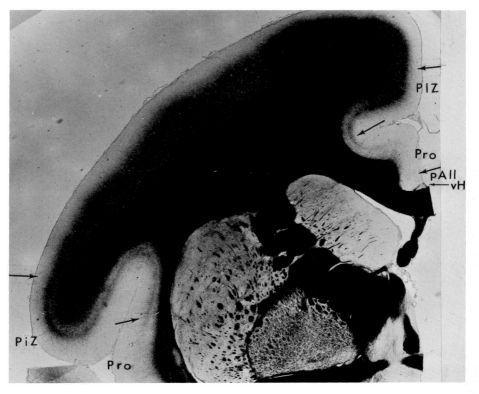

Figure 6. Coronal section through sensorimotor region of *Saimiri* demonstrating the myelination trends from medial to lateral, x 8. After Sanides. 1968. Brain Res., 8:97-124.

of its cortex is considerably less than in man. Therefore, a relatively overstained Heidenhain section was used to demonstrate the stepwise myelination from both limbic bordering cortices. On the convexity we find, as in other primates, the full expression of the classic sensorimotor regions with maximum myelination.

Pursuing the differential trend from the archicortex, we first note that the vestigia hippocampi (vH, induseum griseum) are still represented as gyrulus, covered by myelinated fibers (tenia tecta). Then a small section of pAll is present, with its faintly myelinated fibers demonstrable only at higher magnification. It also has relatively well developed tangential fibers in layer 1, a feature typical for all subdivisions of All. The adjacent cell stained section shows in pAll the typical two-cell-strata stage with a more pronounced inner one. The bulk of the cingulate gyrus is occupied by Pro, with its dense, fine radiate fibers, and an indication of an outer stripe of Baillarger. The transition to PlZ takes place in the bottom of the cingulate sulcus with a sharp increase in myelination of the outer stripe of Baillarger. The full expression of this area can be seen in the upper wall of the cingulate sulcus after cessation of the curvature influence (Sanides, 1962b). The transition into the area Gig (Fig. 6, arrow), halfway to the edge of the hemisphere, is marked by an increase in thickness of the radiate fibers and of the outer stripe of Baillarger. Thus we visualize after the initial stage of allocortex primitivus the stages of periallocortex, proisocortex, para-limbic zone, and finally classic motor region with increasing myelination.

On the lateral side we do not find the initial stage of paleocortex, that is allocortex primitivus, or the next stage, pAll, (both of which are more rostrally located in the base of the frontal lobe and the ventrolateral insula, respectively), but rather find the three subsequent stages of the myelination trend. Here we should note a peculiarity of Saimiri's cortical configuration, which is not present in Old World monkeys, that is, the large share of insula not underlaid by claustrum. This is an important point because the cortex superficial to the claustrum is more primitive in structure than the rest of the insular cortex. In Figure 6 note that, with the vanishing of the thin grey layer beneath the insular cortex (claustrum), a sudden increase in cortical myelination occurs. This is a similar transition as on the medial surface from Pro to PlZ, but here the transition is to the parinsular zone (PiZ). The latter was proved by Benjamin and Welker (1957) to contain the second sensorimotor representation (SmII). PiZ is, as in *Nycticebus* (Fig. 16), in cytoarchitectonic terms a prokoniocortex (proK) which exhibits here three subdivisions, corresponding to the three steps of myelination with gradual transitions in the bottom of the sulcus circularis and at the ventral tip of the operculum. The arrow (Fig. 6) on the outer side of the operculum marks the final transition to the koniocortex with its maximum myelination, particularly of the deeper horizontal fibers.

The Relationship of the Sulcal Pattern to Finer Cortical Organization and the Notion of Homology.

In the primate brain with the highest degree of gyrification, that of man, we demonstrated that the vast majority of the limits of architectonic fields are located in the bottoms of the sulci, fissurets, and dimples (Sanides, 1962b; 1964). In sub-human primates (Sanides and Krishnamurti, 1967; Sanides and Schiltz, 1967) and other mammals (Sanides and Hoffmann, 1969), the majority of the sulci and dimples also form architectonic field limits. However, since in lower mammals there are more field limits than indentations, only some are bound to the sulci. This relevance of the sulcal and gyral pattern to finer cortical organization was also a conclusion of Woolsey and his co-workers after two decades of comparative electrophysiological studies on localization of function in the mammalian cerebral cortex (Woolsey, 1959; Welker and Campos, 1963).

Thus sulci and gyri defined by architectonic and electrophysiological methods become more meaningful for comparative neurology. Within this context a reappraisal of the concept of homology as a tool of comparative neurology is presented.

At first we will follow a historical review by Starck (1950) on this subject. The origin of the concept "homology" goes back to the middle of the nineteenth century when it was introduced and defined by Owen (1848). He stated that homologous refers to the same organ in different animals under every variety of form and function. In this early definition, which is also called the typological one, the organ appears determined by the local relationships within the typus. After the general acceptance of the theory of evolution, the concept of homology was redefined by Haeckel: *Homol-*

ogy is the relation between two organs which have the same descent. In other words, organs are homologous in two different organisms if they derive from a common ancestral organ.

In the central nervous system, however, we cannot define homology by gross morphology only. For example, the cerebral cortex reveals its units only when we study its histology, that is, its architectonics as shown by specific staining techniques. On the other hand the common derivation of architectonic fields from ancestral forms is virtually impossible to prove. These are reasons which make the application of the notion homology questionable for the pattern of cortical units.

Our architectonic studies of the sensorimotor region in *Macaca* and *Saimiri* allow a test of the applicability of the notion of homology to the gyral pattern of New and Old World monkeys. The vast majority of the sulci of the mammalian cerebral cortex are "limiting sulci" rather than "axial sulci" (Elliot Smith, 1907). The latter are located well within a cortical field (e.g., calcarine fissure within the area striata). Thus we can characterize sulci in comparative neurology by the architectonic structure of the cortex of which they form the boundary.

Other than the Old World monkeys, the New World monkeys are unique in their wide range of brain differentiation from the small marmoset (*Hapale*) to the spider monkey (*Ateles*) with its fifth limb in the form of the highest developed prehensile tail. *Saimiri* occupies an intermediate position in this spectrum.

Both superfamiles of the primates (Old and New World monkeys) are known to have their common ancestors in presumably different prosimian stocks as far back as the early Tertiary period (Starck, 1953), i.e., prior to the elaboration of the present gyral pattern in the frontal lobe in the form of a central sulcus and a frontal arcuate sulcal complex. Yet both groups of monkeys reveal striking similarities in the formation of these sulci. Though this similarity is, by architectonic terms, far from identical, we are dealing here with one of the most astonishing examples of the phenomenon of parallel evolution, a phenomenon, which is intergraded with convergence. However, the comparative morphological phenomenon of convergence is by definition just contrary to homology, since it can be produced as a functional differentiation or even remodelling on different ancestral substrata or organs. For this reason, we prefer to come back to the term which the Vogts substituted for homology in the central nervous system, anatomical "equivalence." The equivalence of sulci, then, can safely be determined only be revealing the cortical architecture on both sides of the indentation.

The central sulcus of the primates usually is looked upon as a typical limiting sulcus between motor and somatic sensory areas. This, however, is an undue simplification because, technically, this is only true for the central sulcus of man. Even here we find in the bottom of the central sulcus a slight forward extension of area Ism (3a Vogts). In such apes as the chimpanzee (Strasburger, 1937) and Gibbon (Sanides, unpublished data) the somatic sensory cortex at the ventral end of the central sulcus extends a little farther rostral. In Old World monkeys, there is a definite protrusion of the somatic sensory fields at the ventral end of the central sulcus and a lesser one at the dorsal edge of the hemisphere (see Fig. 7, after the Vogts; confirmed in my cytomyeloarchitectonic studies on *Macaca*). The ventral protrusion beyond the central sulcus corresponds to part of the somatic face area. In the New World monkeys *Ateles* and *Cebus*, however, the rostral protrusion of the face area, investigated

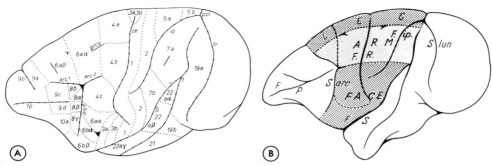

Figure 7. (a) Cytoarchitectonic map of *Cercopithecus* by, C. and O. Vogt (1919 J. Psychol. Neurol., 25:279-462.) Suffixes a-c and α-δ indicate subdivisions of Brodmann's map, the more detailed partitioning is based on stimulation experiments and architectonic control. (b) Somatotopic partitioning of the sensorimotor and parietal cortex of *Macaca mulatta* by the method of local strychninization from Dusser de Barenne (1941. J. Neurophysiol., 4:324-330.). arc, sulcus arcatus; arc 1, horizontal branch; arc 2, caudal spur; arc 3, vertical branch; ce, sulcus centralis; fp, sulcus principalis; ip, sulcus interparietalis; prcs, sulcus precentralis superior; S, fissura Sylvii; si, sulcus simialis, lun, sulcus lunatus.

electrophysiologically by Woolsey and co-workers, was much more extensive (Chang et al., 1947; Hirsch and Coxe, 1958). *Saimiri* also has a very pronounced rostral protrusion of the somatic face area (Benjamin and Welker, 1957), as is confirmed by our map (Figs. 8 & 9).

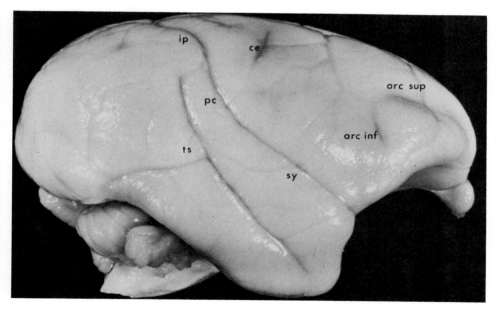

Figure 8. Lateral aspect of the cerebral hemisphere of *Saimiri*. arc inf, arc sup, sulcus arcuatus inferior and superior; ce, sulcus centralis; ip, sulcus intraparietalis; pc, sulcus postcentralis; sy, fissure Sylvii; ts, sulcus temporalis. From Sanides. 1968. Brain Res. 8:97-124.

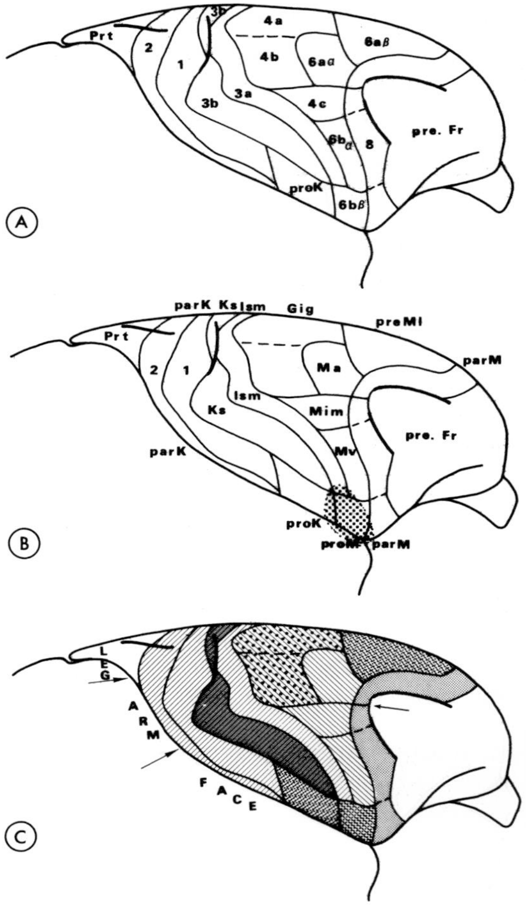

Figure 9. Architectonic map of *Saimiri's* frontal lobe. (a) Nomenclature after Brodmann-Vogt; (b) my nomenclature, see Table 1; deep taste area dotted; (c) areas in patterns. From Sanides. 1968. Brain Res., 8:97-124.

The relationships of the sensory and motor regions of *Saimiri* to the short central sulcus will be discussed (Figs. 8 and 9). A slight rostral protrusion of Ks is present at the dorsal end of the central sulcus similar to *Macaca*. In the dorsal half of the central sulcus Ks lies on the caudal wall and Ism on the rostral wall of the central sulcus. The latter is unknown for Old World monkeys. In the midlength of the sulcus there is a shift of Ks through the bottom of the sulcus to the rostral wall, so that at the ventral end of the sulcus the whole Ks is displaced to the rostral side. This shift from caudal to rostral occurs (based upon electrophysiological data) approximately at the level of the limit of leg and arm area (see arrows in Fig. 9c). We can conclude that in architectonic terms the equivalence of the central sulcus in Old and New World monkeys is incomplete. Rather one should speak here of a *regional* equivalence instead of an *areal* equivalence where the sulcus limits the same areas throughout. In terms of regional equivalence the central sulcus can be referred to as an axial sulcus of the primary sensorimotor region.

This common feature of New World monkeys can also be recognized in Vogts' map of *Alouatta's* motor cortex (Fig. 10) based on electrical stimulation experiments and cytoarchitectonics (C. and O. Vogt, 1907).

Sulcal Pattern in Evolution

Our cytoarchitectonic and microelectrode study on the sensorimotor region of a prosimian, *Nycticebus* (Sanides and Krishnamurti, 1967) demonstrated the delineating role of the sulci for architectonically and functionally defined cortical areas. Furthermore, we could trace the evolution of sulcal development and concluded that "we apparently enter a new phase of more thoroughgoing realization and interpretation of the different types of sulcal patterns and of their particular variants, relying on the cortical substratum itself, its electrophysiologic expression, and its architectonic structure." In the meantime two papers of Radinsky on extant and fossil brain fissuration (1968a, b) confirmed our prediction.

The value of paleoneurology was first demonstrated by Tilly Edinger (1948) in her great systematic study of the 55,000,000 years of brain evolution of the fossil *Equidae* up to extant horse. The fact that the leading structure in the mammalian brain as an end product of a long evolutionary process of rostralward migration of functions (v.Monakow 1911) settled as a "cortex," the cerebral cortex, at the utmost end of the forebrain, offers the unique opportunity to explore its expansion and even its sulcal and gyral pattern by endocranial casts of fossil skulls or by their own natural cast (Steinkern). A fundamental result of these studies on mammalian brain evolution is the growing pallium as such, and within the latter the increasing share of neopallium against the ventrolateral paleopallium. This is reflected in the steady downward movement of the rhinal fissure through the whole Tertiary period.

We will first consider general rules of the sulcal pattern in living mammals. Lower forms such as insectivores and the small specimens of all higher mammalian orders possess, with the exception of the rhinal fissure, a smooth cerebral surface; i.e., they are lissencephalic, whereas larger specimens have increasingly gyrencephalic brains. Gyrification, according to the law of Baillarger-Dareste (Ariens Kappers et al., 1936), is a function of brain size. This is basically geometric reasoning: The cortex, bound by its laminated structure, cannot increase proportionally in thickness with growing

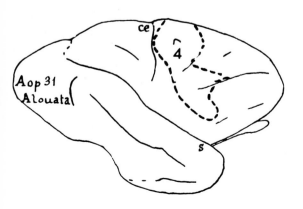

Figure 10. Motor cortex (area 4) of *Alouatta*. From C. and O. Vogt. 1907. J. Psychol. Neurol., 8:277-456.

brain size in evolution. Remaining a thin surface layer of the hemisphere it folds in order to compensate for the two-dimensional surface increase in contrast to the three-dimensional volume increase. In the largest primate brains, those of hominoids, the well-known enormous expansion of frontal and parieto-occipito-temporal integration cortices is added. It culminates in the extreme gyrification in man.

The first to develop further concepts on gyrus formation in phylogenesis was Le Gros Clark (1945). The starting point of his speculation on sulcal and gyral evolution is the statement that gyrus formation in phylogenesis and ontogenesis appears to proceed vertical to the lines of stress. The ventrolateral thickening of the hemisphere by the basal ganglia laterally and the formation of the corpus callosum medially are sites of counterpressure against the increasing distention of the hemisphere, causing prevailing lines of coronal stress. This effect is reinforced by the fact that our ur-trends of differentiation and growth of the neocortex course also in coronal direction. This leads to the original longitudinal cortical foldings* as they are found in such primitive mammals as the musk-deer, sloth, *Procavia* (hyrax), *Orycteropus* (aardvark), and *Galeopithecus*.

In the prosimians, except the smaller ones which are still semilissencephalic, the sagittal sulcal pattern prevails over the convexity. This, however, is combined in the posterior part of the hemisphere with the formation of a temporal lobe—a product of the sagittal rotation which is caused by the expansion of the parieto-occipito-temporal integration cortex with simultaneous fanlike deployment of the insular cortex.

With the increasing expansion of the frontal integration cortex and of the parieto-occipito-temporal integration cortex, as is characteristic in primate evolution, the sagittal growth stress is more and more brought into play. Thus, after some incomplete precursors in *Perodicticus* (Zuckerman and Fulton, 1941) and *Nycticebus* (Fig. 11; Sanides and Krishnamurti, 1967), the stress causes the definite simian coronal pattern of central, precentral, and postcentral sulci and lunate sulcus. The great spread of visual cortex contributes to the latter sulcus.

Thus, from the original sagittal sulcal pattern, one can trace a bifurcation (1) a sequence leading on the one hand to the carnivore and ungulate arcuate sulcal pattern by a kinking around the ventrolateral thickening of the hemisphere as a fixation point and (2) another sequence leading to the coronal pattern of simian primates with more or less pronounced vestiges of the sagittal sulci (see below). The basic structural difference can be recognized at the insular point of kinking or rotation. The rotation in primates, going hand-in-hand with a deployment of the insular cortex, is accompanied by the development of a flat laminar claustrum underlying that cortex. The kinking in the brains with an arcuate pattern does not coincide with a flat insula and is accompanied by the development of a relatively compact claustrum. Correspondingly we have in primate evolution a gradual overlapping of the insular stem lobe by the formation of frontal, parietal, and temporal opercula leading to the typical sylvian

---

* The sulcus cinguli is a paradigm of a longitudinal sulcus from which Le Gros Clark developed his rule that sulci and gyri form vertical to lines of stress. This sulcus can be found running parallel to the corpus callosum in all eutherian mammals. The triad of lack of cingulate sulcus, presence of radiate sulci, and absence of a corpus callosum is found in marsupials and humans with congenital agenesis of the corpus callosum (Sanides, 1962b).

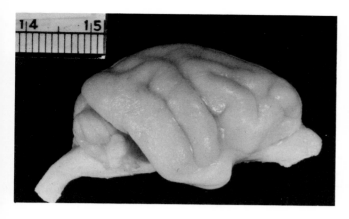

Figure 11. Lateral aspect of the cerebral hemisphere of *Nycticebus* showing the prevailing sagittal sulcal pattern.

fissure, whereas in the brain with the arcuate pattern the opercularization of part of the arcuate gyri leads to a pseudosylvian fissure.

So far we have followed Le Gros Clark's concept on sulcus and gyrus formation. We can go further by enclosing the fossil brains in this design and thus arrive at a pedigree of sulcal pattern in evolution (Fig. 12).

Actually, the fossil brains of carnivores (Radinsky, 1969) and ungulates in the early Tertiary period, i.e., those orders which display the elaborate arcuate sulcal pattern, exhibit the sagittal pattern (Fig. 13). One reason this point has not yet been recognized may be that the transitions from sagittal to arcuate pattern in ungulates are gradual, whereas only the primate order unifies in itself the most striking contrasts from lissencephalic over sagittal to coronal pattern without substantial intermediate forms. Thus, Le Gros Clark as a primatologist was the first to conceive the sulcal pattern from a *developmental* point of view. Obviously, Edinger (1948) had no knowledge of his 1945 essay. Actually, Edinger compares the fossil brain of *Orohippus,* the second stage of equine evalution in middle Eocene, to that of *Procavia* (hyrax), one of Le Gros Clark's paradigms for the sagittal pattern brain. "In several important characters our *Orohippus* brain material resembles the slightly smaller brain of the much smaller hyrax." Then, however, she refers to the "long, arched suprasylvian sulcus" of *Procavia* which actually should be called lateral sagittal sulcus. A much shorter parasagittal sulcus, designated lateral sulcus, corresponds in our view to the medial sagittal sulcus. The *Orohippus* brains as illustrated were not complete enough to provide evidence of the sagittal pattern. The lower Eocene *Eohippus* brain (Fig. 13a) however, shows the two sagittal sulci beyond any doubt. Again the medial one was called lateral sulcus by analogy with the extant arcuate brain lateral sulcus, indeed equivalence with only the anterior part of the latter is to be suggested. The lateral sagittal sulcus of *Eohippus,* which was designated suprasylvian sulcus, shows a slightly lateral convex bending. It is in such an anterior position as to probably occupy the sensorimotor region of this primitive mammal. In other words what in the older paleoneurologic literature generally was called *lateral* and *suprasylvian* sulci in early Tertiary fossil brains actually should better be designated *medial* and *lateral* sagittal sulci, respectively.

In this context it appears that it was possible to solve the riddle of the meaning

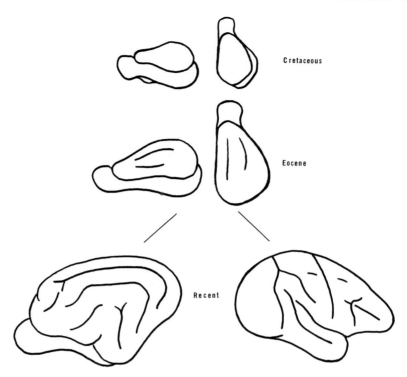

Figure 12. Pedigree of the sulcal pattern in evolution with final bifurcation into arcuate pattern and coronal pattern brains. Cretaceous: Lissencephalic brain of Protoinsectivora, compare with the recent *Erinaceus.* Eocene: Sagittal pattern brain of ancestors of Ungulata, Carnivora and Prostimiae, compare with the recent *Procavia.* Recent: Arcuate pattern brain (cat on left) and coronal pattern brain (*Macaca on right*). Note the steady downward movement of the rhinal sulcus (at the ventral border of the neopallium) which in the monkey has vanished from the lateral surface.

of the sagittal sulci of prosimians in *Nycticebus* (Fig. 11) by our combined approach with architectonic and electrophysiological methods. The main portion of these sulci lies within the sensorimotor region. They delimit the cortical representations of distinct body subdivisions. That is, the medial sagittal sulcus lies between the leg and arm representations, and the lateral one lies between the arm and head representations.

Further evidence that the riddle of the prosimian sagittal sulcal pattern finds its explanation by somatotopic subdivisions was found in the neurophysiological literature. The long sulcus rectus of lemurs, apparently equivalent to the lateral sagittal sulcus, was found by Vogt (1906) to separate motor hand and head areas. The same is the case with the shorter sulcus rectus of *Perodicticus* (Zuckerman and Fulton, 1941). To designate this kind of sulci adequately we introduced the term "somatotopic sulci."

We will now elucidate the factors which are involved in specific sulcus formation. Coronal or sagittal growth stress determines the general direction of developing sulci,

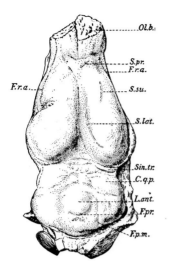
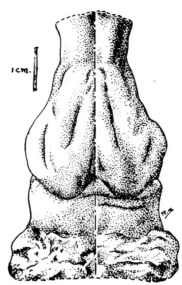

Figure 13. Sagittal pattern brains from Eocene. (a) *Eohippus* brain endocast. From Edinger. 1948. Geology Soc. Amer. Memoir, 25, x 177 pp. (b) *Arctocyon* brain endocast. From Edinger. 1964. Amer. Zool., 4:5-19.

that is, vertical to the lines of stress. The particular site where this stress is exerted requires another explanation, which was basically presented by Le Gros Clark. It is known, that if a beam of uneven dimension is subjected to lateral compression, there is a great concentration of stresses at the junctional zone where the material changes in thickness or consistency. Once a deformation at such a borderline has been initiated, the deflection of the lines of stress will increase the tendency still farther. Since similar conditions obtain at the junctional margins between cortical areas a plausible explanation is offered for the site of limiting sulci, e.g., of the cortical zones of the primate frontal lobe (Fig. 1).

There is also neurophysiological evidence that surface indentations, shallow and deeper ones, are the products of immediately adjacent evolving cortical areas (Welker and Seidenstein, 1959; Welker and Campos, 1963). In the raccoon an extensive behavioral use of the forepaws in manipulation and tactile exploration of the environment is correlated with a relatively large cortical hand representation. Within this region there is a discrete individual projection without any overlapping of single digits and palm pads, and nearly all individual parts are separated on a somatotopic basis by sulci, dimples, and spurs. The enlarged sensory somatic forepaw representation of the raccoon moreover is separated by an anterior limiting sulcus from the motor forelimb area, which implies that a partial equivalent of a central sulcus has developed which is not found elsewhere in the arcuate pattern brain.

Still further evidence for the relationship between development of limiting sulci and local elaboration of cortical areas in association with development of specializations of functions was presented by Woolsey (1959). A pertinent instance is the appearance of two short limiting sulci between the greatly enlarged motor and sensory representations for the prehensile tail of *Ateles* and the adjoining hindlimb representations in precentral Msl and postcentral Sml. There is no doubt that these two limiting sulci represent a new acquisition which occurred in connection with the very prominent enlargement of the sensorimotor areas for the prehensile tail in this genus.

Summarizing these particular examples of somatotopic sulci, we can formulate the rule: *In evolution fast-growing cortical areas exert growth pressure at their borderlines which, under conditions of counterpressure, brings limiting sulci into appearance.* Radinsky presented further convincing findings in extant prosimians (1968b) and fossil and extant carnivores (1968a). The author himself created a decisive prerequisite for the comparative study of endocranial casts by improving the latex casting technique, so that preparation of such casts can be done without damaging the skulls. Another precondition is that the "faithfulness of reproduction of external brain morphology appears to hold true for endocranial casts of all genera of mammals except for the largest brained ones, such as cetaceans, elephants and large primates" (Radinsky, 1968b). His pilot study comprised all but one of the extant prosimian genera. Pertinent are the results on indriids vs. lemurids. The greater outbulging of the area between the anterior section of medial and lateral sagittal sulci in the former led the author, referring to our findings in *Nycticebus*, to the interpretation of a differential enlargement of motor hand area. It is telling that this coincides with a more advanced frontalization of the eyes in the indriids than in the lemurids, for the combination of skill of the hands with stereoscopic vision (by overlapping peripheral visual fields) is the most important trend in primate evolution. It is the integration of both functions which is bound to the steadily growing parietal integration cortex of primates, culminating in man.

In the other study Radinsky (1968a) deals with endocasts of living and fossil otters, revealing particular elaborations of the gyral pattern of the sensorimotor region, which can be correlated with somatic sensory specialization due to anatomical and behavioral observations. In particular Radinsky found that in those otter genera which have a great reduction or loss of the claws of the hand, a special elaboration of the cortical hand area has occurred. He could show by fossil endocasts that such specializations developed as far back as about 10 million years ago. This somatotopic cortical elaboration has its behavioral correlate in that these small-clawed and clawless otters feed mainly on crustaceans and molluscs rather than on fish and probably use their hands for feeling around in mud and under stones to locate food (Walker et al., 1964)—an amazing parallel to the conditions in the raccoon!

For the evaluation of the sulcal and gyral pattern of the otters Radinsky (1968a) refers to the electrophysiological localization studies of Woolsey and co-workers in carnivores (Woolsey, 1959, containing further references). The most important pertinent finding is the somatotopic character of the coronal sulcus, which in all genera investigated separates somatic sensory and motor hand areas from head areas. This proves that the coronal sulcus is equivalent to the lateral sagittal sulcus of prosimians.

Moreover, Woolsey (1959) demonstrated the somatotopic character of the short sagittal sulci or fissurets of simians' sensorimotor region. In Old and New World monkeys the caudal spur of the arcuate sulcus delimits the motor head from motor hand areas, and in chimpanzee this somatotopic limit on the precentral gyrus is continuous with the inferior frontal sulcus. In other words there is obvious equivalence between the lateral sagittal sulcus of prosimians and this posterior spur of the monkey's arcuate sulcus as it is with the coronal sulcus of carnivores.

There are, however, in simian primates further obvious relics of the ancient prosimian sagittal pattern. The superior precentral and postcentral sulci, both short fissurets in New and Old World monkeys and chimpanzee, delimit hindlimb from forelimb areas. These are obviously relics of the medial sagittal sulcus of prosimians. The somatotopic significance of these relics of the ancient sagittal sulci in monkeys is moreover confirmed by Dusser de Barenne's strychnine neuronographic studies (1941, see Fig. 7b).

There are apparently relics of the ancient sagittal sulci even in the increasingly expanding integration cortices of higher primates, including man. Since this appears puzzling in such highly differentiated cortical areas, we will discuss our view based on comparative neurology, of the frontal and parieto-occipito-temporal integration cortices.

Because of the overwhelming growth of these integration cortices in higher primates and particularly in man, and because of the difficulty in delineating these limited areas of lower mammals (beside the motor and sensory areas), the idea had been put forward that the integration areas were principally later elaborations in evolution than motor and sensory areas. Thus the latter were referred to as primary regions and the former as secondary regions (Kuhlenbeck, 1928). The results of Flechsig's myelogenetic investigation (1920) of the human cerebral cortex favor this concept. Indeed, the motor and sensory areas are the first to differentiate in the perinatal gradual maturation process of myelination of immediate subcortical projection fibers. However, the Vogts (1919) had already stated the remarkable fact that it is the areas with the heaviest definitive myelin content which begin to myelinate first. This is just the case with these primary sensory and motor areas. Obviously this is a general ontogenetic counterrule which interferes with the biogenetic rule of Haeckel. This counterrule appears to signify that such tissues or histological elements which present a particularly high level of differentiation in the mature stage begin to differentiate irrespectively earlier in fetal life.* This leads to sequence dislocations of the ontogenetic maturation process compared with the pertinent phylogenetic periods.

We can also refer to Bishop's findings which we summarized as "myelination trend in evolution," that is, the finer myelinated fibers of related systems are basically older in evolution than the heavier myelinated ones. This conclusion, of course, is contradictory to the assumption that the primary sensory and motor areas are primary in evolution. On the contrary, from this ensues that the koniocortices, which are the heaviest myelinated cortical areas within the sensory regions, represent the most recent stage in sensory cortex evolution and that the area gigantopyramidalis, which is the heaviest myelinated motor area, represents the most recent stage in motor cortex evolution, an inference which is likewise suggested by the highest architectonic specialization of these areas and is parallelled by the highest functional specialization.

---

* Yakovlev and Lecours (1967), studying the whole myelogenetic cycles of the brain, came to similar conclusions. "Those systems with special functional importance to a given species generally appear earlier, but have longer cycles of myelination than those systems with more universal and less specific functions which differentiate later, but have shorter cycles of myelination."

Moreover, we were able to trace the initial existence of the anterior and posterior integration cortices in the neocortex of the European hedgehog (Erinaceus europaeus). This most primitive insectivore exhibits, together with the neocortex of representatives of Chiroptera, the most primitive neocortex of placental mammals so far investigated.

Thus, what had been recognized as a main feature of neocortical evolution—the appearance and immense growth of the integration cortices, particularly in the primate series up to man—was actually not understood. Overwhelmed by this vast expansion of apparently functionally silent regions, that is, the integration cortices, and preoccupied with their neuropathologic and psychopathologic analysis, or had overlooked the fact that we are dealing with a typical feature of primates—*the most generalized neocortical structure is bound to become the enormously prevailing one, with the widest scope of further differentiation during life.*

In this view, the presence of apparent relics of the ancient sagittal sulci in the integration cortices, even of higher primates, can be expected. In the monkey's frontal lobe it is the sulcus principalis which, after a short interruption by the paramotor areas (Brodmann's 8) inside the arcuate sulcus, continues the direction of the motor region relic of the lateral sagittal sulcus, that is, the posterior spur of the arcuate sulcus (Fig. 7). In apes and man we found, as already discussed, the inferior frontal sulcus to be equivalent to the sulcus principalis. This assumption derived from the fact that both sulci delimit the dorsomedial zone of the frontal granular cortex, marked by the prevailing mediolimbic architectonic influence, from the ventrolateral zone, marked by the prevailing insulolimbic influence. The mediolimbic and insulolimbic directions of differentiation could, however, also be traced within the precentral motor cortex of man in the form of subdivisions (Sanides, 1962b). This showed that the basic borderline through the precentral gyrus is located at the same level as in the prefontal cortex, in continuation with the inferior frontal sulcus. In the somatotopic partitioning of the human motor cortex this level corresponds to the limit between head and hand representations. This is the case with the posterior spur of the arcuate sulcus of the *Macaca,* and the same level is valid for the chimpanzee (Fig. 14).

The superior frontal sulcus corresponds to the level of the limit between leg and arm areas of the precentral gyrus and thus appears to correspond to the medial sagittal sulcus of *Nycticebus.* A corresponding sulcus does not exist in the prefrontal granular cortex of monkeys.

The result of these considerations is that the inferior and superior frontal sulci of man and apes are part-equivalents of the lateral and medial sagittal sulci of prosimians, the somatotopic significance of which we have clarified. This sounds as if somatotopic partitioning also determines the character of the frontal integration cortex.* Indeed, that this is so in architectonic terms could be shown in the parietal integration cortex of *Nycticebus.* The somatic koniocortex (Ks=3b Vogts) exhibits a clear-cut cytoarchitectonic tripartitioning into subdivisions corresponding to hindlimb, forelimb, architectonic tripartitioning into subdivisions corresponding to hindlimb, forelimb, and head areas, separated by the two sagittal sulci. These subdivisions distinguish themselves prevalently by the size of the few efferent lamina V pyramidal cells within

---

* An application of this view of the primate prefrontal cortex is to be found in a paper based on delayed response testing ablation experiments of rhesus monkeys (Sanides and Schlitz, 1967).

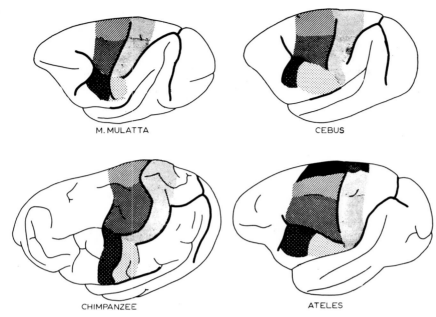

Figure 14. Brains of four primates (left, Old World; right, New World) showing corresponding somatopic sensorimotor subdivisions of MsI, and SmI into head, forelimb, and hindlimb areas. Note enlarged tail areas (black) in *Ateles*. For limiting sulci see text. From Woolsey. 1959. *In* Structure and Function of the Cerebral Cortex. Elsevier.

the otherwise light lamina V of area Ks. The largest are to be found in the hindlimb area, intermediate ones in the forelimb area, and smaller ones in the face area. This corresponds to the general experience in higher primates of a decrease in size of the giant pyramidal cells in the area Gig from leg to arm area and an absence of such giant pyramidal cells at all in the face area.

Corresponding architectonic subdivisions, somatotopically correlated and separated by the two sagittal sulci, were found also in the somatic parakoniocortex (parK=1 Brodmann). Here the large lamina V pyramidal cells which are even more numerous than in Ks show the same size differences between medial and lateral subdivisions, as they are separated by the medial sagittal sulcus. A lateral subdivision was not found in *Nycticebus*, since the parK fuses at this level with proK. In the cat, however, all three subdivisions of parK corresponding to leg, arm, and head area with the same gradation of size of the V lamina pyramidal cells as in Ks could be demonstrated. In both *Nycticebus* and cat in the caudally contiguous parietal integration cortex corresponding architectonic subdivisions could be traced. The somewhat smaller and denser lamina V pyramidal cells of these areas show the same gradation in size between medially, intermedially, and laterally.

It is important that the sulcus intraparietalis which plays the limiting role between the apparent leg subdivision and the apparent arm subdivision of the parietal integration cortex is located at the level of the medial sagittal sulcus. And that in some of the slow loris specimens investigated (Krishnamurti, 1966) it is a direct caudal continuation of the medial sagittal sulcus. The intraparietal sulcus of higher primates, in the corresponding location, then, appears to be equivalent to this part of the medial sagittal sulcus. Even in man, the similar cytoarchitectonic findings of the parietal integration areas are known and are parallelled by the myelin content, which decreases with the diminution of the average cell size ventrally from the intraparietal sulcus (Hopf and Vitzthum, 1957). From the neuropathologic point of view, Schaltenbrand (1950) even designated the superior parietal lobule as part of his "leg brain" and the inferior parietal lobule as part of his "arm brain" with the intraparietal limiting sulcus separating them.

The evidence of the equivalence of the prosimian somatotopic sagittal sulci in higher primates and in extant carnivores is based not only on gross morphology but also on architectonics and electrophysiological results. For evaluation of the gyral pattern of fossil brains we will of course always depend on extrapolations concerning the functional character of area delimited by certain sulci.

After our presentation of Le Gros Clark's theoretical deductions of the development of the sulcal pattern and after our generalizations based on the interdisciplinary approach to the prosimian sagittal pattern, it may be justified to interpret the three early Tertiary fossil brains which are paradigms of our pedigree of the sulcal pattern in evolution, *Eohippus* (Fig. 13a), Notostylops, and *Arctocyon* (Fig. 13b), as marked by the same type of somatotopic sagittal sulci as the prosimians (Fig. 11).

Concerning the endocranial cast of the notoungulate Notostylops of Lower Eocene age, Edinger (1948) gives the following account of the configuration of the hemisphere: "The small neopallium had only two, more or less distinct longitudinal sulci and possibly a Sylvian fissure." The endocranial cast of *Arctocyon* of Upper Paleocene displays the same pattern, and Arctocyanidae were ancestral to all later Carnivora, as *Eohippus* was to Equidae.*

To secure the general validity of the somatotopic character of the sagittal sulci in fossil brains ancestral to extant arcuate pattern brains it appears important to examine the same in nonprosimians, that is, in the few recent aberrant primitive mammals mentioned above, using electrophysiological and/or cytoarchitectonic methods.

Organization Of The Sensorimotor, Gustatory, And Visual Areas

THE SENSORIMOTOR AREAS

Since the discovery of the secondary sensory and motor representations, the classic scheme of the motor, somatic sensory, auditory, and visual cortical areas has been fundamentally shaken. A new array including the additional representations has, in spite of the increasing amount of detailed knowledge on the sensory input areas, not

---

* In a recent publication on "Outlines of canid and felid brain evolution" (Ann. N.Y. Acad. Sci. 167:277-288, 1969) Radinsky illustrated the endocast of Mesperocyon, the oldest known specimen of the canid family of Carnivora from the Middle Oligocene. This fossil brain still shows the two sagittal sulci pattern with only incipient arching of the lateral one.

yet been found. This state of affairs appears not too much changed since Bucy's opening remarks to the second edition of the great monograph *The Precentral Motor Cortex* (1949) which he edited:

> "The discovery of the second motor and sensory centers by Adrian (1941), Woolsey (1943, 1944) Woolsey and Wang (1945), and Sugar, Chusid, and French (1948) is one of the most intriguing new developments. As yet, however, our understanding of these is not sufficient to allow us to correlate their activity with the activity of other cortical and subcortical centers."

Our cytoarchitectonic and myeloarchitectonic studies of the sensorimotor region in several primates which in the prosimian *Nycticebus* were correlated with a microelectrode recording study, as well as our cytoarchitectonic and myeloarchitectonic studies on the taste areas in *Saimiri* and *Macaca* which were correlated with Benjamin and co-worker's systematic electrophysiological studies, provide a basis for new discussion of the pertinent data of the literature. These will be confronted with our concept of neocortex evolution.

Considering our ur-trends of differentiation in evolution from archicortex via the cingulate gyrus medially and from paleocortex via the insula laterally, it was conceived that the supplementary motor (Mpl) representation (fig. 19), lying in the medial phylogenetic trend, is an earlier stage of motor control, and the second somatic sensory (SmII) representation lying in the lateral phylogenetic trend is an earlier stage of *sensory* control than the respective classic representations.

As we stated in 1962b, Mpl, as discovered by Penfield and Rasmussen in man (1952), actually lies mainly in the paralimbic zone (PlZ, Figs. 1 and 26) of our human map, that is, in an intermediate stage of architectonic differentiation between anterior cingular Pro and FmZ. SmII corresponds in its location to a parinsular zone (PiZ) on the inside of the central operculum, which in architectonic terms is intermediate between the insular Pro and the postcentral SmI.

When we, in our frontal lobe monograph (1962b) formulated the hypothesis for the additional sensorimotor representations we had no knowledge of the important paper about the somatic areas I and II of Woolsey and Fairman (1946) who, on electrophysiological grounds concerning SmII and AII, came to a similar assumption as we did:

> "Duality, therefore, appears to be a general principle of cortical organization. The position of somatic and auditory areas II between the rhinencephalon and insula on the one hand and the more highly differentiated areas I on the other suggests that the 'second' areas may be phylogenetically more ancient and primitive."

The microelectrode recording study of *Nycticebus'* somatic sensory cortex (Figs. 11 and 15) revealed a fundamental correlation between morphologic and cytoarchitectonic features and projection patterns from peripheral receptive fields. Thus we actually succeeded in outlining architectonically a parinsular area, proK, representing SmII. As a particular feature we found this area partly responsive to auditory stimuli, another indication of the limited specialization compared with the so-called

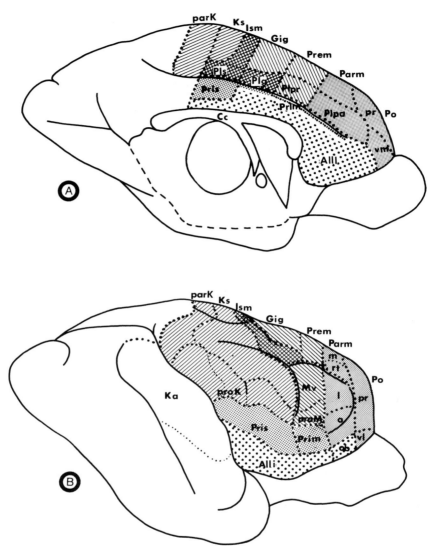

Figure 15. Cytoarchitectonic map of sensorimotor, insular, limbic, and prefrontal regions of *Nycticebus*. See Table 1 for abbreviations and Figure 9 for equivalent areas in Brodmann's nomenclature. From Sanides and Krishnamurti. 1967. J. Hirnforsch., 9:225-252.

primary areas. This overlapping of somatic and auditory receptive units in SmII previously has been systematically explored in the cat by Berman (1961a, b).

Since *Nycticebus* still possesses an exposed insular cortex (better designated claustrocortex, after Brockhaus, 1940), with the exception of a caudal fringe covered by a small temporal operculum, it offers the unique opportunity of studying the lateral ur-trend, within which Sm II lies, without interference of sulci or opercula, up to the somatic koniocortex of the head area (Fig. 16). Beginning at the anterior

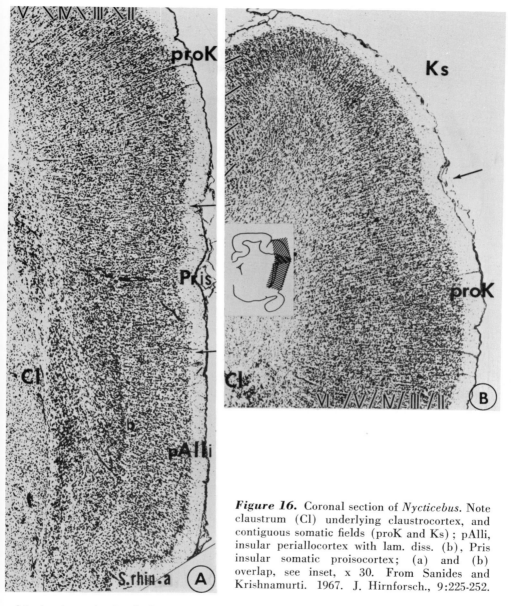

Figure 16. Coronal section of *Nycticebus*. Note claustrum (Cl) underlying claustrocortex, and contiguous somatic fields (proK and Ks); pAlli, insular periallocortex with lam. diss. (b), Pris insular somatic proisocortex; (a) and (b) overlap, see inset, x 30. From Sanides and Krishnamurti. 1967. J. Hirnforsch., 9:225-252.

rhinal sulcus, the borderline to the paleocortex (allocortex primitivus), we find as a first step the insular pAll which is composed essentially of two-cell-strata with a more prominent inner one and a rather inconspicuous lamina dissecans (b) in between. Both strata show a cell condensation externally. The outer lamina can be traced to the dense cell band of the paleocortex beyond the rhinal sulcus. In pAll this cell band is in the position of a second layer, though composed of densely packed multiform cells which are larger than granule cells. These cell condensations fade out towards the area limit to the proisocortex (Pris). Nevertheless, in Pris the layer II cells remain coarser than in contiguous proK.

In addition Pris is somewhat less prominent on the inner stratum, and instead of the lamina dissecans an incipient granular lamina IV appears. At the area limit of proK (i.e., SmII) the emphasis switches to the outer stratum where laminae II, III, and IV are almost fused. Laminae II and IV are composed partly of small pyramidal cells and partly of granule cells. Lamina V exhibts medium-sized pyramidal cells on a lighter background. Lamina VI is again denser and composed of medium-sized cells.

We can summarize the prevailing trends as a shift of emphasis from inner to outer stratum and a stepwise granularization. This also holds true for the transition of proK to Ks. Here the granularization reaches its maximum with almost complete fusion of laminae II, III, and IV, resulting in the dense outer stratum. Lamina V is light since it has less pyramidal cells than proK. The dense lamina VI is composed of smaller cells.

Thus we recognize proK, the area of the SmII representation, to be an intermediate step between insular proisocortex (Pris) and Ks; i.e., it is, compared with Ks, preliminary in granularization, preliminary in the density of the outer stratum (laminae II, III, and IV), and preliminary in the lightening of lamina V. In all these features we note proK as an area of much lesser specialization than Ks. Hence we referred to it as a "prokoniocortex" (proK), occupying part of the parinsular zone.

Similarly a paralimbic zone (Fig. 15) is delineated with intermediate areas (Pls, Plg, Plpr, Plpa) between Pro of the cingulate gyrus (Prlm and Prls) and the pertinent convexity areas. This zone probably contains Mpl, although this has not yet been established in *Nycticebus*. The intermediate stage of this zone can be recognized in Figure 17 in its location within the medial ur-trend. In the lower left we see the dorsal part of the cingulate gyrus with pAll and limbic motor proisocortex (Prlm). Adjacent to pAll ventrally would be the vestigia hippocampi. The periallocortex is, as the insular one, composed of two cell strata with a more prominent inner one. There is no lamina dissecans. As in the insular cortex, a bandlike condensation of cells appears at the surface. It is composed of densely packed small multiform cells, which are larger than granule cells. This cell band can be easily traced through the proisocortex (Prlm) to the bottom of the cingulate sulcus where it disappears at the transition with the paralimbic Plpr. Area Prlm exhibits, as does the anterior cingulate gyrus in higher primates, a particularly light lamina III. Its dense medium-sized V pyramidal cells fuse with the dense VI. In Plpr the dense V is composed of somewhat larger pyramidal cells standing out against a lighter VI. Lamina III increases considerably in its width and in the size of its pyramidal cells. The increase of the size of lamina V and lamina III pyramidal cells continues, as in higher primates, into area Gig.

Before we discuss further data of the combined architectonic—electrophysiological approach to the somatic sensory region of *Nycticebus*, a comment is included on our nomenclature as it is used in our maps (Figs. 9, 15). The sequence of the numbers used to name Brodmann's well-known areas was determined by the order of the appearance of each architectonic area in the horizontal serial sections of the human brain arranged from the crown to the base. The numbers have, as such, no reference

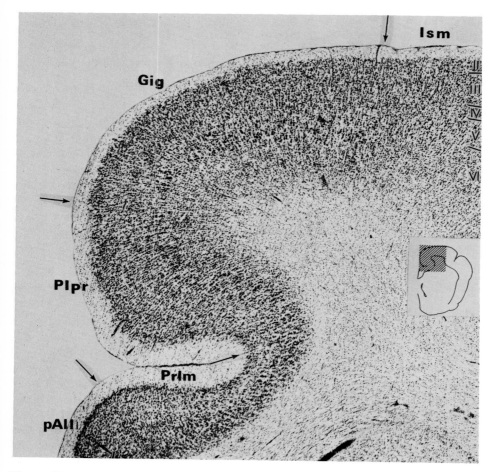

Figure 17. Coronal section of *Nycticebus* through anterior cingulate gyrus and adjacent motor cortex, pAll 1, limbic periallocortex; Prlm, limbic motor proisocortex; Plpr, paralimbic premotor area, x 28. From Sanides and Krishnamurti. 1967. J. Hirnforsch., 9:225-252.

to architectonic or functional qualities of the fields. Also, the paralimbic and parinsular areas were not yet detected by Brodmann, since emphasis was still laid on the convexity areas.

C. and O. Vogt (1919), by combining stimulation experiments in *Macaca* with architectonic controls, subdivided some of Brodmann's fields which have become well established, e.g., area 6ba, the mastication field at the base of the precentral motor cortex. However, the adding of a suffix to an area gives the impression that it is only a subarea of a major area. The dorsal parts of Brodmann's area 6, that is, 6aa and 6aβ have quite a different character functionally and architectonically. They are agranular and serve complex movements, whereas 6ba is dysgranular. Thus Brodmann's area 6 breaks up into incommensurable units.

Considering these fallacies in the current inadequate nomenclature we introduced our own nomenclature utilizing pertinent architectonic features, topology of the areas, and as far as possible functional correlates. In *Saimiri* almost all subdivisions as outlined by the Vogts in *Macaca* (Fig. 7a) could be found again, and both nomenclatures are included in Figure 9.

Of significance is the partitioning by the Vogts of Brodmann's somatic area 3 into 3a and 3b. We refer to 3b as somatic koniocortex, Ks, since it forms the hypergranular core of the somatic sensory region. Such a hypergranular core is also typical for the visual regions, i.e., visual koniocortex, Kv, and for the auditory region, i.e., auditory koniocortex, Ka. Area 3a shows rather intermediary character between Ks and Gig; that is, it exhibits more V pyramidal cells than Ks but is less granular than Ks. Therefore we designated this area intersensorimotor area, Ism, suggesting also its double function. With its less specialized sensory character Ism resembles the posterior somatic belt which we call parakoniocortex (parK). In *Saimiri* as in all simian primates so far investigated there are two fields in this belt, Brodmann's area 1 and 2, whereas in parK in *Nycticebus* only one clear-cut area was differentiated which exhibted at its caudal border a small magnocellular rim suggestive of an area parK$_2$ "in statu nascendi." The term koniocortex also refers to a general field bordering a koniocortex; it is distinguished by its conspicuously large pyramidal cells in lamina IIIc (Sanides and Hoffman, 1969).

We have now to consider some details of the electrophysiological results in *Nycticebus* and their relationship to the somatic sensory partitioning. For evaluation of the cortical points responsive to the peripheral tactile stimulus the relative size of the receptive field, the modality, and the ability to drive clusters of units were decisive. Maximal responses of this type were confined to the core of the somatic sensory region, i.e., Ks. Somatic sensory responses were also found in penetrations in the areas which border Ks rostrally and caudally, that is, in area Ism and parK (Fig. 18), respectively; here, however, light mechanical stimulation was ineffective, relatively strong mechanical stimulation was required to elicit activity. An evoked surface positive wave was found in these areas as in Ks, but units here were not so reliably driven as in Ks, and their peripheral receptive fields were larger. Thus the highest architectonic specialization, i.e., the koniocortex, was correlated with the highest functional specialization, providing the largest sensory discriminative power.

To complete the description of *Nycticebus*' somatic sensory region we have to mention the small paralimbic field Pls (Fig. 15) which resembles the intermediate field Ism but has more densely packed lamina Va pyramidal cells, which can be considered a characteristic of the anterior limbic lobe. A common feature of area Pls and area Ism is the occurrence of single unusually slender large pyramdial cells in lamina Vb which strongly resemble the conspicuous rod cells of the anterior limbic region in man.

Thus somatic koniocortex appears surrounded by four related granular fields (Fig 15). Three of them—the parinsular prokoniocortex (proK), the caudal parakoniocortex (parK), and the oral intermediate area (Ism)—have somatic input, while the paralimbic one (Pls) is possibly a part of the supplementary sensory representation of Penfield and Rasmussen (1952). This is similar to the architectonically and physiologically based concept of the auditory region of the cat (Rose and Woolsey, 1949). Rose and Woolsey proposed a fourfold partitioning such that the central koniocortical field AI is surrounded by three fringe areas which are architectonic transitions to the neighboring areas and are known also to receive auditory input. One of these is the parinsular AII which we classify as prokoniocortex. The fringe areas have, apart from the direct auditory input, corticocortical connections with the central primary field.

According to our findings in man, which will be discussed later, such a ringlike organization around a core koniocortex holds true also for the visual region. In this region, there are two concentric fringe areas (18 and 19 Brodmann's) for which direct visual input and corticocortical connections from the striate area have been demonstrated. To these can be added a visual prokoniocortex, designated prostriate area, which we found in a parasplenial location. Rostrally, it completes the ring around the striate area.

The uniqueness of the somatic sensory and of the precentral motor regions lies in the fact that they are based on both sides on proisocortex, i.e., the dorsal claustrocortex and the anterior limbic cortex, to which they are linked by parinsular fields laterally and paralimbic fields medially. This suggests a differentiation from *both* ur-trends. Another peculiarity is that these two regions possess a common fringe area in the intermediate field Ism.

The auditory and visual regions, on the other hand, with their respective parinsular (AII) and paralimbic (prostriata) links appear differentiated from *one* focus of origin only—the auditory region from caudoinsular cortex, the visual region from caudolimbic cortex.

The ringlike arrangements of the mammalian neocortical somatic sensory, motor, auditory, and visual regions and their relation to the ur-trends of neocortex differentiation will be discussed below.

Now we have to consider our pertinent findings in the New World monkey *Saimiri* which will be compared with findings in the Old World rhesus monkey. The ringlike organization of the somatic sensory and of the motor region holds true for both animals. In spite of the special New World monkey configuration with rostral protruding of the face representations, the somatic and motor fields exhibit similar architectonics in both monkeys. In the fringe of the premotor fields which surround area Gig in *Saimiri* (Fig. 9) the most rostral agranular field, preMl, will be discussed. As in other primates we distinguished at the medial surface in *Saimiri* a paralimbic field, plM, with very dense, smaller lamina V pyramidal cells. Area preMl, contiguous to the latter following the limbic ur-trend, exhibits somewhat larger and looser lamina V pyramidal cells. However, their great density as a limbic feature as compared with the other motor fields has prompted us to give the area the suffix 1. For the equivalent field 6aβ in *Macaca* the Vogts noted particularly adversive movements which were elicited at the lowest thresholds, whereas in the caudally adjacent area 6aα these movements could be elicited only at a higher threshold. The Mpl representation, as described by Penfield and Rasmussen in man (1952), corresponds grossly to our paralimbic zone. In *Macaca*, Woolsey (1958) found the same location of Mpl on the medial surface, with little encroachment upon the convexity (Fig. 19). Here, too, it corresponds mainly

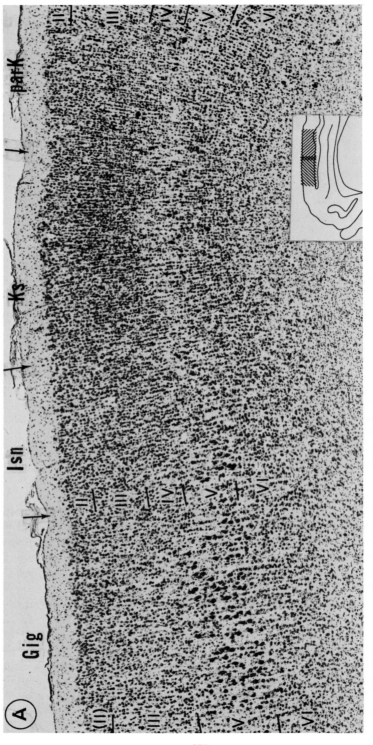

Figure 18. Parasagittal section of *Nycticebus*, illustrating the somatic fields parK, Ks, Ism; the motor fields Gig, Prem; the prefrontal field Parm; (a) rostral to and contiguous with (b), see inset. x 54. From Sanides and Krishnamurti. 1967. J. Hirnforsch, 9:225-252.

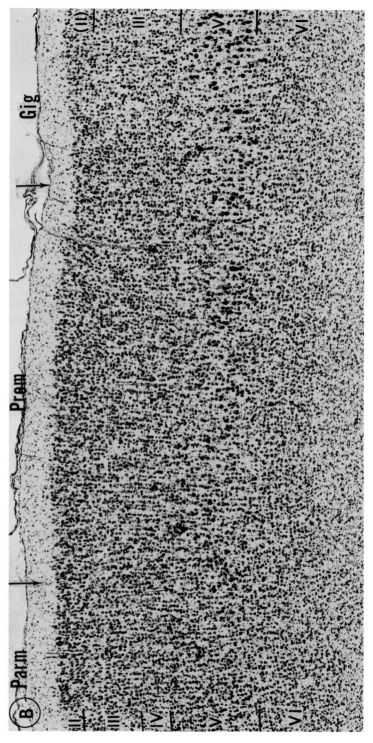

Figure 18. Parasagittal section of *Nycticebus*, illustrating the somatic fields parK, Ks, Ism; the motor fields Gig, Prem; the prefrontal field Parm; (a) rostral to and contiguous with (b), see inset. x 54. From Sanides and Krishnamurti. 1967. J. Hirnforsch., 9:225-252.

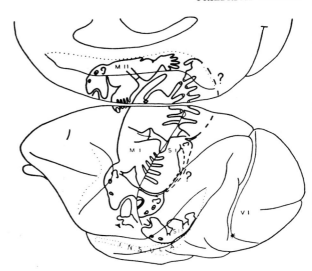

Figure 19. Diagram of neuro-physiologic mapping of the sensorimotor regions in *Ma-caca*. MI and SI, classic precentral and postcentral sensorimotor representations. SII, parinsular somatic; MII, paralimbic motor representations. From Woolsey, C. N. *In* Schaltenbrand and Woolsey eds., "Cerebral Localization and Organization. (Madison, The University of Wisconsin Press 1964, pp. 17-32.)

to our paralimbic field and encroaches, particularly with the peripheral parts of the arm representation, upon 6aβ. Thus only Mpl in *Saimiri* appears to encroach so far upon the surface to cover the whole of preMI.

In our concept, plM ·and preMI are parts of the motor belt surrounding the highest specialized motor core, area Gig, plM remaining in a paralimbic stage and preMl being differentiated further. The conflicting physiologic findings raise the question whether the so-called adversive movements elicited by the convexity parts of 6aβ in *Macaca* by the Vogts (1919) correspond actually to the reactions elicited by the area designated as supplementary motor area at the same site in *Saimiri* (Benjamin and Welker, 1957).

The unsolved question of the cortical motor patterns can be attributed to the fact that the electrical excitation of motor responses is still the most unphysiologic method among the neurophysiologic techniques of investigating the cerebral cortex. From quite another approach, that of hodology of cortical fiber connections, a strong argument for the entity of the supplementary motor representation in a paralimbic site is provided by Pandya and Kuypers (1969) in *Macaca*. Using the Nauta technique, they found, after ablation of the second sensory area, numerous degenerating fibers projecting to the site of the ipsilateral Mpl at the medial wall of the hemisphere. We had already postulated such connections. In our view, the present stage of sensorimotor organization, with the classic precentral motor and postcentral somatic regions flanked medially by paralimbic supplementary motor and ventrolaterally by parinsular second sensorimotor areas, is preceded in evolution by a stage where the paralimbic and parinsular representations were still contiguous. Therefore interaction of both original motor and sensory areas by subcortical connections was strongly suggested. Thus in the results of Kuypers and Pandya, we can recognize a suggestion that the convexity cortex of the motor fringe areas are fundamentally different from the areas on the medial wall of the hemisphere. This is in line with our architectonic findings.

THE CORTICAL TASTE NERVE AREAS

The taste projections to the cortex have been investigated by Benjamin and co-workers in a series of electrophysiological studies (Benjamin and Pfaffmann, 1955; Benjamin and Akert, 1959; Benjamin, 1963; Benjamin and Burton, 1968; Benjamin et al., 1968). Our architectonic studies are correlated with their findings in *Saimiri* (Sanides, 1968) and with unpublished data in *Macaca*. By courtesy of the authors we had occasion to study microscopically several of the experimental brains and to examine the two sites (1) the surface area and (2) the opercular/insular cortex which yielded positive responses to the stimulation of the taste nerves (chorda tympani and lingual-tonsillar branch of glossopharyngeus). In this way we identified the gustatory nerve projection areas on the convexity of the hemisphere as coinciding mainly with Ks, with the tongue representation. This and the deep gustatory nerve input area were revealed as a well-defined granular field at the anterior border of the insula (Figs. 9 and 20) occupying mainly the most rostral inner aspect of the frontal operculum. The relationship of these areas to the sensorimotor partitioning will be described in order to arrive at an evaluation of their differential stage in the context of our concept of neocortex evolution.

The deep pure taste area, G, turned out to be a rostral continuation of the parinsular belt (containing more caudally the somatic prokoniocortex, corresponding to SmII). We have first to pursue the course of the latter through insular and opercular cortex. In electrophysiological studies of the somatic sensory areas in *Saimiri*, Benjamin and Welker (1957) found the leg and trunk representation of SmII on the caudal half of the insular cortex in that section without an underlying claustrum. The architectonic particularity of this insular section against the ventral Pro is revealed strikingly in Figure 6 by its increase in myelin content. In cytoarchitectonics it exhibits its character as a prokoniocortex (in contrast to the ventral proisocortex) by an increase of granular lamina IV and decrease of the lamina V pyramidal cells. Some arm representation was found on the contiguous inside operculum, but for technical reasons it was not traced further forward. As far as face representation was found in the upper bank of the Sylvian fissure, it corresponds at this level to area parK2. Hence, it has to be designated, not as part of SmII (as was originally done), but as part of the outer somatic belt of SmI.

Microelectrode studies by Benjamin (personal communication) revealed that the tongue representation of SmII occupies the more rostral parts of the inside of the operculum, which are formed by proK. It is in this location that gustatory area G emerges at the level of Horsley-Clarke coordinate A13 to occupy about 3 mm length of the inside of the operculum rostrad up to A16. In its rostral half, area G encroaches within the insula into the region of the levelling off of the sulcus circularis and extends rostrally to the caudo-orbital cortex. At the upper lip of the Sylvian fissure area G is contiguous (1) with a subdivision of proK, (2) with proM (corresponding to caudal half of 6bβ Vogts), and (3) with parM, that is with the opercular subdivision of the slightly granular paramotor belt of the prefrontal cortex (Fig. 9).

The insular cortex, which abuts against area G in the depth of the sulcus circularis, corresponds to an anterior light granular section of the insular Pro which we could

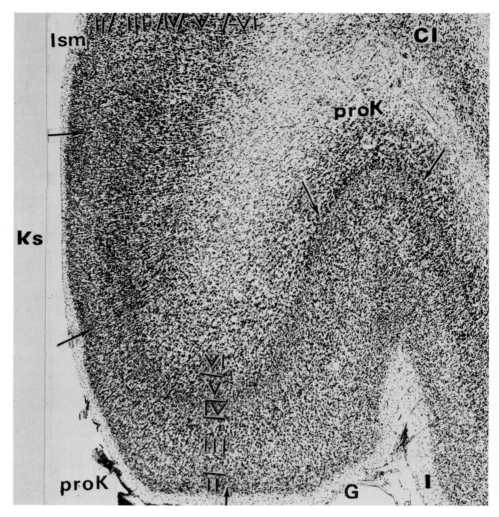

Figure 20. Coronal section of *Saimiri* through central operculum, adjacent insular cortex (I), showing gustatory area G, and somatic areas proK, Ks, Ism, x 37. From Sanides. 1968: Brain Res., 8:97-124.

also distinguish in *Macaca* from a dysgranular middle section with an accentuated dense lamina V which may be related to the precentral motor cortex.

Architectonically, area G is the rostral part of the parinsular belt (Fig. 20). It differs from proK by finer and lighter staining granules in lamina IV, smaller granuloid cells in lamina II, and a somewhat lighter lamina V. On the other hand, area G appears to be not as specialized as the somatic Ks. Rather it approaches the adjacent paramotor area of the prefrontal cortex and is best characterized as an intermediate step between the anterior light granular insular Pro and thus part of the prefrontal cortex.

The basic tripartitioning of the insular proisocortex has been recognized previously only in man by Brockhaus (1940). It appears important that this tripartitioning is also valid for *Saimiri* and *Macaca*. This recalls an older general observation of the Vogts (1919) who noted that the different sections of the insula reflect in their architectonics the different adjacent convexity regions. This, however, is also basically true for the limbic lobe; this means that in the stage of proisocortex differentiation the areal architectonic partitioning of the adjacent neocortical belt is anticipated.

It is an intriguing result of these studies that the pure taste area G appears as one root of prefrontal cortex differentiation. To emphasize the remarkable fact that this is already anticipated in the insular proisocortex we designated this fine granular part of the insular cortex prefrontal insula.

In conclusion, the gustatory input has its main representation in the older parinsular belt rostral to SmII, whereas the gustatory surface projection onto the tactile tongue representation of SmI appears to be an associative function with the latter. Only tactile discrimination, audition, and vision—the sharper localizing and objectifying senses—are represented in recent mammals in so-called primary areas with highest specialized cores of koniocortex. The other chemical sense, olfaction, is represented in the paleocortex itself, which forms one base of the original telencephalon in early vertebrates.

Investigations of the pertinent regions of *Macaca* showed very similar relations to *Saimiri* (Fig. 21). Also here area G (1) encroaches partly upon the anterior fine granular insula, (2) occupies the broad depth of the sulcus circularis and (3) occupies the inside of the rostral operculum. By courtesy of Dr. Benjamin, who allowed an examination of an experimental brain with tracks of the deep gustatory nerve responses, we also could establish that these responsive loci were lying prevalently in area G, that is, particularly in the deeper parts around the bottom of the sulcus circularis. In the hemispheres of two monkeys we made a striking observation. Within area G in the depth of the opercular wall we found a koniocortex focus characterized by an accumulation of granule cells in laminae II and IV, a light lamina V, and a dense lamina VI (Fig. 21). This could be confirmed in adjacent myelin-stained sections in that this clear-cut focus shows a sharp increase in myelination compared with the otherwise faint myelination of area G in which it is lying. This requires further studies in other brains. However, we can regard it as a remarkable phenomenon that in area G, a subdivision of the parinsular stage of *Macaca's* neocortex, a premature koniocortex focus can be found.

A small koniocortex-like subdivision, 68gr in Vogts area 68, was described by Gerhardt (1938, 1940) in man and chimpanzee in the depth of the central operculum. Patton and Ruch (1946) referred to this as a possible taste area. This poorly myelinated area (Gerhardt, 1938) is located too far caudally to be equivalent to area G. The poor myelination would also be in contrast to our finding of a koniocortex focus in area G in *Macaca* and to the general observation of maximum myelination of koniocortices. von Bonin and Bailey (1947) show in their work on *Macaca* a corresponding spot to area 68 gr in the depth of the opercular wall adjacent to the insula. This possible koniocortex focus lies too far caudally, namely below the tip of the central sulcus, whereas area G also in *Macaca* has its caudal limit approximately in the level of the rostral limit of Ks.

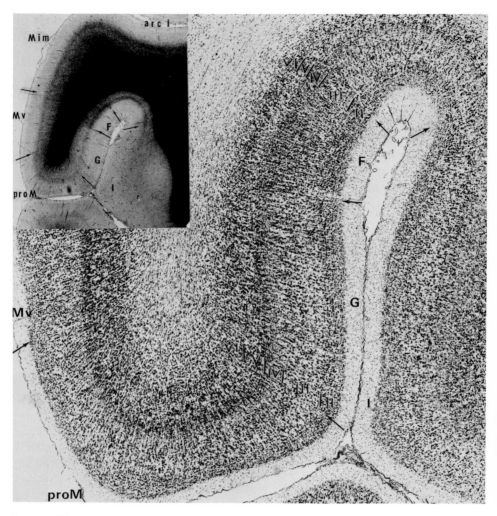

Figure 21. Coronal section of *Macaca* through central operculum and insular cortex (I), with gustatory area G, and motor areas proM, Mv, and Mim. Inset of adjacent myelin-stained (Heidenhain) section, showing the same areas in myeloarchitectonics. Note koniocortex focus F in the large picture, corresponding to heavily myelinated focus F in the inset; arc i, inf. arcuate sulcus, x 27.

Among the previous investigators of the cytoarchitectonics of the sensorimotor region in *Macaca* only Roberts and Akert (1963) included the inside of the opercular cortex in their studies. Their area Ofo on the rostral inside of. the frontal operculum corresponds mainly to our taste area G. Their Plate I shows a good agreement with our outlines. In more rostral levels Roberts and Akert included within area Ofo the external opercular paramotor area. This first prefrontal area corresponds to the anterior half of 6bβ Vogts and has some resemblance to area G because G is intermediate to parM in the differential trend from the prefrontal insula.

This inclusion of opercular area parM is the reason why ablation of area Ofo resulted in retrograde degeneration of the ventral part of the paralamellar portion of the dorsomedial nucleus of the thalamus. Area G itself receives only sustaining input from the ventromedial complex (Benjamin and Burton, 1968).

Thus the pure gustatory area G in *Macaca* is also located beneath proM (caudal half of Vogt's 6bβ) and is contiguous orally with the paramotor belt of the prefrontal cortex. According to its location and architectonic character, area 68 of the Vogts with its hypergranular focus in man and chimpanzee (and the area described above in *Macaca*) appears to be the somatic prokoniocortex, corresponding to SmII.

THE VISUAL AREAS

The primates priority on vision can be recognized not only in the frontalization of the orbits in evolution almost up to a sagittal plane of the medial orbital wall in catarrhines, but also in the enormous expansion of the visual cortex, and in the highest specialized character of its koniocortex, the area striata. Only primates have such a striate area, marked by the strikingly myelinated Gennari's line, that is, an accentuated outer stripe of Baillarger which is not accompanied by an inner stripe of Baillarger (Fig. 22). In myeloarchitectonic nomenclature this type is referred to as singulostriate. The granularization reaches its maximum in the area striata with a particular elaboration of lamina IV.

A ringlike structure for the visual region in primates was already established by Brodmann (1909). After his maps one had the impression that the parastriate area 18 and the peristriate area 19 surround the striate area 17 as a complete double ring.

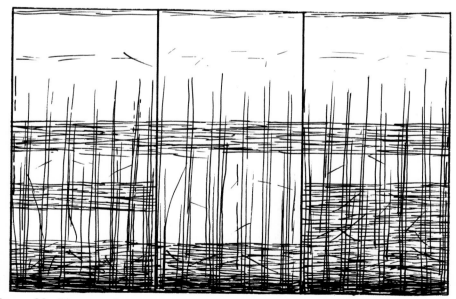

Figure 22. Diagram of main types of myeloarchitectonics of the isocortex. Left, bistriate; middle, singulostriate; right, unistriate.

Concerning the rostral end of the striate area, which is hidden in the depth of the common trunk of the calcarine fissure and parieto-occipital fissure, Brodmann was rather cautious in describing the ring by areas 18 and 19. The first to challenge this apparent closed ring of area 18 and 19 around 17 at the anterior, i.e., paralimbic, end of the striate area was Pfeifer, who depending on his excellent angioarchitectonic method prepared a complete atlas of the angioarchitectonics of the cerebral cortex in *Macaca* (1940). He could demonstrate that the striate area at the rostral end is actually contiguous with areas of limbic character and is not surrounded by areas 18 and 19.

Our comprehensive cytoarchitectonic and myeloarchitectonic studies on the visual region of man and preliminary studies in chimpanzee (Sanides and Vitzthum, 1965; Vitzthum and Sanides, 1966) led us to a similar conclusion. Contiguous to the anterior end of the striate area in the walls of the trunk of the calcarine fissure, which delimits the isthmus of the limbic lobe, neither areas 18 nor 19 are located but a limbic type area with slight myelination, accentuation of the lamina II, and single limbic cells (Figs. 23 and 24). On the other hand, this area belongs to the rare singulostriate type, of which the striate area is the extreme. For a limbic region this area which rostrally borders the striate area is at the same time rather granular and has a rather light lamina V. Thus it exhibits actually a combination of limbic and striata-like features. Seen in the context of the limbic ur-trend of differentiation is appears as an intermediate stage between the periarchicortex of the entorhinal region and the presubiculum anteriorly and the striate area posteriorly (Fig. 23).

This topology and the peculiar architectonics prompted us to designate this area "prostriata," suggesting that we are dealing here with a similar prokoniocortex as the parinsular second somatic and second auditory ones. This assumption proved to be in striking agreement with findings of MacLean and co-workers in microelectrode

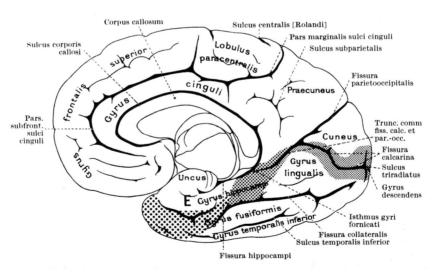

Figure 23. Diagram of the medial aspect of the human hemisphere with area striata (small dots) and two continuous singulostriate limbic areas surrounding the entorhinal region (E): prostriata (medium dotted), anterior V-accentuated area (large dotted). After Vitzthum and Sanides. 1966. *In* Evolution of the Forebrain. Thieme.

studies in *Saimiri* with photic stimulation (Casey et al., 1965; Cuénod et al., 1965). Examining wider areas of the limbic lobe they found a short latency visual receiving area with a corresponding extension from the entorhinal region to the striate area, which is obviously equivalent to the prostriata as described by us in man and confirmed in chimpanzee. Thus it is a visual ProK, the prostriata, which closes the parastriate and peristriate ring around the area striata, the visual Ks. One peculiarity of the prostriata, compared with SmII, AII, and the supplementary motor and sensory representations, lies in the fact that we encounter here already in the stage of the proisocortex a prokoniocortex area which in general is located in the paralimbic/parinsular belts. That may be an indication of the close affiliation of the visual system with the limbic lobe, as conceived by MacLean (Gergen and MacLean, 1964).

We have also to think about the entorhinal region, which is extremely elaborate in higher primates, as an example of an older cortical structure with possibilities for further growth and differentiation or specialization. It is difficult to speculate when this intricate temporal addition to the periarchicortex has arisen. However, it is suggested that this occurred later than the development of the simple periarchicortical presubiculum. This could be the phylogenetic reason why we encounter a proK, the prostriata, at the entorhinal junction. The prostriata may be classified as part of the paralimbic/parinsular growth ring which contains also the other *prokoniocortices*.

Finally we have to add that the area striata presents throughout its rostral to caudal range from its paralimbic border to the occipital pole several grades of myelination with a maximum in the *prepolar* site (Fig. 24). These grades are paralleled by a corresponding increase of cell size in the nongranular layers. The polar and prepolar area striata with their highest myelin content correspond to the central vision (macular region), which is phylogenetically most recently acquired. On the other hand the slightly myelinated oral part of the area striata corresponds to the temporal crescent which in the primates forms the remainder of phylogenetically ancient monocular vision; the middle sections of the area striata with medium myelination correspond to the binocular periphery of the fields of vision.

One can consider Fig. 24 to be an excellent example of the myelination trend in evolution, from the slightly myelinated prostriata through the heavily myelinated macular region of the striate area.

Growth Rings of the Neocortex

The data and ideas developed in the forgoing sections will be synthesized here to elaborate the concept of neocortex evolution. New pertinent material including Golgi studies of specimens of Insectivora, Chiroptera, and Rodentia will be presented, providing further support of this concept.

The new approach to the evolution and eventual definition of the mammalian neocortex resulted from a new combined application of cytoarchitectonics and myeloarchitectonics of the cerebral cortex as a tool for tracing differential trends of evolutionary significance in a series of primates and lower mammals. A pioneer in using the cytoarchitectonic method in such a sense was Abbie, who elaborating on Dart's concept of the duality of the neocortex, demonstrated in monotremes and marsupials

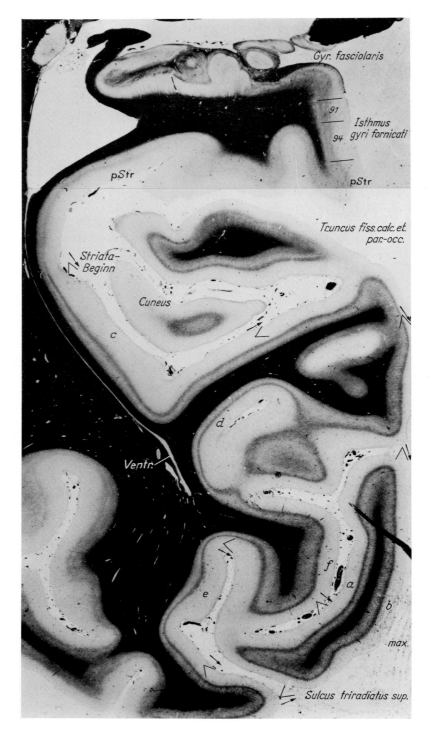

differential trends from the archicortex and paleocortex, resulting in two different moieties of the cerebral neo-cortex. In his second article on this subject Abbie (1942) speaks very descriptively of "successive waves of circumferential differentiation" away from the hippocampus on the one hand and away from the paleocortex on the other. And this is exactly what we have demonstrated in a broad spectrum of *Eutheria*, and for what we would like to propose the term "growth rings of the neocortex."

THE PERIALLOCORTEX AS FIRST GROWTH RING OF THE NEOCORTEX

By now we can formulate the preconditions which neocortex has to fulfill compared to the older paleocortex and archicortex as they are revealed from the comparative neurological literature (Ariens Kappers et al., 1936). Neocortex is a laminated griseum which is located at the periphery of the endbrain between the medial archicortex and the lateral paleocortex and which is lying peripheral to its projection fibers including dorsal thalamic input. As we will see, these preconditions appear fulfilled already by the *periallocortex* which as the first intermediate stage rims the archicortex and paleocortex at the medial and ventrolateral borders of the iso-cortical lobes. The basic resemblance of this stage, whether it borders the archicortex or the paleocortex, is demonstrated in Figures 3, 16, and 17. It is defined as the two-cell-strata pAll with an inner large-celled stratum and an outer medium-celled stratum separated by a more or less well defined lamina dissecans (lam. diss.). From Golgi preparations of the periarchicortex it is known that the lam. diss. is the site of synaptic contact between basal dendrites of pyramids of the outer stratum and horizontal fibers (Lorente de Nò, 1938). This could occur without a clear-cut blank layer at the borderline between both strata so that the lam. diss. is not a necessary prerequisite for the basic organization of pAll. A common feature, however, of all forms of pAll—periarchicortical and peripaleocortical—is cell condensations of medium-sized polymorph cells at the surface of the outer stratum where it borders the zonal layer. This kind of cell condensation which can be traced to the site where they taper off into the next intermediate stage, Pro II, have quite another character than the lamina II of the isocortex which is made up of small mostly pyramidal cells. Although there are areal differences in the cell forms of the lamina II within the isocortex, it appears justified to refute the term "outer granular layer" for it, as done by Globus and Scheibel (1967), and to preserve the term "granular layer" for the lamina IV, which alone is composed predominantly of the star cells of the Golgi picture. As for the lamina II of the isocortex, one may rather refer to its granuloid character.

The significance of such a fine notional distinction is revealed by the progress in synaptology in electron microscopy, in particular by Gray's work in 1959 which proved the synaptic role of the dendritic spines. Pyramidal cell dendrites are more or less studded with spines, whereas true star cells, corresponding to the granule cells

---

Figure 24. Subsplenial horizontal section of man's hemisphere through the isthmus of the limbic lobe and calcarine fissure up to occipital pole. Myelin staining (Heidenhain) showing the singulostriate character of the area striata with several grades of myelination and a prepolar maximum (max). The area striata is rostrally contiguous with the faintly myelinated singulostriate prostriata (pStr), x 3.3. After Sanides and Vitzthum. 1965. Deutsch. Z. Nervenheilk., 187:680-707.

of the isocortical lamina IV and dispersed also over the other isocortical layers, are characterized by their form, by the scarcity or total lack of spines, and by the beaded character of their dendrites.

In the Golgi picture pAll is characterized by the absence of a layer of true star cells, as it lacks in cytoarchitectonics a granular layer, which makes its first cortical appearance in Pro. Thus we could trace star cells in the level of layer IV in the insular Pro of the cat.

Since the true granular lamina IV in the isocortex is the site of the afferent axonal terminal plexus from the thalamus, there is the question, where do the thalamic fibers terminate in pAll.

The problem of thalamic projections to pAll and of their terminations was solved by a new approach to the thalamolimbic and reciprocal connections in the rat by Domesick (1969, and personal communication), who placed small lesions in different regions of the limbic cortex and anterior thalamus and traced the terminal degenerations with the Fink-Heimer technique. The pertinent findings are that the posterior cingulate pAll of the rat (Rose's area retrosplenialis granularis) * receives projections from the anteroventral nucleus thalami and sends reciprocal projections to this nucleus. The presubiculum, the simplest form of pAll receives a large thalamic projection which may originate from all the anterior nuclei (still under investigation). Thus these major parts of the periarchicortex fulfill all conditions of the neocortex definition.

Domesick (1969) presented clear evidence about the site of the thalamic terminations within the posterior cingular pAll. The terminations are in lamina I and in the so-called lamina III. The latter is that part of the outer stratum which lies deep to the external cell condensations. We will come back to these findings when we deal with our Golgi studies. At this point we may add only that the interesting findings of thalamic terminations in the zonal layer of the pAll is surprisingly paralleled by corresponding findings in the visual cortex of the opossum (Nauta, personal communication) and in the neocortex of the hedgehog (Ebner, personal communication). This of course does not exclude thalamic terminations in deeper layers.

Filimonoff (1947) united the peripaleocortex and the periarchicortex under the term "cortex intermedius" or pAll, recognizing the intermediary character of this complete rim around the allocortices sensu strictiori. Fascia dentata, cornu ammonis, subiculum, tenia tecta (induseum griseum corporis callosi) are the subdivisions of the hippocampal allocortex sensu strictiori. Tuberculum olfactorium, the diagonal region, the septum pellucidum, the periamygdalar region, and the prepiriform region are the subdivisions of the paleocortical allocortex sensu strictiori, to which he refers as semicortex or cortex semiseparatus. This emphasizes the fact that in the mature stage this cortex still shows an incomplete separation of the cortical plate from the periventricular cell masses. It is this fact which makes the paleocortex the most conservative mammalian cortical structure, still close to the amphibian stage of endbrain organization with only periventricular cell masses. One might therefore also refer to the paleocortex as a corticoid structure (Yakovlev, 1959). The archicortex on the other hand forms a separate cortical plate during ontogenesis, with some peculiarities, such as late migration and scarcity of cellular elements.

---

* These so-called granules of the outer stratum are of a granuloid character.

From the borders of both these heterogenous cortices has arisen a new cortex, the pAll, which with both its moieties forms a *closed ring* around the next intermediate stage, Pro. How far this similarity extends between the organization of the peripaleocortex and periarchicortex was not recognized by Filimonoff. Our figures demonstrate, however, a lam. diss. between the outer and inner stratum of the peripaleocortex (Fig. 16), as they also show the accentuated superficial cell condensations.

It is true that in higher mammals, particularly in primates, the uniformity of this intermediate ring is somewhat obscured by the fact that the periarchicortex includes beside the simple presubiculum in the temporal lobe the highly specialized entorhinal region. This especially intricate region in higher primates appears to be a kind of integration cortex for olfactory and visual input at the level of pAll; it has preserved the basic structure of the periarchicortex including one or two lam. diss. and a particular elaboration of cell condensations—glomeruli—in the accentuated lamina II. Ramon y Cajal (1955) described the lamina II in the entorhinal region as composed of large stellate cells. His figures and those of Lorente de Nò show that these "star cells" are studded with spines, in contrast to the star cells of the isocortex. A layer of true star cells are not to be found in the entorhinal region, another confirmation of its pAll character.

An important difference in the relationships to the allocortices appears at the outer borderline of both moieties of pAll. The outer stratum of the peripaleocortex becomes continuous with the dense cell band of the paleocortex (Fig. 16), whereas the inner stratum of the periarchicortex becomes continuous with the cell band of the archicortex (Figs. 3 and 25). We are dealing here with the well-known superpositions at the limits of the primitive allocortices, which in our context suggest the common origin of both periallocortices in that the outer stratum appears derived from the paleocortex and the inner stratum appears derived from the archicortex.

Thus the pAll is recognized as the incipiently laminated neocortex with uniform main features throughout its periarchicortical and peripaleocortical extensions, which are adjacent to these dissimilar types of ancient cortex—the archicortex and the paleocortex. Hence the ring of pAll can best be understood as having evolved during phylogeny as a common derivation of both older cortices.

What now presents itself as a ringlike cortical structure, i.e. the first growth ring of the neocortex, must have been originally, in the extinct links between reptiles and mammals, a core of new cortex, built up from both, the paleocortex and the archicortex.

ORGANIZATION OF THE PROISOCORTICAL AND PARALIMBIC/PARINSULAR GROWTH RINGS

During the phylogeny of the neocortex, ever new waves of growth and differentiation evolved, and each time a new cortex developed as a new core, displacing the previous core to a ringlike structure. Thus a sequence of concentric growth rings has been formed by the effect of both differential ur-trends. The next stage is Pro, which is the last step prior to the mature isocortex. Progress in cellular lamination characterizes this step. A main feature is the incipient appearance of a granular lamina IV made up of true star cells, which in a sense fill the gap the lam. diss. had left between the two strata (Fig. 16). Now the new dorsal thalamic input enters this layer of

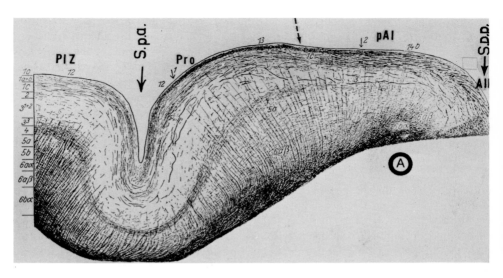

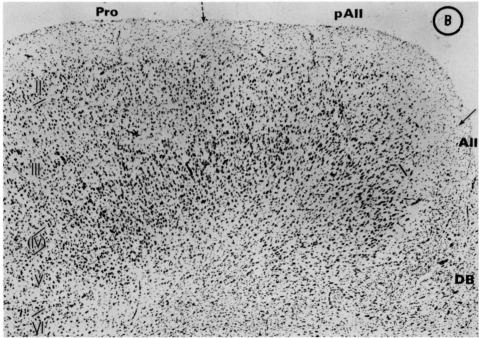

Figure 25. Horizontal sections through man's area adolfactoria (a) Myelin staining (Weigert-Kulschitzky). After C. and O. Vogt 1919. J. Psychol. Neurol., 25:279-462. (b) Nissl staining, x 32. After Sanides 1962b. Mongr. Neurol. Psychiat., 98. b, blank layer; DB, diagonal band; Spa and Spp, sulcus parolfactori anterior and posterior; (See Table 1 for abbreviations.)

star cells, forming the afferent plexus of the outer stripe of Baillarger and establishing a new kind of synaptic contact in the cortex.

As mentioned, there are already at the level of Pro such regional architectonic patterns which anticipate the architectonic areas of the next differential stage, the paralimbic/parinsular one, and even the next succeeding step with differentiation of koniocortex, which is the last in the sensory regions. We have already noted that the Pro of the anterior cingulate gyrus, which dorsally borders Mpl in the paralimbic zone, is cytoarchitectonically agranular as is the latter and the dorsally adjacent FmZ (Fig. 1).

We must emphasize that we cannot recognize whether any of the medium-sized perikarya are star cells in the poorly developed lamina III of the anterior cingulate Pro. So far we only know that the fine clear-cut granules of lamina IV of sensory and integration cortices correspond to the typical small star cells of the Golgi picture. But there are also larger star cells, which fulfill all pertinent criteria of star cells. They are not necessarily recognized in the Nissl picture. Therefore, it appears important that recent Golgi studies by Marin-Padilla (1969) demonstrated star cells in all layers of the human frontomotor zone, but predominantly in what would correspond to the level of lamina IV of granular cortex.

We now can demonstrate how this switch from zonal layer and outer stratum synaptic contact of the thalamic afferents in pAll to lamina IV synaptic contact in Pro and isocortex is reflected in cytoarchitectonics and myeloarchitectonics. For this purpose we refer to Vogt's graphic representation of a Weigert-Kulschitzky stained preparation—the most discretely working myelin method—of a horizontal section through man's area adolfactoria (Fig. 25a), and to compare it with a Nissl stained section in a corresponding plane (Fig. 25b).

The important role of the zonal layer in myeloarchitectonics of the older cortices is well known. Olfactory afferents of the paleocortex form the heavily myelinated outer part of the zonal layer of the prepiriform cortex. Tufted, lophodendritic cells of the cortical cell layer spread their dendrites into the olfactory fiber plexus. The pAll still possesses a much more pronounced fiber plexus in the zonal layer than the isocortex. Our figure allows survey of the gradual decrease of the archicortical strength of the zonal fiber plexus over pAll into Pro.

At the right of both figures is the sulcus parolfactorius posterior where cells of the diagonal band (DB) meet the wedgelike beginning of the primitive allocortex (rudimentary precommissural hippocampus). Here the entering tangential fibers of the medial stria olfactoria form almost the outer half of the cortex. This primitive allocortex, composed of thick spindle cells and lesser pyramidal cells is seen in Figure 25b to be continuous with the inner stratum of pAll at the area limit. The superposed outer stratum is composed of scattered cells of different sizes. Pronounced cell condensations are lacking at the surface of the stratum in this human material, but some typical agglomerations of medium-sized polymorph cells are present. Throughout pAll the emphasis is on the inner stratum, which also has typical limbic cell forms as rod cells and fork cells. A clearly-cut lam. diss. cannot be distinguished. In the myelin picture the strong tangential fibers of the zonal layer are gradually tapering off to a thinner subpial layer toward the area limit to Pro. However, the zonal fiber plexus is thinning and the outer stripe of Baillarger is gradually building up. This gradual increase continues into Pro. Thus we are dealing with a gradient of the architectonic changes and not with a gradation, i.e., stepwise change, as is the rule within the *isocortex*. The building up of the cytoarchitectonics of the proisocortex occurs gradually. There is a widening lamina III separated from a denser lamina II with medium-sized cells. A striking observation in such transitions is that before the dysgranular lamina IV emerges, a blank layer (b) between inner and outer stratum is discernible. Finally within this Pro the inner stratum differentiates into two layers: pyramidal-celled lamina V and more spindle-celled lamina VI. Beyond the sulcus parolfactorius anterior we find PlZ, with a thicker granular lamina IV and more pronounced lamination. The myeloarchitectonics in PlZ exhibit finer tangential fibers of the zonal layer and a stronger outer stripe of Baillarger coinciding with the granular lamina IV. At the same time thicker, deeper horizontal fibers of laminae V and VI begin to appear as they are known for their intracortical associative function. The radiate fibers are important in our context. Radiate fibers penetrate all layers up to lamina 1 in pAll and in the adjacent section of the Pro (supraradiate type Vogts). In Pro at the same time more radiate fiber bundles are ending at the outer stripe of Baillarger (infraradiate type Vogts), and in the paralimbic zone more heavily myelinated radiate fiber bundles are present which, as it is typical for the mature isocortex, pass the outer stripe of Baillarger and penetrate into the outer third of lamina 3 (euradiate type Vogts).

Concerning the described behavior of the tangential fibers of the zonal layer, the level of penetration of the radiate fibers, and the emergence of deeper horizontal fibers, bundling in the form of the stripes of Baillarger, principally similar changes take place in the *claustrocortex* of the *insula*. That is in the domain of the lateral ur-trend which is paleocortical in origin dependent in its initial stages on the *lateral* olfactory tract input.

The basic resemblance of the cytoarchitectonic and myeloarchitectonic changes in the respective spheres of both ur-trends has already been discussed previously. However, each ur-trend places its own architectonic marks. This seeming contradiction has to be elucidated: The basic resemblance of both ur-trends reveals itself in our view as an expression of the fact that each of the corresponding consecutive beltlike stages (rings) of both moieties was at the time of their original formation the integrate part of one new differentiated core. On the other hand, each moiety is subject to a prevailing, moulding influence from the pertinent spring territory, which may be thought to be exerted by means of the corticocortical fiber connections and the subcortical afferents and efferents.

Nauta's above quoted observation "on a certain dualism in the prefrontolimbic associations" can be regarded as an example of the persisting dependence of the higher differentiated moieties of the growth rings upon their respective territories of origin.

This moulding influence of the spring territories is also reflected in the functional architecture of the primate neocortex. Thus the frontal lobe, which is not only in its precentral motor cortex of a predominantly effector type (Sanides and Schiltz, 1967), is architectonically predetermined more by the hippocampal spring territory, which is an effector structure par excellence. Only the inferior frontal gyrus appears determined more by the paleocortical spring territory which is pure olfactory sensory. This is also reflected by the faster and greater granularization within the frontal lobe of the successive stages of the lateral ur-trend. That is even valid for the precentral motor cortex which includes Vogt's mastication field 6b. In all primates investigated this field is not agranular as the rest of the pyramidalized precentral motor cortex, but dysgranular. A slight granularization extends to the limit of head and arm representation.

In contrast, we came to the conclusion that in the sensory integration cortex of the parietal lobe the prevailing influence of the lateral ur-trend extends up to the intraparietal sulcus, including the arm brain.

The third neocortex growth ring is also formed by two moieties: the medial paralimbic zone and the lateral parinsular zone. This then is the site of the additional sensory and motor representations: AII, SmII, and the taste area G laterally and supplementary motor and sensory representations and prostriata medially. The lesser degree of functional differentiation of these representations is particularly evident for the sensorimotor areas. These show much less preference for the apices of the limbs and still include a major ipsilateral share of both features, quite in contrast to the primary areas. The intermediate architectonic character of those areas between insular Pro and pertinent koniocortex was discussed previously. Furthermore the intermediate architectonic character of the prostriata between the entorhinal region and the visual koniocortex was noted. To characterize this intermediate stage we introduced the term prokoniocortex.

LAST WAVE OF GROWTH AND DIFFERENTIATION OF THE NEOCORTEX

It is in the koniocortex that granularization reaches its culmination. It was Rose (1949) who pointed out how much the koniocortex in man (which resembles that of all higher primates) differs in appearance from that of other mammals e.g. the cat. Only simian primates appear to have granule cells with such clearly-demarcated small and rounded perikarya in their lamina IV. The prosimian *Nycticebus* (Fig. 16) has, instead of such clearly-demarcated granule cells, somewhat larger and irregularly shaped cells as has the cat (Sanides and Hoffmann, 1969). Nevertheless we could fashion a workable definition of the koniocortex first in *Nycticebus*, which, including the factor of cell density, appears to be the same in all mammals of the size range of monkeys, prosimians, cats, dogs, and smaller species. The relative cell density in these animals and the dispersion of small cells in the koniocortex result in a partial fusion of the cell layers of the outer stratum (II, III, and IV), with blurring of the lamination. This is accentuated in the layers of the inner stratum with its outstanding light lamina V and the dense lamina VI. Thus we have in the koniocortex a preponderance of the outer stratum which is more involved with afferent input and intracortical processing, as contrasted to the inner stratum which has predominantly an efferent function.

The high specialization of the koniocortex of higher primates is also revealed by the study of Cragg (1967), who showed that the cell density is much higher than in nonprimate brains of comparable weight. This is basically the product of the extreme granularization in higher primates. In the light of the new meaning of the star cells in synaptology compared to other small cells with dendritic spines, one can speak of stellarization as a trend in higher neocortex evolution.*

Our comparative studies in insectivores and bats suggest that the formation of the koniocortices as well as of the gigantopyramidalis i.e. the latest step in sensory and motor cortex evolution occurred in somewhat advanced mammals about 50 million years ago, in the *Eocene*, with the rise of modern orders and suborders of mammals, since *Erinaceus*, for example, also referred to as a survivor of the Paleocene when archaic mammals were dominant (Romer 1949), did not reach this stage.

With the primary motor and sensory areas of this last wave of growth and differentiation of the neocortex, we arrived at the convexity cortex of most recent mammals. The comparative architectonic and electrophysiological data of these areas indicate that the generalized design of these regions were derived from the prokonio-cortices of the preceding growth ring. It will be much more difficult to indicate how the general design of the evolutionary pattern of the integration cortices was derived. Therefore, we will propose a tentative design only for the frontal cortex, about which we have collected much data in a wide range of primates (Fig. 26).

Once more we have to imagine that the paralimbic/parinsular growth ring originally occurred as a core within the Pro growth ring. The above quoted findings of Pandya and Kuypers (1969) of the corticocortical projections of *Macaca's* parinsular SmII to paralimbic supplementory motor area support this concept. The somatic, auditory, and visual koniocortices and the gigantopyramidalis are new growth cores which displaced the paralimbic and parinsular moieties to growth rings. In addition new emerging cores of the integration cortices were involved. Therefore in the paralimbic/parinsular stage we encounter components of separate growth rings for sensory, motor, and integration cortices with parts as the premotor areas and para-koniocortex areas crossing the hemisphere and no longer revealing their origin so easily in the coronal directions of differentiation of the ur-trends.

A ringlike structure was first described for the auditory region of the cat (Rose and Woolsey, 1949). Examining the cytoarchitectonics and myeloarchitectonics we arrived at the interpretation of AII as a proK intermediary between the insular Pro and AI, the area of the auditory koniocortex. The ringlike structure of the visual region was closed rostrally by the prostriata, the limbic visual proK intermediary to the area striata (the visual koniocortex). In the sensorimotor regions we encountered particular relations caused by the tight interlocking of tactile and motor functions, and because the somatomotor representations were primarily built up by the medial ur-trend, whereas the somatic sensory representations were primarily built up by the lateral ur-trend. Thus we find here a double sensorimotor ring with the common inter-connecting fringe area, the intersensorimotor Ism (Vogts 3a) lying in the depth of simian primates' central sulcus.

Now we can resume our interpretations from a study of the sensory and motor

---

* At this point a principal observation of Lorente de Nò appears relevant. Comparing his elaborate Golgi studies of the mouse neocortex as represented in his article in Fulton's textbook (1938) with the human neocortex, he states: "The reduction of the numbers of cells with short axons, without essential modification of the long links in the chains of cortical neurons, makes the cortex of the mouse the 'skeleton' for the human cortex."

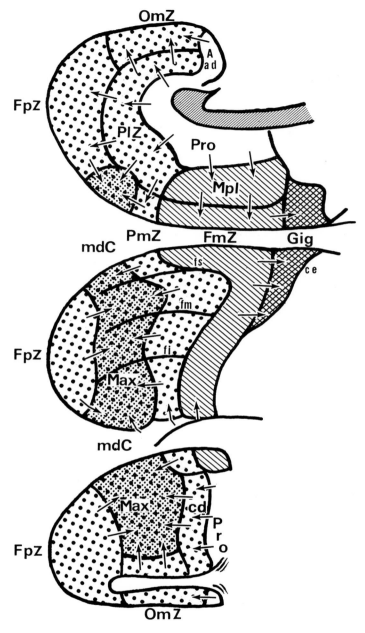

Figure 26. Architectonic map of man's frontal lobe with precentral motor cortex and prefrontal cortex: (a) medial, (b) lateral, (c) orbital aspects; frontomotor zone (FmZ) with highest specialized core, Gig. Prefrontal growth ring (dotted) and highest differentiated midfrontal core (mdC) with two differentiation maxima (Max); Aad, area adolfactoria; ce, sulcus centralis; fi, fm, fs, inferior, middle, superior frontal sulci.

regions of *Nycticebus* and *Saimiri* (Sandies, 1967). In the older paralimbic and parinsular representations, central foci have arisen with denser thalamic input and higher specialized structure, resulting in the most refined sensory and motor representations and relationships with peripheral sense organs and muscles. Prevailing in most recent mammals these sensory and motor fields were first detected and designated as primary fields. During later development the linking paralimbic and parinsular prokoniocortices and supplementary sensorimotor areas lagged behind; their representations at the periphery were less differentiated. The persisting original cortices became involved in associative sensory functions (parK); they retain connections with the respective koniocortex cores and with the adjacent integration cortices.

Approaching the problem of the growth rings of the frontal integration cortex (prefrontal cortex) in higher primates including man, we have first to consider that there are at the caudo-orbital and the insulo-opercular border of the frontal lobe the representations of the chemical senses, olfactory and gustatory, respectively. They are not intermediate to koniocortices. The olfactory paleocortex is rimmed by a caudo-orbital Pro (Fig. 26) of unknown function. Adjacent to this a particularly sudden differentiation in rostral direction takes place leading in man over a paralimbic belt and another intermediate area to the highest differentiated center of the orbital cortex (Vogts area 60; Fig. 4). The other chemical sense, taste, occupies the most rostral site in the parinsular belt, and it is intermediate between the prefrontal insula and the paramotor belt of the prefrontal cortex (Fig. 9).

In a way the amazing manifold architectonic partitioning of man's enormous frontal lobe, as revealed first by the Vogts with the myeloarchitectonic method (1910), then by Ngowyang with the cytoarchitectonic method (1934), and by us with the combined cytomyeloarchitectonic approach (1962b), was instrumental in finding and tracing main directions of architectonic differentiation. In their standard work the Vogts (1919) had described the phenomenon of architectonic gradations by the example of four frontal areas of *Macaca* which form a sagittal sequence: 4a, premotor 6aα, and 6aβ, and prefrontal 9. They explained that the extreme cytoarchitectonic differences of areas 4a and 9 are bridged by intermediate changes of the architectonic features in the areas 6aα and 6aβ. Thus the principle of architectonic sequences was detected and designated "areal gradations," emphasizing the stepwise change from area to area, as is the rule in the isocortex. Brockhaus (1940) was the first to elaborate this principle of architectonic differentiation for a whole region, the human insular cortex. Virtually he described what we later called lateral ur-gradation. However, he did not pursue this sequence to the operculum or make an evolutionary interpretation.

Instead of the term medial and lateral "ur-gradations" as used in our frontal lobe monograph (1962a) we now prefer to speak of medial and lateral ur-trends, since there is a minor difference if we deal with stepwise changes, i.e., gradations as dominant in the isocortex, or with gradual changes, i.e. gradients as demonstrated in the area adolfactoria. The direction of differentiation is the constant and is better referred to as differential trend.

We described the differential sequences of man's frontal lobe and traced them back to the territories of origin, the concept of primary and secondary cortical regions as developed by Kuhlenbeck (1928) was still dominant, with seeming support from Flechsig's misunderstood myelogenesis (1920). The sensory and motor areas were looked upon as primary and the overlooked integration cortices of lower mammals as secondary. There is also a sequence of increasing granularization and reduction of lamina V pyramidal cells from the precentral motor cortex to the frontopolar zone (FpZ), that is, from so-called primary to so-called secondary regions. We referred to this sequence with some reluctance as "poleward gradation" and classified it as being more recent than the ur-gradations (ur-trends). The reluctance was caused by the fact that there was also a component of decrease of the average cell size and of the myelin content. Both factors have the effect of a higher resemblance of FpZ to adjacent PlZ, suggesting that it is the medial ur-trend which exerts the main influence. The basic evolutionary significance of the myelination trend as it is reflected in both ur-trends (Figs. 5 and 6) was derived later through Bishop's work. On the other hand the integration cortices have as a whole a somewhat finer myelination than the sensory and motor projection areas.

Finally the finding of small clear-cut anterior (frontal) and posterior integration areas in the European hedgehog led us to a revision of the "poleward gradation." A poleward differential trend appears now only valid from the paramotor belt to a midfrontal cortical belt (Figs. 26a, b). Corresponding to the sensory and motor growth rings we again arrive at the assumption of an older growth ring and a more recent core. The ring of older prefrontal cortex exhibits incipient granularization in its paralimbic and paramotor zone and in a caudo-orbital paralimbic belt and persisting paralimbic features combined with somewhat higher granularization in OmZ and FpZ. The more recent midfrontal core appears then to be the product of concentric differentiation of this growth ring, as are the koniocortices within their fringe areas. This prefrontal core comprises (1) the two maxima of frontal differentiation (Max) in the convexity and orbital parts of the inferior frontal gyrus, (2) the middle section of the middle frontal gyrus, and (3) the adjacent part of the superior frontal gyrus. This core is highly granularized and possesses large lamina III pyramids and a relatively weak lamina V.

The paramotor belt was so named for its resemblance to the premotor areas, combined, however, with incipent granularization. It contains the frontal eye fields, Broca's area * in man, and in its ventral part an area from where respiration is influenced. The intermediate area from the prefrontal insula is formed by the gustatory area G.

For further substantiation of the prefrontal growth ring, detailed study of the thalamic dependencies appears promising, since there is some evidence that the thalamus exhibits a correlated concentric zonation within the mediodorsal nucleus (MD). The dorsal paralamellar part of MD projects to the motor eye fields of the paramotor belt (Scollo-Lavizzari and Akert, 1963). The ventral paralamellar part of MD projects to the ventral part of the paramotor belt (Roberts and Akert, 1963). FpZ and OmZ receive projections from the medial magnocellular portion of MD (Hassler, 1950). On the other hand, the midfrontal core (Fig. 26) receives projections from the central parvocellular portions of MD. According to Le Gros Clark (1930) it is this small-celled element which becomes progressively more conspicuous in higher

---

* The frontomotor speech center could be a peculiar elaboration in man of an older primitive vocalization center in a comparable site.

primates. However, a complete parallelism between the growth and differentiation of the prefrontal cortex in higher primates up to man and that of the mediodorsal nucleus cannot be expected, since as a matter of fact the enormous expansion of human prefrontal cortex exceeds by far the rate of growth of MD.

CONFIRMATION OF THE EVOLUTIONARY STAGES OF THE NEOCORTEX IN PRIMITIVE EUTHERIA

In tracing the differential ur-trends in primates and describing growth rings of the neocortex we tried to extrapolate into the unknown of brain evolution. However, there is one group of recent mammals—the order of insectivores—which is known to be the most primitive among placentals. An architectonic and Golgi study of specimens of this group and the related Chiroptera was performed to validate our concept. Of course, a "survivor of the Paleocene" (*Erinaceus*) would not have survived if it would still represent completely the original stage of brain evolution. In some way, this species must have undergone further differentiation and specialization. If, however, one finds characteristics of their whole neocortex in common with those postulated older stages of neocortex differentiation of the bulk of placentals, this would be evidence for the correctness of the postulation.

This is exactly the case with specimens of Erinaceinae, *Erinaceus* and *Hemiechinus*, and of Chiroptera, *Myotis lucifugus*. Their neocortex exhibits no trace of koniocortex and gigantopyramidalis, which are typically found in such comparable-sized rodents as mouse and rat. Furthermore they share a specific characteristic of the whole neocortex with only limbic and insular cortices of other placentals. This is the accentuated lamina II, which is formed by darkly staining densely packed polymorph cells larger than granular cells; the peculiar character of which is revealed by the Golgi method. We drew the attention to this phenomenon in all our descriptions of the initial stages of the neocortex (Figs. 3, 16, and 17). In pAll we referred to it as cell condensations at the surface of the outer stratum. These cell condensations are continuous with an accentuated lamina II of Pro. We were able to trace this peculiar feature through several mammalian orders we investigated, including primates. At first we overlooked it in the insular and cingulate gyri of man. In the entorhinal region of man—this specialized, intriguing temporal periarchicortex—the emphasis on lamina II with formation of conspicuous glomeruli is best known. In man's insular cortex and cingulate gyrus we can now recognize this feature after our experience with lower mammals. It is much less pronounced because of the low general cell density.

In the rat's cerebral cortex (Fig. 27) we can demonstrate the conspicuous feature of the accentuated lamina II, surrounding the isocortex in a ringlike fashion in the limbic and insular boundary regions. It comprises the first (pAll) and second (Pro) neocortical stages. The peripaleocortex (pAll) begins near the rhinal sulcus. Its outer stratum with the superficial cell condensations is continuous with the dense band of the prepiriform cortex (Pal). The claustrum which is easily recognizable in the depth of Pal, fuses with the inner stratum of pAll and Pro and is almost indiscernible in these lower mammals. The inner stratum of pAll is formed by darkly staining larger pyramidal cells and is separated from the outer stratum by an indication of a lam. diss. (broken line). Within Pro the lamina II accentuation is less pronounced and tapers off toward the area limit of proK. More caudal sections show the lamina II accentuation ventrolaterally to be as pronounced as at the medial limbic boundary region of Figure 27.

Erinaceus (Fig. 28) with its small neocortical cap shows the accentuated lamina II all over the poorly laminated neocortex. It is continuous with Pal laterally. A careful scrutiny shows the precommissural hippocampus (H) to be continuous with the inner stratum of pAll. *Myotis* (Fig. 29) has a relatively larger neocortex over its reduced paleocortex (Stephan, personal communication). Again the entire poorly laminated neocortex exhibits an even sharper accentuated lamina II. The supracom-

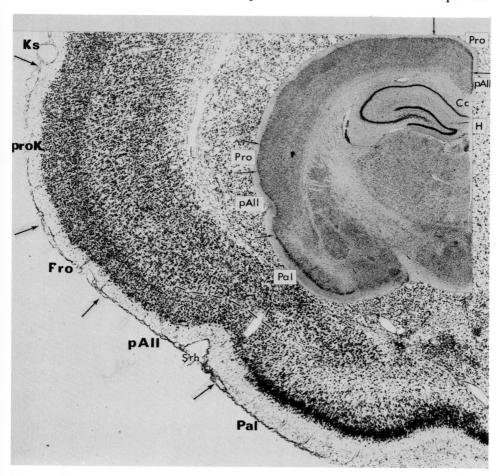

Figure 27. Coronal section through the hemisphere of the rat showing the sequence from paleocortex (Pal) to two-strata periallocortex (pAll, with indicated lam. diss., dashed line), to Pro, ProK, and Ks, x 40; inset shows a more candal section with peri-archicortical pAll and Pro, and peripaleocortical pAll and Pro. Note the accentuated II in pAll and Pro. S.rh., rhinal sulcus.

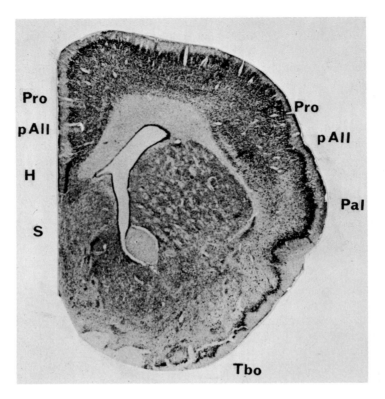

Figure 28. Coronal section through the hemisphere of *Erinaceus*. Ventrolateral is the large olfactory tubercle (Tbo). The small neocortical cap exhibits the lamina II accentuation all over the convexity. S, septum, x 10.

missural hippocampus (H), forming a gyrulus, is continuous with the inner stratum of pAll. Pal is continuous with the outer stratum of pAll. At this point we can add that in a recent work on the cytoarchitectonics of several Chiroptera (*Nyctalus noctula, Nyctalus leisleri, Vespertilio pipistrellus, Plecotus auritus*) Kurepina (1968) comes to the conclusion that "the cortex of the bat's brain is primitively developed, which corresponds to their low position in the phylogenetic scale." Kurepina's illustrations of the cytoarchitectonic structure of the bat's cortex reveal the lamina II accentuation over the convexity of the neocortex to be similar to our Figure 29. The author did not mention this as a particular characteristic. Comparative studies of another insectivore, the mole, and of *Tupaia* showed that the former also exhibits, though in a lesser degree, an accentuation of the lamina II, perhaps with the exception of the frontopolar region. In the mole, however, the convexity cortex already shows somewhat better lamination. Compared with the mole, the tree shrew (*Tupaia*) possesses far better lamination and typical koniocortices, the lamina II accentuation does not reach farther than that of the rat (Fig. 27).

Finally we have evidence for the existence of the lamina II accentuation in the

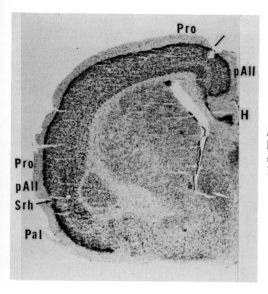

Figure 29. Coronal section through the hemisphere of *Myotis Lucifugus.* The small neocortical cap illustrates the lamina II accentuation all over the convexity, x 12.

convexity cortex of Metatheria and Prototheria. In an examination of a brain series of the American opossum, we found that the neocortex exhibits a relatively sharp accentuation of the lamina II. This, however, was combined with a fairly good lamination and granularization of the convexity cortex. Examining the figures of Abbie (1942) of a more primitive marsupial, *Perameles,* we found again a sharply accentuated lamina II over a laminated cortex, and a rather similar appearance can be discerned in Abbie's figures (1940) of the different areas of the monotremes *Echidna* and *Platypus.*

Summarizing our findings about the phenomenon of the accentuated lamina II we can say that it is a common characteristic of the more ancient neocortex growth rings in most of the recent placentals but is present all over the neocortex in some primitive mammals (insectivores * and bats). A similar condition of the II is found in the Metatheria so far investigated and in the Prototheria.

At lower magnification the future isocortex of a human fetus of about eight months shows approximately the same picture as the neocortex of the bat: a moderately differentiated cortex is covered by a sharp accentuated dense lamina II. Thus we recognize this peculiar feature persisting in a late ontogenetic stage. Of course the fate of these undifferentiated cells is quite different. Von Economo speculated about the possibility that at birth the dense lamina II is the source of nerve cells for the deeper layers. It is our impression that the consummation of the dense lamina II in other mammals may be rather protracted, since we have observed a relative density of lamina II in most mammals which were more or less immature. Corresponding

---

* Reviewing illustrations of the cerebral cortex of insectivores by Stephan and Andy (1962) and Stephan and Spatz (1962) we could realize the accentuated lamina II in the following insectivores: Tenrec ecaudatus, Setifer setosus, Chlorotalpa stuhlmanni, Elephantulus fuscipes, and Potamogale velox.

observations can be made in photomicrographs of the cortex of immature monkeys (Powell and Mountcastle, 1959).

In conclusion we can say, the lack of koniocortex and gigantopyramidalis combined with poor lamination and granularization in the specimens of Erinaceiniae and Chiroptera indicate that the last stage of sensory and motor cortical differentiation has not been attained in these insectivores and "flying insectivores." This is obviously the paralimbic/parinsular stage of neocortical evolution. In most placentals the conspicuous lamina II accentuation does not extend beyond Pro limit. The fact that this peculiar feature is present all over the neocortex is indicative of an additional conservative character in these primitive placentals, combined even with the third stage of neocortex evolution.

In the marsupial virginian opossum, a more advanced neocortex shows the persistence of this peculiar accentuated lamina II. It is possibly an aberrant expression of neocortical evolution.

A cytoarchitectonic study (Gerebtzoff and Goffart, 1966) and a sensory projection study (Meulders et al., 1966), on the cerebral cortex of the sloth have produced significant data. The sloth, is one of the living primitive mammals with a sagittal sulcus pattern and a sharply accentuated lamina II all over its neocortex. It is composed of medium-sized darkly staining cells. This characteristic, combined with the poor lamination and poor granularization of the whole neocortex, suggested to these authors that this cortex was comparable to the juxta-allocortex of other mammals. In our view this cortex actually corresponds approximately to a predominant paralimbic/parinsular stage as demonstrated in the bat and hedgehog (Figs. 28 and 29). On the other hand the sagittal sulci would suggest that there exists SmI. The evoked potential study sustains this view and demonstrates that the two sagittal sulci delimit the forelimb area medially and laterally. The authors found, however, only a very limited area for the head. SmII on the other hand was completely overlapped by auditory input and lacked somatotopic partitioning. It is interesting that this aberrant primitive mammal evolved the sagittal sulcal pattern with the new coronal somatotopic representation but did not evolve a koniocortex.

A Golgi study (Tungsten modification of Golgi-Cox after Ramon-Moliner, 1958) was made of the brains of *Hemiechinus*, *Myotis lucifugus*, rat and cat. Slides counterstained with cresylviolet verified the relationships to the cytoarchitectonic layers. The general distribution of cortical neurons showed a predominance of pyramidal cells in all layers with typical apical and basal dendrites rich in spines. There were few typical star cells lying in middle and outer layers of the cortex, more so in the hedgehog than in the bat. Only the cells of the lamina II exhibited a well-developed dendritic pattern (Fig. 30), which is not found in the isocortical lamina II of the rat or cat. In the Golgi preparations of the latter animals, in lamina II typical or atypical pyramidal cells with short shaft or direct spreading of two bifurcating dendrites from the perikaryon into lamina I were found, as described by Globus and Scheibel (1967). We confirm the observation made by these authors that the apical bouquets and the basal dendrites of the pyramidal cells have the same horizontal spread. Thus the dendritic fields of the apical dendrites and the basal skirts together form a cylinder. Neurons of this type were not met in the densely packed lamina II of *Myotis lucifugus* and *Hemiechinus* but were already found at the inner border of

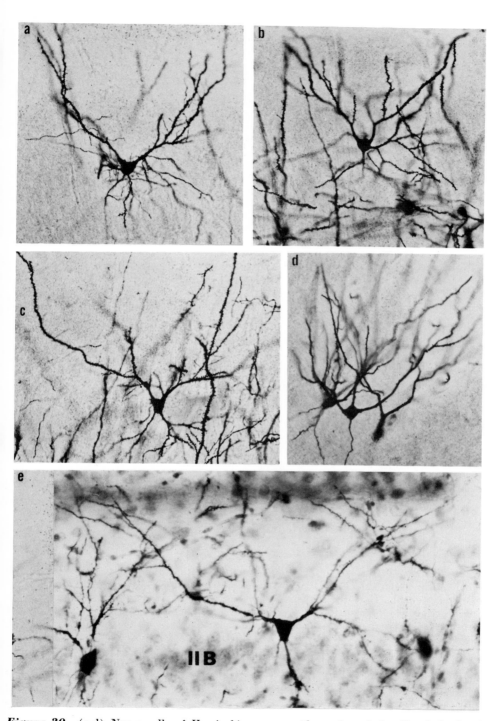

Figure 30. (a-d) Nerve cells of *Hemiechinus*; a-c, wide angle tufted cells of the band-like accentuated lamina II of the convexity cortex; (d) tufted cell of the prepiriform cortex (Golgi method,) x 200; (e) wide angle tufted cell of the bandlike accentuated lamina II (IIB) of the convexity cortex of *Myotis Lucifugus*; (Golgi method, counter-stained with cresylviolet,) x 300.

197

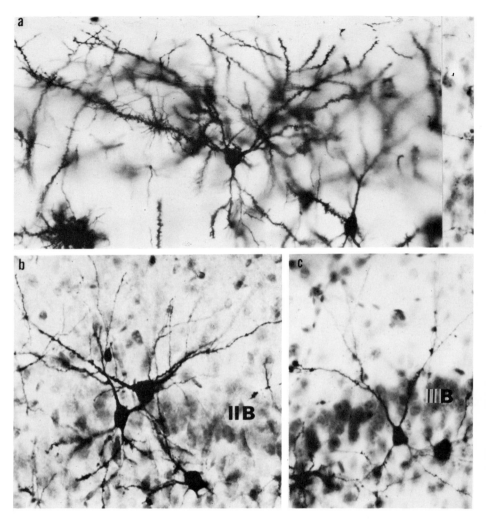

Figure 31. (a-c) Nerve cells of *Myotis Lucifugus*; (a) wide angle tufted cell of the bandlike accentuated lamina II of the convexity cortex; (b) similar cell type of the accentuated lamina II (IIB) of the entorhinal region; below and left of this cell a large starlike type; (c) immediately below the accentuated lamina II (IIB) of the convexity cortex usual atypical pyramidal cell; (Golgi method, (b) and (c) counterstained with cresylviolet,) x 300.

lamina II (Fig. 31c). The dendritic pattern of the accentuated lamina II neurons is shown in Figures 30e and 31a for the bat and Figure 30a-c for the hedgehog. These cells were the tufted type,* with particularly wide spreading of extraverted dendrites extending directly from the perikaryon without any shaft. The underdeveloped fine

* It is a pleasure to acknowledge the valuable advice of Dr. Ramon-Moliner in these studies.

basal dendrites did not reach the spread of the extraverted dendrites. Both types of dendrites were rich in spines with more spines on the outer dendrites.

Compared with other tufted neurons, for example those of the prepiriform cortex of *Hemiechinus* (Fig. 30d), the extreme wide spreading of the thick external dendrites was striking. The wider spread was common in the bat. These neurons have a similar dendritic pattern to the neurons of the frog endbrain (Fig. 32A; Ramon y Cajal, 1909). The axons of these neurons appear to terminate in deeper layers of the cortex. In essence the dendritic pattern of these neurons is characterized by an extensive overlapping of the external dendritic fields of the accentuated lamina II cells within the zonal layer. Although the neurons of lamina II of the hedgehog in general did not show such wide spreading apical bouquets, the incongruity between the very fine and shorter basal dendrites and the zonal layer dendritic spread was striking. Similar cell types were found in lamina II of the entorhinal region. Among those which Ramon y Cajal referred to as large star cells (Fig. 31b; compare also with Lorente de Nò, 1933, Fig. 3 of the entorhinal region of the mouse). However, the basal dendrites in both cases were relatively thick, the thicker external dendrites covering a wider dendritic field. As our Figure 32 from Ramon y Cajal demonstrates, this investigator traced the parallelism of the dendritic pattern of pallial neurons in phylogenesis and ontogenesis: A, B, C, and D representing major stages in phylogeny (amphibian, reptile, lower mammal, man), a, b, c, d, e, representing ontogenetic

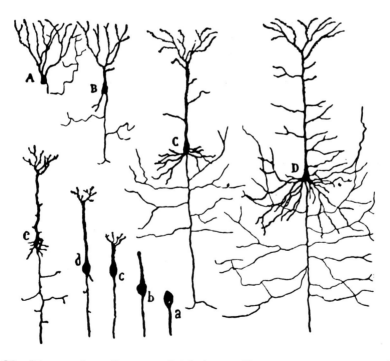

Figure 32. Diagram from Ramon y Cajal (1909. Histologie du Système Nerveux des Vertébrés, Maloine.) Showing phylogenesis of pallial neurons (A-D), parallelled by ontogenesis of a pyramidal cell of a mouse (a-e). A, frog; B, lizard; C, mouse; D, man.

stages of pyramidal cells of the mouse cortex. Thus the development of the lopho-dendritic cells towards pyramidal cells has been established, in the course of which basal dendrites appear in later stages than the apical ones.* A telling detail is that in contrast to Globus and Scheibel's rule, elaborated predominantly in rabbits, the basal skirt in man has a wider extent than that of the apical bouquet. We conclude that the apical bouquet is a conservative feature and that the basal skirt is a progressive feature in pallial neurons evolution.

The perikarya of the predominant cell type of the accentuated lamina II of hedgehog and bat appear to be shaped by the strong extraversion and wide dendritic spread into the zonal layer, in that they mostly had a broad base above and a tip or curve below. This peculiar type of extraverted cell is a specimen of the tufted cortical neurons, which have their extreme in mammals in the dentate fascia neurons without any basal dendrites. The extraversion of the related allocortical neurons is an expression of the fact that the zonal layer still represents in allocortex and periallocortex the main afferent and association plexus of the cortex.

In summary the dendritic pattern of our extraverted wide angle cells in the bat and the hedgehog neocortex indicates a conservative expression, which agrees with the observation in the hedgehog that the thalamic terminations reach the zonal layer. These terminals make synaptic contact with the extensively overlapping external dendrites. Such thalamic terminations in the zonal layers were described in the pAll of the rat, too.

The conclusion that the investigated specimens of Erinaceinae and Chiroptera did not reach the last stage of sensory and motor cortex evolution but persist at the paralimbic/parinsular stage and based on comparative cytoarchitectonics and myeloarchitectonics and Golgi studies. In neurophysiologic terms this would mean that in these animals the so-called primary sensory and motor areas are absent while, the so-called secondary ones (SmII, AII, supplementary motor and sensory areas, prostriata, and the gustatory area G) are present. The possibility of intermediate stages or aberrant development has also to be considered.

Microelectrode recording studies in the neocortex and thalamus of *Erinaceus* by Diamond and co-workers (1967), which we discussed recently (Sanides, 1968), lend support to our view that this "survivor of the Paleocene" did not yet reach the stage of the classic sensory and motor representations. The sensory relay nuclei of the thalamus should also reflect the neocortex stages as a kind of interdependent growth ring of the forebrain, as was indicated for the dorsomedial nucleus (noted above). Actually Diamond's (1967) and Bauchot's (1959) anatomical observations indicate that this mammal has the most primitive stage of thalamic differentiation among placentals. This corresponds to Diamond's electrophysiological results that the somesthetic nucleus (VP) and the auditory thalamic nucleus (medial geniculate body) are not yet "the exclusive target of one modality." Thus in the thalamus the specific relay nuclei may have differentiated during evolution as a core in a more generalized older ground area. An indication for such thalamic ground areas is the pulvinar-posterior system as presented by Rose and Woolsey (1958).

---

* Noback and Purpura (1961), tracing the postnatal ontogenesis of neurons in cat neocortex confirmed this developmental sequence and discussed electrophysiological implications.

The recording study of the sensory cortex (Diamond, 1967) is suggestive for nonclassic representations. The unusual large tactile receptive fields were found in the periphery, indicated a reduced discrimination power. Moreover, the predominance of sustaining input to the sensory cortex was found. This phenomenon, first revealed by Rose and Woolsey (1958), is characteristic for the sensory areas surrounding the koniocortex cores. The latter receives "essential" input (discussed in Sanides, 1968).

THE GROWTH RINGS OF THE NEOCORTEX AND THE RELATIONSHIP OF SMII AND MPL TO THE CLASSIC SENSORIMOTOR REPRESENTATIONS

We will now review the stages of forebrain evolution and present a tentative design of how the coronal somatotopic pattern of classic sensorimotor representations may have developed from the sagittal paralimbic and parinsular patterns of the secondary (secondarily detected!) representations. We demonstrated above that not only primates began their gyrification of the neocortex in evolution with a sagittal pattern, but also ungulates and carnivores, which represent the most successful groups with the arcuate patterned brain. The somatotopical significance of this sagittal pattern in terms of functional architecture was clarified and traced through recent carnivores and most advanced primates including man. The medial and lateral sagittal sulci which determine the sagittal patterned brain separate hindlimb, forelimb, and head areas not only in the classic sensorimotor regions but apparently also in the integration cortices. The question is whether we can find, looking backward from this point of departure, an explanation as to why and how the classic sensorimotor areas may have arisen following an earlier phylogenetic stage on which the so-called secondary representations of the paralimbic/parinsular zone "had done the job."

The principle of building of new nervous centers to meet new adaptive needs of an everchanging world during geological times is reflected in what von Monakow (1911) described as the rostralward migration of functions during brain evolution. This leads to the intricate sequential reorganization of the brain stem and diencephalon as seen in comparative neurology and ontogenesis. The rostralward migration terminated at the utmost end of the endbrain by forming the cerebral cortex and exploiting the new source of pial blood supply. Further waves of growth and differentiation making the adaptive responses to an everchanging environment (on land even more so than in the water) were now established as concentric growth rings of respective new cortices parallelled by corresponding waves of growth and differentiation of the interdependent thalamic nuclei, together with the differentiation of the affiliated peripheral sense organs. Thus we have traced in a series of mammals the sequence of four neocortex waves: Periallocortex, proisocortex, parinsular/paralimbic belt, and koniocortex plus gigantopyramidalis of the sensory and motor regions. Of course we can not easily determine the answer as to which requirements were fulfilled by the earliest growth ring, the pAll.

The raison d'etre of the next growth ring with its Pro is more easily surmised. We know that the insular Pro and cingular Pro are involved in a form of motor expression in the context of emotional and autonomic reactions (Showers, 1959; Showers and Lauer, 1961). The parinsular/paralimbic growth ring is composed of the prokoniocortices and supplementary motor areas, which may be functionally conceived as sensory and effector expressions which are largely emancipated from the realm of emotions and concommitant autonomic reactions. We can now focus on the sensori-motor areas which have assumed the central position in the cerebral hemispheres. Their somatotopic organization is expressed in the gyral pattern as well as in the architectonics. The basic problem is why were the sagittal paralimbic and parin-sular representations of SmII and Mpl supplanted and displaced in the Tertiary by the coronal patterned new classic representations. In the large series of sensorimotor figurines of rodents, lagomorphs, primates, and carnivores as electrophysiologically elaborated by Woolsey and his co-workers, we find in such lower animals as the rat and rabbit the striking predominance of the head representations (especially muzzle!), and already here the forelimb area is about twice as large as the hindlimb area. This preference of the forelimb is growing in the carnivores leaving behind not only hindlimb, but head area, too. In prosimians, on the other hand, the hand and foot as prehensile limbs are developed correlating with large pertinent cortical areas.

We can conclude that preference for the representation of the forelimb in SmI and MsI compared with hindlimb is expressed in the original design of classic sensori-motor organization. This preference of the forelimb representation is not yet expressed in the older paralimbic and parinsular sensorimotor areas of non-primates. This indi-cates that these representations of the third neocortex growth ring serve a general tetrapod function.

The preference of the forelimb within the classic sensorimotor representations in the next growth ring is another expression related to the adaption to terrestial life. Thus the forelimb is partly released from the compulsory tetrapody to serve roles as a scouting function and as a weapon in attack and defense.

The significance of the new sensorimotor representation which expands and dif-ferentiates as a core between the paralimbic motor and parinsular sensory representa-tions of the third growth ring could have evolved to serve this adaptive function of the forelimb. One can speculate that this new sensorimotor representation began with the development of the classic forelimb area and that this new expanding area between the older sagittal representations brought, under the counterpressure of the latter, its two sagittal sulci into appearance. (For example during evolution the growing pre-hensile motor tail representation of *Ateles* brought its limiting sulcus into appearance). Both sagittal sulci still delimit the classic hand area in recent prosimians, however against the complemented classic hindlimb area on the one hand (medial sagittal sulcus) and the classic head area on the other lateral sagittal sulcus.

THE DETERMINATION OF THE MAMMALIAN NEOCORTEX AND ITS PRE-CURSOR IN REPTILES

There appears to be a general agreement in relating the isocortex with neocortex, and the allocortex sensu ampliori (including periallocortex) with archicortex and paleocortex, (von Economo and Koskinas, 1925). This does not hold true for pAll, which we conceive as first growth ring of neocortex composed of a periarchicortex moiety and a peripaleocortex moiety.

This first wave of mammalian neocortex is a two-cell-strata cortex with emphasis on the larger celled inner stratum. Both strata are separated by a more or less clear-cut lam. diss. Another characteristic of this primary neocortex is the condensations of medium-sized tufted cells at the surface. Their dendritic tufts in the zonal layer receive synaptic contacts from the fibers of the surface-bound olfactory system and from the thalamic afferents. In the next wave of neocortex differentiation, Pro, the thalamic input switches from axodendritic synaptic contacts in the zonal layer and outer stratum to axosomatic synapses in the star-celled lamina IV. This is reflected in myeloarchitectonics as the decrease in the zonal afferent plexus and the development of the outer stripe of Baillarger afferent plexus (Fig. 5).

The latter organization of a multilaminar cortex is not reached in the reptiles. The question arises whether reptiles have somewhere, a general cortical organization equivalent to the primary neocortex—the two-cell-strata pAll of mammals. The dorsal or general cortex of reptiles which was once assumed to be the precursor of the mammalian neocortex (because of the lack of thalamic afferents) is now precluded (Kruger and Berkowitz, 1960). Rather it represents part of the hippocampal complex, as suggested by Rose (1923). Recall that the inner stratum of mammalian pAll is continuous with the hippocampal subiculum medially and that the outer stratum of pAll is continuous with the paleocortex laterally. There is an analogous condition in reptiles at the site where the dorsolateral component of the dorsal cortex underlies the lateral paleocortex. This occurs in the order Squamata (lizards and snakes) and in the order Chelonia (turtles). We note the wide divergence of the phyletic lines within the reptiles. The actual diversification of the forebrain structure of the reptilian orders has been recently traced thoroughly by Northcutt (1967). He concluded that the dorsolateral cortex underlying the paleocortex has a different character in the lizards and turtles. Only in turtles the efferent character in the form of pyramidal cells is preserved. It is functionally linked to the motor systems in the lateral forebrain bundle. In the group of reptiles which gave rise to birds—the saurapsid line which includes all living reptiles except the turtles—the dorsolateral component of the dorsal cortex has an associative role rather than a motor function.

In turtles, another requirement for the equivalence with the mammalian pAll is met. The dorsolateral component underlying part of the paleocortex receives thalamic afferents. Whether such afferents reach into the zonal layer of the superimposed paleocortex has not been established. This projection is suggested by the investigation of Orrego and Lisenby (1962) of the electrical activity in the turtle cortex. They concluded that there are sensory afferent paths terminating on apical dendrites of the general cortex.

The turtle cortex is divided into two strata—(1) an inner one, the dorsolateral cortex which is hippocampal in origin and efferent in character, and (2) an outer stratum, which is part of the paleocortex. This morphological organization appears to be the equivalent of the mammalian periallocortex. In turn, this is an expression of the primordium of a neocortex in evolution.

REFERENCES

Abbie, A. A.   1940.   Cortical lamination in the Monotremata. J. Comp. Neurol., 72: 428-467.

—— 1942. Cortical lamination in a polyprotodont marsupial, *Perameles nasuta*. J. Comp. Neurol., 76:509-536.

Adrian, E. D. 1941. Afferent discharges to the cerebral cortex from peripheral sense organs. J. Physiol. (London), 100:159-191.

Ariëns Kappers, C. N., G. Huber, and E. C. Crosby. 1936. The Comparative Anatomy of the Nervous System of Vertebrates, Including Man. New York, Macmillan.

Bailey, P., and G. von Bonin. 1951. The Isocortex of Man. Urbana, University of Illinois Press.

Bauchot, R. 1959. Étude des structures cytoarchitectoniques du diencéphale de *Talpa europaea (Insectivora talpidae)*. Acta anat. (Basel), 39:90-140.

Benjamin, R. M. 1963. Some thalamic and cortical mechanisms of taste, *In* Zotterman, Y., ed. Olfaction and Taste. Oxford, Pergamon, vol. 1, 309-329.

—— and K. Akert. 1959. Cortical and thalamic areas involved in taste discrimination in the albino rat. J. Comp. Neurol., 111:231-260.

—— and H. Burton. 1968. Projection of taste nerve afferents to anterior opercular-insular cortex in squirrel monkey (*Saimiri sciureus*). Brain Res., 7:221-231.

—— R. Emmers, and A. J. Blomquist. 1968. Projection of tongue nerve afferents to somatic sensory area I in squirrel monkey (*Saimiri sciureus*). Brain Res., 7: 208-220.

—— and C. Pfaffmann. 1955. Cortical localization of taste in albino rat. J. Neurophysiol., 18:56-64.

—— and W. I. Welker. 1957. Somatic receiving areas of cerebral cortex of squirrel monkey (*Saimiri sciureus*). J. Neurophysiol., 20:286-299.

Berman, A. L. 1961a. Overlap of somatic and auditory cortical response fields in anterior ectosylvian gyrus of cat. J Neurophysiol., 24:595-607.

—— 1961b. Interaction of cortical responses to somatic and auditory stimuli in anterior ectosylvian gurus of cat. J. Neurophysiol., 24: 608-620.

Bishop, G. H. 1959. The relation between nerve fiber size and sensory modality: phylogenetic implications of the afferent innervation of cortex. J. Nerv. Ment. Dis., 128:89-114.

—— 1965. My life among the axons. Ann. Rev. Physiol., 27:1-18.

—— and J. M. Smith. 1964. The size of nerve fibers supplying cerebral cortex. Exp. Neurol., 9:484-501.

Bonin, G. v., and P. Bailey. 1947. The neocortex of *Macaca mulatta*. Ill Monogr. Med. Sci., 5:1-163.

Brockhaus, H. 1940. Die Cyto- und Myeloarchitektonik des Cortex claustralis und des Claustrum beim Menschen. J. Psychol. Neurol., 49:249-348.

Brodmann, K. 1909. Vergleichende Lokalisationslehre der Grosshirnrinde. Leipzig, Barth.

Bucy, P. C. 1949. The Precentral Motor Cortex, 2nd ed. Urbana, University of Illinois Press.

Casey, K. L., M. Cuénod, and P. D. MacLean. 1965. Unit analysis of visual input to posterior limbic cortex. II. Intracerebral stimuli. J. Neurophysiol., 28:1101-1117.

Chang, H. T., C. N. Woolsey, L. W. Jarcho, and E. Hennemann. 1947. Representation of cutaneous tactile sensibility in the cerebral cortex of the spider monkey. Fed. Proc., 6:89 (abstract).

Clark, W. E. Le Gros. 1930. The thalamus of the *Tarsius*. J. Anat., 64:371-414.

—— 1945. Deformation patterns in the cerebral cortex. *In* Clark. W. E. Le Gros, ed. Essays on Growth and Form. Oxford, Clarendon Press.

Cragg, B. G. 1967. The density of synapses and neurons in the motor and visual areas of the cerebral cortex. J. Anat., 101:639-654.

Crosby, E. C. 1917. The forebrain of *Alligator mississippiensis*. J. Comp. Neurol., 27: 325-402.

Cuénod, M., K. L. Casey, and P. D. MacLean. 1965. Unit analysis of visual input to posterior limbic cortex. I. Photic stimulation. J. Neurophysiol., 28:1118-1131.

Dart, R. A. 1934. The dual structure of the neopallium: its history and significance. J. Anat., 69:3-19.

Diamond, I. T. 1967. The sensory neocortex. Contrib. Sens. Physiol., 2:51-100.

Domesick, V. 1969. Projections from the cingulate cortex in the rat. Brain Res., 12: 296-320.

Dusser de Barenne, J. G. 1941. Functional organization of sensory and adjacent cortex of the monkey. J. Neurophysiol., 4:324-330.

Economo, C. von, and G. N. Koskinas. 1925. Die Cytoarchitektonik der Hirnrinde des Erwachsenen Menschen. Berlin-Wien-Heidelberg, Springer.

Edinger, T. 1948. Evolution of the horse brain. Geology. Soc. Amer. Memoir, 25:177 pp.

——— 1964. Midbrain exposure and overlap in mammals. Amer. Zool. 4:5-19.

Filimonoff, I. N. 1947. A rational subdivision of the cerebral cortex. Arch. Neurol. Psychiat., 58:296-310.

Flechsig, P. 1920. Anatomie des Menschlichen Gehirns und Rückenmarks auf Myelogenetischer Grundlage. Leipzig, Thieme.

Gerebtzoff, M. A., and M. Goffart. 1966. Cytoarchitectonic study of the isocortex in the sloth (Choloepus hoffmanni Peters). J. Comp. Neurol., 126:523-534.

Gergen, J. A., and P. D. MacLean. 1964. The limbic system: Photic activation of limbic cortical areas in the squirrel monkey. Ann. N. Y. Acad. Sci., 117:69-87.

Gerhardt, E. 1938. Der Isocortex parietalis beim Schimpansen. J. Psychol. Neurol., 48:329-386.

——— 1940. Die Cytoarchitektonik des Isocortex parietalis beim Menschen. J. Psychol. Neurol., 49:367-419.

Globus, A., and A. B. Scheibel. 1967. Pattern and field in cortical structure: The rabbit. J. Comp. Neurol., 131:155-172.

Gray, E. G. 1959. Axo-somatic and axo-dendritic synapses of the cerebral cortex, An electron microscope study. J. Anat., 93:420-433.

Hassler, R. 1950. Über die anatomischen Grundlagen der Leukotomie. Fortschr. Neurol. Psychiat., 18:351.

Haug, H. 1956. Remarks on the determination and significance of the grey cell coefficient. J. Comp. Neurol., 104:473-492.

Hirsch, J. F., and W. S. Coxe. 1958. Representations of cutaneous tactile sensibility in cerebral cortex of Cebus. J. Neurophysiol., 21:481-498.

Hopf, A. 1956. Über die Verteilung myeloarchitektonischer Merkmale in der Stirnhirnrinde beim Menschen. J. Hirnforsch., 2:311-333.

——— 1966. Über eine Methode zur objektiven Registrierung der Myeloarchitektonik der Hirnrinde. J. Hirnforsch., 8:301-314.

——— 1968. Registration of the myeloarchitecture of the human frontal lobe with an extinction method. J. Hirnforsch., 10:259-269.

——— and H. Vitzthum. 1957. Über die Verteilung myeloarchitektonischer Merkmale in der Scheitellappenrinde des Menschen. J. Hirnforsch., 3:79-104.

Johnston, J. B. 1915. The cell masses in the forebrain of the turtle, Cistudo carolina. J. Comp. Neurol., 25:393-468.

Krishnamurti, A. 1966. The external morphology of the brain of the slow loris Nycticebus coucang coucang. Folia Primat., 4:361-380.

Kruger, L., and E. C. Berkowitz. 1960. The main afferent connections of the reptilian telencephalon as determined by degeneration and electrophysiological methods. J. Comp. Neurol., 115:125-141.

Kuhlenbeck, H. 1928. Das Zentralnervensystem der Wirbeltiere. Jena, Fischer.

Kurepina, M. 1968. Einige Besonderheiten der Struktur des Neocortex bei Fledermäusen im ökologischen Aspekt. J. Hirnforsch., 10:39-48.

Lorente de Nò, R. 1933. Studies on the structure of the cerebral cortex. I. The area entorhinalis. J. Psychol. Neurol., 45:381-438.

——— 1938. Cerebral cortex: architecture, intracortical connections, motor projections. *In* Fulton, J. F., ed. Physiology of the Nervous System. New York, Oxford University Press.

Marin-Padilla, M. 1969. The basket cells of the human motor cortex, Anat. Rec., 163: 225 (abstract).

Meulders, M., J. Gybels, J. Bergmans, M. A. Gerebtzoff, and M. Goffart. 1966. Sensory projections of somatic, auditory, and visual origin to the cerebral cortex of the sloth (*Choloepus hoffmanni* Peters). J. Comp. Neurol., 126:535-546.

Meynert, T. 1872. Der Bau der Grosshirnrinde und Seine Örtlichen Verschiedenheiten, Nebst Einem Pathologisch-anatomischen Corollarium. Neuwied, J. H. Heuser.

Monakow, C. v. 1911. Lokalisation der Hirnfunktion. J. Psychol. Neurol., 17:185-200.

Nauta, W. J. H. 1964. Some efferent connections of the prefrontal cortex in the monkey. *In* Warren, J. M., and K. Akert, eds., The Frontal and Granular Cortex and Behavior. New York, McGraw Hill.

Ngowyang, G. 1934. Die Cytoarchitektonik des menschlichen Stirnhirns. Nat. Res. Inst. Psychol. Sinica, 7:1.

Noback, C. R., and D. P. Purpura. 1961. Postnatal ontogenesis of neurons in cat neocortex. J. Comp. Neurol., 117:291-307.

Northcutt, R. G. 1967. Architectonic studies of the telencephalon of *Iguana iguana.* J. Comp. Neurol., 130:109-148.

Orrego, F., and D. Lisenby. 1962. The reptilian forebrain. IV. Electrical activity in the turtle cortex. Arch. Ital. Biol., 100:17-30.

Owen, R. 1848. Report on the archetype and homologies of the vertebrate skeleton. British Association for the Advancement of Science, 16th Meeting.

Pandya, D. N., and H. G. J. M. Kuypers. 1969. Cortico-cortical connections in the rhesus monkey. Brain Res., 13:13-36.

Patton, H. D., and T. C. Ruch. 1946. The relation of the foot of the pre- and post-central gyrus to taste in monkey and chimpanzee. Fed. Proc., 5:79.

Penfield, W., and T. Rasmussen. 1952. The Cerebral Cortex of Man. A Clinical Study of Localization of Function. New York, Macmillan.

Pfeifer, R. A. 1940. Die Angioarchitektonische Areale Gliederung der Grosshirnrinde. Leipzig, Thieme.

Powell, T. P. S., and V. B. Mountcastle. 1959. The cytoarchitecture of the postcentral gyrus of the monkey *Macaca mulatta.* Bull. Hopkins Hosp., 105:108-120.

Radinsky, L. B. 1968a. Evolution of somatic sensory specialization in otter brains. J. Comp. Neurol., 134:495-507.

——— 1968b. A new approach to mammalian cranial analysis, illustrated by examples of prosimian primates. J. Morph., 124:167-180.

——— 1969. Outlines of canid and felid brain evolution. *In* Petras, J. and C. Noback, eds. Comparative and Evolutionary Aspects of the Vertebrate Central Nervous System. Ann. N.Y. Acad. Sci., 167:277-288.

Ramon y Cajal, S. 1909a. Histologie du système nerveux de l'homme et des vertébrés. Paris, Maloine. Reprinted in 1955 by the Consejo Superior de Investigaciones Cientificas, Madrid.

——— 1909b. Histologie du Système Nerveux des Vertébrés, Paris, Maloine, vol. II.

——— 1955. Studies on the Cerebral Cortex (Limbic Structures). London, Lloyd-Luke (Medical Books) Ltd.

Ramon-Moliner, E. 1958. Tungstate modification of the Golgi-Cox method of Ramon-Moliner. Stain. Techn., 33:19-29.

——— 1962. An attempt at classifying nerve cells on the basis of their dendritic patterns. J. Comp. Neurol. 119:211-227.

Roberts, T. S., and K. Akert. 1963. Insular and opercular cortex and its thalamic projection in *Macaca mulatta.* Schweiz. Arch. Neurol. Psychiatr., 92:1-43.

Romer, A. S. 1949. The Vertebrate Body. Philadelphia-London, Saunders.

Rose, J. E. 1949. The cellular structure of the auditory region of the cat. J. Comp. Neurol., 91:409-440.

———— and C. N. Woolsey. 1949. The relation of thalamic connections, cellular structure and evocable electrical activity in the auditory region of the cat. J. Comp. Neurol., 91: 441-466.

———— and C. N. Woolsey. 1958. Cortical connections and functional organization of the thalamic auditory system of the cat. In Harlow, H. F., and C. N. Woolsey, eds. Biological and Biochemical Bases of Behavior. Madison, University of Wisconsin Press, pp. 127-150.

Rose, M. 1923. Histologische Lokalisation des Vorderhirns der Reptilien. J. Psychol. Neurol., 29:219-272.

Sanides, F. 1962a. Entwicklungsprinzipien des menschlichen Stirnhirns. Naturwissenschaften, 49:

———— 1962b. Die Architektonik des Menschlichen Stirnhirns. Monogr. Neurol. Psychiat., 98. Berlin-Wien-Heidelberg, Springer.

———— 1964. The cyto-myeloarchitecture of the human frontal lobe and its relation to phylogenetic differentiation of the cerebral cortex. J. Hirnforsch., 6:269-282.

———— 1968. The architecture of the cortical taste nerve areas in squirrel monkey (Saimiri sciureus) and their relationships to insular, sensorimotor and prefrontal regions. Brain Res., 8:97-124.

———— and J. Hoffmann. 1969. Cyto- and myeloarchitecture of the visual cortex and surrounding association areas in the cat. J. Hirnforsch. (In press.)

———— and A. Krishnamurti. 1967. Cytoarchitectonic subdivisions of sensorimotor and prefrontal regions and of bordering insular and limbic fields in slow loris (Nycticebus coucang coucang). J. Hirnforsch., 9:225-252.

———— and K. A. Schlitz. 1967. Abtragungsversuche zur funktionellen Anatomie der Präfrontalrinde der Primaten. Nervenarzt, 38:348-360.

———— and H. Vitzthum. 1965. Zur Architektonik der menschlichen Sehrinde und den Prinzipien ihrer Entwicklung. Deutsch. Z. Nervenheilk., 187:680-707.

Schaltenbrand, G. 1950. Das Lokalisationsproblem der Hirnrinde. Deutsch. Med. Wschr., 75:533-536.

Scollo-Lavizzari, G., and K. Akert. 1963. Cortical area 8 and its thalamic projection in Macaca mulatta. J. Comp. Neurol., 121:259-270.

Shariff, G. A. 1953. Cell counts in the primate cerebral cortex. J. Comp. Neurol., 98:381-400.

Showers, M. J. 1959. The cingulate gyrus: additional motor area and cortical autonomic regulator. J. Comp. Neurol., 112:231-301.

———— and E. W. Lauer. 1961. Somatovisceral motor patterns in the insula. J. Comp. Neurol., 117:107-116.

Smith, G. Elliot. 1907. New studies on the folding of the visual cortex and the significance of the occipital sulci in the human brain. J. Anat., 41:198-207.

———— 1919. A preliminary note on the morphology of the corpus striatum and the origin of the neopallium. J. Anat., 53:271-291.

Starck, D. 1950. Wandlungen des Homologiebegriffes. Zool. Anz., 145: 957-969.

———— 1953: Morphologische Untersuchungen am Kopf der Säugetiere, besonders der Prosimier. Z. Wiss. Zool., 157:169-219.

Stephan, H. 1963. Vergleichend-anatomische Untersuchungen am Uncus bei Insektivoren und Primaten. Prog. Brain Res., 3:111-121.

———— and O. J. Andy. 1962. The Septum. J. Hirnforsch. 5:229-244.

Strasburger, E. H. 1937. Die myeloarchitektonische Gliederung des Stirnhirns beim Menschen und Schimpansen. J. Psychol. Neurol., 47:461,565.

Sugar, O., J. G. Chusid, and J. D. French. 1948. A second motor cortex in the monkey (Macaca mulatta). J. Neuropath. Exp. Neurol., 7:182-189.

———— and H. Spatz. 1961. Vergleichend-anatomische Untersuchungen an Insektivorengehirnen. IV. Gehirne afrikanischer Insektivoren. Versuch einer Zuordnung von Hirnbau und Lebensweise. Morphol. Jahrbuch 103:108-174.

Vitzthum, H., and F. Sanides. 1966. Entwicklungsprinzipien der menschlichen Sehrinde.

In Hassler, R., and H. Stephan, eds. Evolution of the Forebrain. Stuttgart, Thieme, pp. 435-442.

Vogt, C., and O. Vogt. 1907. Zur Kenntnis der elektrisch erregbaren Hirnrindengebiete bei den Säugetieren. J. Psychol. Neurol., 8:277-456.

———— and O. Vogt. 1919. Allgemeinere Ergebnisse unserer Hirnforschung. J. Psychol. Neurol., 25:279-462.

Vogt, O. 1906. Über strukturelle Hirncentra, mit besonderer Berücksichtigung der strukturellen Felder des Cortex pallii. Anat. Anz., 29 Erg. Bd.:74-114.

———— 1910. Die myeloarchitektonische Felderung des menschlichen Stirnhirns. J. Psychol. Neurol., 15:221-232.

Walker, E. P., F. Warnick, K. I. Lange, H. E. Uible, S. E. Hamlet, M. A. Davis, and P. F. Wright. 1964. Mammals of the World. 3 vols. Baltimore, Johns Hopkins Press.

Welker, W. I., and G. B. Campos. 1963. Physiological significance of sulci in somatic sensory cerebral cortex in mammals of the family Procyonidae. J. Comp. Neurol., 120:19-36.

———— and S. Seidenstein. 1959. Somatic sensory representations in the cerebral cortex of the raccoon. J. Comp. Neurol., 111:469-499.

Woolsey, C. N. 1943. "Second" somatic receiving areas in the cerebral cortex of cat, dog, and monkey. Fed. Proc., 2:55. (abstract).

———— 1944. Additional observations on a "second" somatic receiving area in the cerebral cortex of the monkey. Fed. Proc., 3:43 (abstract).

———— 1958. Organization of somatic sensory and motor areas of the cerebral cortex. *In* Harlow, H. F., and C. N. Woolsey, eds. Biological and Biochemical Bases of Behavior. Madison, University of Wisconsin Press, pp. 63-81.

———— 1959. Some observations on brain fissuration in relation to cortical localization of function. *In* Tower, D. B., and J. P. Schadé, eds. Structure and Function of the Cerebral Cortex. Amsterdam-London-New York, Elsevier.

———— and D. Fairman. 1946. Contralateral, ipsilateral and bilateral representation of cutaneous receptors in somatic areas I and II of the cerebral cortex of pig, sheep, and other mammals. Surgery, 19:684-702.

———— and G. H. Wang. 1945. Somatic areas I and II of the cerebral cortex of the rabbit. Fed. Proc., 4:79.

Yakovlev, P. I. 1959. Pathoarchitectonic studies of cerebral malformations. III. Arhinencephalies (Holotelencephalies). J. Neuropath. Exp. Neurol., 18: 22-25.

———— and A. R. Lecours. 1967. The myelogenetic cycles of regional maturation of the brain. *In* Minkowski, A. ed. Regional Development of the Brain in Early Life. Oxford and Edinburgh, Blackwell Scientific Publications.

Zuckerman, S., and J. F. Fulton. 1941. The motor cortex in *Galago* and *Perodicticus*. J. Anat., 75:447-456.

7

The Fossil Evidence of Prosimian Brain Evolution*

LEONARD B. RADINSKY

Department of Anatomy
University of Chicago
Chicago, Illinois, 60637

Introduction

A considerable amount of new neurologic and paleontologic information on the evolution of primate brains has become available in recent years. While studies of the brains of contemporary primates are necessary to interpret the evolutionary trends that resulted in living primate brains, the only real record of those trends is provided by fossil endocranial casts. Fortunately, endocranial casts of most primates, including all living prosimians, reproduce most of the external morphology of the brain (Bauchot and Stephan, 1967; Radinsky, 1968) and therefore can provide significant information on brain evolution. Knowledge of early fossil primate endocranial casts was recently reviewed by Hofer (1962). The description since then of several new specimens motivated the present review.

Tertiary Prosimian Endocranial Casts

TETONIUS

The oldest primate endocranial cast, known for over 80 years but only recently (Radinsky, 1967b) adequately prepared and figured, is that of *Tetonius homunculus*, a North American Early Eocene (approximately 55 million years old) anatomorphid (or anatomorphine omomyid) prosimian. The brain of *Tetonius* was remarkably ad-

* For permission to study specimens in their charge and for providing casts of important specimens, I am grateful to Dr. C. L. Gazin, U.S. National Museum; Dr. D. A. Guthrie, Claremont College; Dr. M. C. McKenna, the American Museum of Natural History; Dr. E. L. Simons, Yale Peabody Museum; Dr. J. A. Wilson, University of Texas; and Dr. K. Oakely and the Trustees of the British Museum (Natural History). I thank Dr. M. Goldberger for valuable discussions of primate neurology. This research was supported by National Science Foundation Grant GB-7071X.

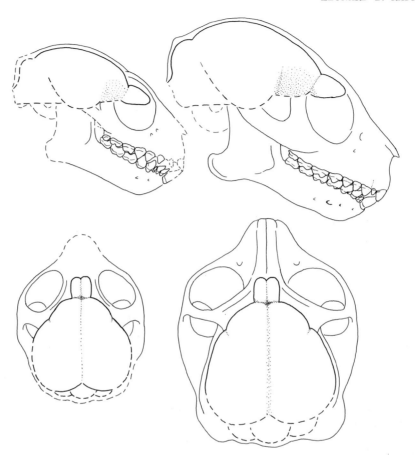

Figure 1. Left, *Tetonius homunculus*, restored from American Museum of Natural History 4194 and figured mandibles. Right, *Necrolemur antiquus*, composite from Yale Peabody Museum 18302 and Hürzeler (1948. Schweiz. Paläont. Abh., 66:3-46.). Dashed lines indicate restored portions x 1.5.

vanced for its time in having enlarged occipital and temporal lobes (the size of the former may have been responsible for the moderately overlapped cerebellum) and reduced olfactory bulbs (see Fig. 1), which are features that characterize modern primate brains. Compared with later primates, however, *Tetonius* was primitive in having a relatively small frontal lobe (here used, in the absence of a central sulcus, to denote the area rostral to the Sylvian fissure), and relatively large olfactory bulbs. Except for a barely visible Sylvian fissure, the brain of *Tetonius* was lissencephalic. That condition cannot be considered a primitive feature in *Tetonius*, since modern prosimian brains of equal size display a similar lack of sulci.

The occurrence of expanded occipital and temporal lobes in *Tetonius* suggests visual and possibly also auditory specialization, and the reduced olfactory bulbs indicate a decrease in importance of olfaction compared to the condition in other early mammals for which endocranial casts are known. The presence of these sensory specializations in such an ancient primate as *Tetonius* suggests that they may have been among the critical adaptations that were responible for the Eocene radiation of primates. It would be extremely interesting to know if brain specialization played a role in the first radiation of primates, which occurred in the Paleocene, but the only Paleocene primate braincase known is that of the plesiadapid *Plesiadapis* (Russell, 1964), for which no endocranial cast has yet been made. The relatively great bitemporal width of the *Plesiadapis* braincase suggests that it had expanded occipital lobes, but that suggestion cannot be confirmed without examination of the inside of the braincase.

SMILODECTES

After *Tetonius*, the next oldest primate for which the endocranial anatomy is known is *Smilodectes gracilis*, a North American Middle Eocene (approximately 45 million years old) notharctid (or notharctine adapid) prosimian. Gazin (1965) described an endocranial cast of *Smilodectes* (U.S. National Museum 23276) that lacked only the olfactory bulbs, and I have prepared the right side of another specimen (Yale Peabody Museum 12152) that includes much of the olfactory bulb (Fig 2).

The brain of *Smilodectes* was extraordinarily specialized for its time in the degree to which the neocortex was expanded and the olfactory bulbs reduced. The cerebrum is extremely broad posteriorly, with a maximum width/length index of about 1.20, as compared to about 1.05 in *Tetonius* and under 1.00 in most living prosimians. The cerebellum is less overlapped in *Smilodectes* than in *Tetonius*, which may indicate relatively less expansion of the visual cortex or may be simply a difference resulting from the larger size of *Smilodectes*. In any case, the neocortex appears to have expanded mainly laterally in *Smilodectes* as opposed to laterally and caudally in *Tetonius*. Unlike the condition in *Tetonius*, there is no trace of a Sylvian fissure in *Smilodectes*, which may be correlated with the larger size of the latter, since its relatively smaller orbits impinged less on the brain. On Y.P.M. 12152, but not on U.S.N. M. 23276, two low, ventrally convergent, transverse ridges in the region where a Sylvian fissure would be expected appear to be casts of subdural blood vessels. Both *Smilodectes* endocranial casts have a shallow longitudinal sulcus high on the cerebrum that appears to be the homolog of the lateral sulcus (?=intraparietal), and U.S.N.M. 23276, but not Y.P.M. 12152, has a second, more ventral, very shallow longitudinal sulcus that converges rostrally with the first (see Fig. 2). Gazin (1965, p. 5) suggested that the second sulcus was the homolog of the suprasylvian sulcus, and comparisons with other Eocene mammal endocranial casts support that interpretation. *Smilodectes* is the only primate known to have a suprasylvian sulcus in that position, and it is also unique among primates in lacking a Sylvian fissure. The two features are probably related, for with increasing rostrocaudal compression of the cortex, whether from increase in relative orbit size or from expansion of particular cortical areas or both, a Sylvian fissure would develop and the low longitudinal suprasylvian sulcus would be obliterated. In any event, the discontinuity of the presumed suprasylvian sulcus on one side of U.S.N.M. 23276 and its absence in Y.P.M. 12152 indicate that its development was quite variable in *Smilodectes*.

The rhinal fissure is not evident on the *Smilodectes* endocranial casts. Presum-

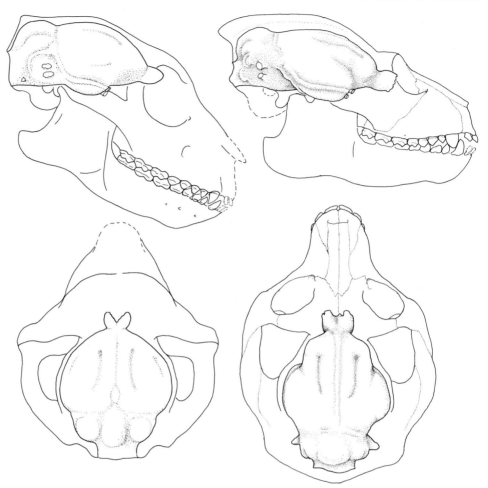

Figure 2. Left, *Smilodectes gracilis*, composite from Yale Peabody Museum 12152 and Gazin (1965. Smithsonian Misc. Coll., 149:1-14.). The lower of the two sulci, here identified as the suprasylvian sulcus, is present on only one of the two known specimens. Right, *Adapis parisiensis*, composite from a cast of the British Museum endocranial cast figured by Clark (1945. J. Anat., 79:123-126.) and American Museum of Natural History 11045 (cast of skull). Both natural size.

ably it occurred, as in modern prosimians, at the level of the vascular canal that extends rostrocaudally low on the temporal lobe. The olfactory bulbs were relatively smaller than in *Tetonius* but, as in the earlier species, lay entirely rostral to the frontal lobes. A complete cast of the olfactory bulb chamber of *Notharctus*, a Middle Eocene genus closely related to *Smilodectes*, reveals that olfactory bulbs were widely separated and faced anteromedioventrally. In summary, advanced features of the brain of *Smilodectes* included expansion of the cerebral cortex in occipital and temporal regions and reduction in size of the olfactory bulbs. Primitive features, for a primate, are the dorsally exposed cerebellum, small frontal lobes, and lack of a Sylvian fissure.

ADAPIS

The next oldest primate endocranial casts are from two genera from the Late Eocene (about 40 million years old) of Europe. An endocranial cast of *Adapis parisiensis*, an adapid lemuroid, was figured and described by Clark (1945), refigured under the name *Adapis magnus* by Piveteau (1957), and discussed again by Hofer (1962). The *Adapis* endocranial cast (see Fig. 2), is similar to that of *Smilodectes* in having broad occipital and temporal lobes, a coronolateral sulcus, olfactory bulbs rostral to the frontal pole and facing anteromedioventrally, and a dorsally exposed cerebellum. The brain of *Adapis* was more advanced than that of *Smilodectes* in having a well-developed Sylvian fissure and relatively larger frontal lobes. Expansion of the frontal lobes in *Adapis* may have been responsible for the development of the Sylvian fissure, for there are no orbital impressions on the brain of *Adapis*. The width/length index of the *Adapis parisiensis* cerebrum is about 1.10. The brain of *Adapis* is more primitive than that of living prosimians in having relatively smaller frontal lobes, a more exposed cerebellum, and pedunculate olfactory bulbs (presumably related to the small frontal lobes).

NECROLEMUR

An endocranial cast of *Necrolemur antiquus*, a tarsiid contemporary of *Adapis*, was described and figured by Hürzeler (1948), and more recently discussed by Hofer (1962). The resemblance to the endocranial cast of *Tetonius* is striking, for the brain of *Necrolemur* also had voluminous temporal and occipital lobes, a moderately over-lapped cerebellum, relatively small frontal lobes and relatively large (for a primate) olfactory bulbs (see Fig. 1). The only discernible advance over the condition seen in *Tetonius* is a slightly better developed Sylvian fissure. The restoration of the *Necrolemur* endocranial cast presented in this paper shows relatively more narrow temporal lobes than does Hürzeler's (1962) figure because of a slight difference in orientation of the skull (in Fig. 1 it is oriented with the basicranial axis perpendicular to the line of sight). Also, Hürzeler's illustration shows relatively shorter olfactory bulbs because they were not fully uncovered from the bone.

ROONEYIA

Hofer and Wilson (1967) described a partly exposed natural endocranial cast of *Rooneyia viejaensis*, a North American Early Oligocene (about 35 million years old) omomyid prosimian (Fig. 3). The occipital lobe overlaps the cerebellum about as much as in approximately comparable-sized modern lorisoids, such as *Galago crassicaudatus* and *Perodicticus potto*, which is more than in similar-sized modern lemuroids such as *Lepilemur ruficaudatus* and *Lichanotus laniger* (illustrated in Radinsky, 1968). A shallow Sylvian fissure separates the deep temporal lobe from a frontal lobe that is relatively larger than in any of the Eocene primates described above (except possibly for *Adapis*) but that is relatively smaller than in similar-sized modern prosimians (see Fig. 7). The brain of *Rooneyia* was also more primitive than that of comparable-sized modern prosimians in lacking sulci other than the Sylvian. In fact,

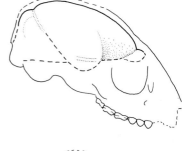

Figure 3. *Rooneyia viejaensis,* University of Texas 40688-7. The lateral view outline of the olfactory bulbs is restored from the bulge on the medial orbital wall. Natural size.

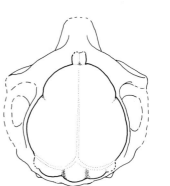

although the cerebrum of *Rooneyia* is about as large as that of *Smilodectes* and *Adapis,* it lacks even the shallow coronolateral sulcus that had already appeared in those Eocene forms.

KOMBA

The only other fossil prosimian endocranial cast known for the rest of the Tertiary is one of a lorisoid from the Miocene (exact age unknown; see Simpson, 1967) of Africa. The specimen, which lacks olfactory bulbs, was originally described by Clark and Thomas (1952) under the name *Progalago* sp., discussed by Hofer (1962), and referred by Simpson (1967) to cf. *Komba robustus.* In general proportions it is similar to equal-sized endocranial casts of modern lorisoids, such as *Galago senegalensis* and *Euoticus elegantulus,* except for being somewhat flatter and less deep. Clark and Thomas (1952, p. 18), noted that the cerebellum was more exposed than in *Galago senegalensis,* but I agree with Hofer (1962, p. 22) that in view of the variability of that feature in modern galagines, the difference is not significant.

The frontal lobes of cf. *Komba robustus* are less tapering in dorsal view than are those of the *Galago senegalensis* specimen figured by Clark and Thomas (1952, Fig. 2B) and reproduced by Hofer (1962, Fig. 5) but have about the same contour as in the *G. senegalensis* endocranial cast available to me (Radinsky, 1968, Fig. 4). Sulci evident on the cf. *Komba* endocranial cast are the anterior part of the coronal sulcus (? = sulcus rectus) on the frontal lobe and a Sylvian fissure that appears to extend slightly less dorsally than in living lorisoids. The only sulcus present in similar-sized modern galagine brains and not evident on the figure of the Miocene specimen is the

posterior suprasylvian sulcus (=parallel or superior temporal sulcus), which is, however, only faintly indicated on the modern endocranial casts.

Extinct Malagasy Lemuroid Endocranial Casts

The remaining record of prosimian brain evolution, excluding living forms, consists of endocranial casts of several genera of extinct giant lemuroids from Pleistocene
to Recent deposits in the Malagasy Republic. Although too late in time to shed light
on modern prosimian brain evolution, the extinct giant Malagasy lemuroids are of
interest for demonstrating what happened to brains on the prosimian level of organization that were enlarged to the monkey to ape size range. The known forms exhibit
two basic skull types: short-faced ones, with relatively large braincases, such as
Archaeolemur, Hadropithecus, and *Mesopropithecus,* and long-faced forms with relatively small braincases, such as *Megaladapis, Palaeopropithecus,* and *Archaeoindris.*

ARCHAEOLEMUR

Endocranial casts of *Archaeolemur* have been described by Smith (1908) (under
the name *Nesopithecus*), Clark (1945), and Piveteau (1948, 1950, and 1956), and I
have prepared another specimen (Fig. 4). Smith (1908, p. 171) stated that the endocranial cast of *Archaeolemur* displayed a typical indriid pattern, but Clark (1945,
p. 125) considered it similar to anthropoid brains except for having a relatively smaller
frontal lobe. Piveteau (1950, pp. 99 and 101) identified a sulcus immediately rostral
to the lower part of the Sylvian fissure as the arcuate sulcus and considered the sulcal
pattern of the frontal lobe of *Archaeolemur* to place it on a level of evolution comparable to that of advanced ceboids or cercopithecoids. Comparison with endocranial
casts of living monkeys and the indriids *Propithecus* and *Indri* leads me to conclude
that the *Archaeolemur* endocranial cast displays the morphology one would expect to
see in an indriid of that size and that the arrangement of sulci is indriid rather than
ceboid or cercopithecoid in pattern. The sulci Piveteau (1950, p. 99) labelled as the
arcuate and fronto-orbital, I identify as the fronto-orbital and a spur of the orbital
sulcus, respectively, and the sulcus Clark (1945, Fig. 6) labelled the central sulcus, I
interpret as the rostral end of the lateral sulcus, or the ansate sulcus (see Fig. 4).

The differences in pattern of the *Archaeolemur* frontal lobe sulci from what is
seen in the living indriids seems attributable to the larger size of *Archaeolemur* and,
resulting from its larger size, its shallower orbital impressions. Because of the much
shallower orbital impressions, the fronto-orbital sulcus lies on the broad convex edge
of, rather than within, the concavity of the orbital impression in *Archaeolemur.* The
degree to which the central sulcus is developed in *Archaeolemur* is no greater than
occurs in *Propithecus* or the lorisoid *Perodicticus,* and therefore it cannot be considered an advance over modern prosimians.

One feature in which *Archaeolemur* does appear uniquely specialized is the elaboration of its coronal gyrus (between coronal sulcus and Sylvian fissure), which is
relatively broad and is subdivided by two secondary sulci. Since that cortical area
includes the primary somatic sensory (SmI) representation of the face (Sanides and

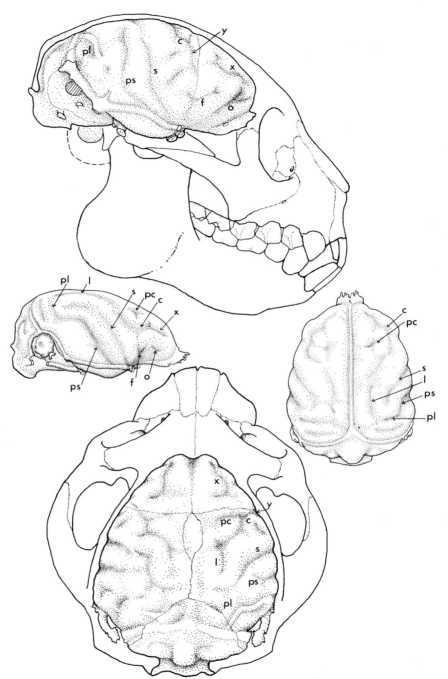

Figure 4. Above and below, *Archaeolemur majori*, American Museum of Natural History 30007. Left and right, *Indri indri*, one of the largest-brained modern prosimians. Abbreviations: c, coronal sulcus; f, fronto-orbital sulcus; l, lateral sulcus (?=intraparietal sulcus); o, orbital sulcus; pc, postcruciate sulcus, the transverse portion of which is homologous with part of the central sulcus; pl, postlateral sulcus (=lunate sulcus); ps, posterior suprasylvian sulcus (=postsylvian, superior temporal or parallel sulcus); S, Sylvian fissure (=anterior suprasylvian sulcus); x, rostral continuation of coronal sulcus (?=sulcus rectus); y, ventral continuation of postcruciate sulcus (=central sulcus), x ¾.

Krishnamurti, 1967; Welker and Campos, 1963), it may indicate specialization for tactile sensitivity on the face of *Archaeolemur*, or, since increased cortical folding is often associated with increased size, it may simply be an allometric phenomenon. A medially directed sulcal spur at the caudal end of the isolated rostral part of the coronal culcus is better developed in *Archaeolemur* than in *Indri* or other prosimians and may delimit the rostral boundary of part of the primary motor cortex (MsI), in which case it would be homologous to the cruciate sulcus of carnivores.

HADROPITHECUS

An endocranial cast of *Hadropithecus stenognathus*, a form closely related to *Archaeolemur*, has been figured in lateral view by Piveteau (1956), and its relationship to the skull may be interpreted from the X-ray of the cranium shown in that paper (Fig. 5D). Except for having a flatter frontal lobe and apparently lacking secondary sulci within the coronal gyrus, the *Hadropithecus* endocranial cast appears to be similar to that of *Archaeolemur*. The flatter frontal lobes and less tucked-under olfactory bulbs appear to be correlated with the relatively larger skull of *Hadropithecus*. The *Archaeolemur* endocranial cast figured by Piveteau (1950, p. 99) has a frontal profile more similar to that of *Hadropithecus* than is seen in my *Archaeolemur* specimen, so that even that difference may not distinguish the genera.

MESOPROPITHECUS

Endocranial casts of the extinct indriid *Mesopropithecus pithecoides* have been figured by Smith (1908, pp. 169-170) and Clark (1945, p. 125). They are about the same size and apparently similar in sulcal pattern to endocranial casts of the living *Indri* (compare Figs. 5A and 5B), from which they differ in being slightly narrower rostrally and higher at about the level of the temporal lobes.

MEGALADAPIS

Megaladapis is the largest and best known of the long-skulled giant lemuroids. Endocranial casts of it have been described by Smith (1902, p. 364), Clark (1945), and Hofer (1954), and I have prepared another specimen (Fig. 6). Features usually not seen in prosimian endocranial casts are the predunculate olfactory bulbs set out on extremely long olfactory tracts, the relatively forward position of the optic chiasma, the lack of orbital impressions, the poor reproduction of cerebral sulci, and the open Sylvian depression. The first three obviously resulted from the size increase that produced such a long skull. The faintness of sulci is also an allometric phenomenon and may be seen in large-brained anthropoid endocranial casts as well. Besides the Sylvian fissure, a shallow coronolateral sulcus and a very faint posterior suprasylvian sulcus are the only sulci evident on the endocranial cast. The open Sylvian depression may have resulted from the relatively forward position of the orbits, which do not impinge on the frontal lobes. A similar lack of opercularization of the Sylvian region is seen in living primates only in the aberrant lemuroid *Daubentonia*, where it is also correlated with lack of orbital impressions (Radinsky, 1968, p. 172). This suggests that

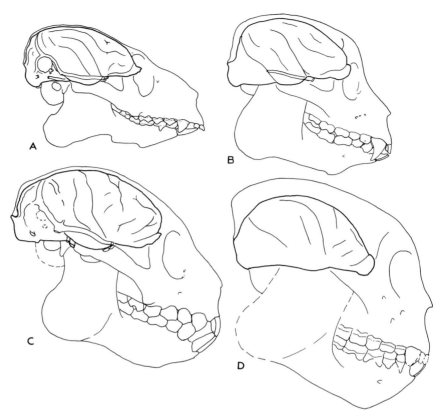

Figure 5. Selected indriids and archaeolemurids. A, *Indri indri*, from Radinsky (1968. J. Morph., 124:167-180.). B, *Mesopropithecus pithecoides*, composite from Standing (1908. Trans. Zool. Soc., 18:59-162.) (skull) and Smith (1908. Trans. Zool. Soc., 18:163-177.) and Clark (1945. J. Anat., 79:123-126.) (endocranial casts). C, *Archaeolemur majori*, American Museum of Natural History 30007. D, *Hadropithecus stenognathus*, composite from Piveteau (1956. Ann. Paléont., 42:139-150; and 1957. Traité de Paléontologie, 7. Paris, Masson.). x ½.

the limiting of rostrocaudal expansion of frontal lobe cortex by the orbits may be one of the factors involved in development of the primate Sylvian fissure.

PALAEOPROPITHECUS

Endocranial casts of one other long-skulled giant prosimian, the indriid *Palaeopropithecus maximus*, have been described by Smith (1908), Clark (1945), and Piveteau (1950). From the illustrations (see Fig. 6), it appears to resemble endocranial casts of *Megaladapis* in general proportions, faintness of sulcal impressions, lack of orbital impressions, and the open Sylvian depression. The olfactory tracts appear to have been relatively long, as in *Megaladapis*, although their full extent is not preserved in any of the figured specimens.

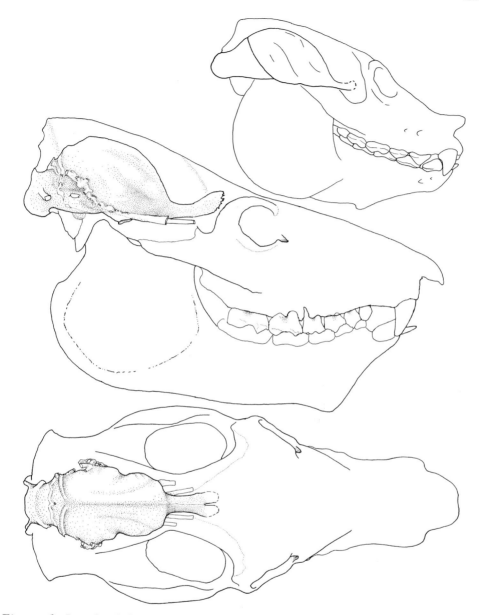

Figure 6. Long-headed giant lemuroids. Above, *Palaeopropithecus maximus*, composite from Standing (1908. Trans. Zool. Soc., 18:163-177.) (skull), Saban (1963. Mém Mus. National d'Hist. Nat., 29:1-378.) (X-ray of skull), and Piveteau (1950. Ann. Patéont., 36:85-103.) (endocranial cast). Middle and below, *Megaladapis edwardsi*, American Museum of Natural History 30024, x ⅜.

Discussion

The scanty evidence now available on the early evolution of prosimian brains, all of which has been reviewed above, indicates that as far back as the Early Eocene (55 million years ago), primates had, compared to other contemporary mammals, relatively large occipital and temporal lobes and relatively small olfactory bulbs. Those are features that characterize modern primate brains, but since the oldest known primate endocranial cast is from a member of the second (Eocene) major primate evolutionary radiation, it is still not known whether those neurological specializations characterized the earliest members of the order.

Expansion of the frontal lobe lagged behind that of the rest of the cortex, since even by Early Oligocene (35 million years ago), frontal lobes were relatively smaller than in modern prosimians (with the exception of *Tarsius*). A Miocene lorisoid endocranial cast (cf. *Komba*), probably 15 to 20 million years old, has frontal lobes of modern prosimian proportions. Endocranial casts of giant Malagasy lemuroids, such as *Archaeolemur*, indicate that although brain size comparable to that of large anthropoids was attained, the sulcal pattern remained basically similar to that of the smaller prosimians. Endocranial casts of the long-skulled giant lemuroids, such as *Megaladapis*, indicate the extreme distortion of normal brain proportions that may result from extrinsic factors.

Similarities in neuroanatomy between fossil and recent prosimians may be suggestive of phylogenetic relationship, but the evidence should be viewed critically. Clark (1962, p. 235), Edinger (1961, p. 69), and others have emphasized the similarities in proportions between endocranial casts of *Tetonius* and *Necrolemur* and that of the living *Tarsius*, and Clark (1962) considered the Eocene specimens to indicate that the tarsoid type of brain had already evolved that far back in time. However, I agree with Hofer (1962, p. 10) that it is the retention of relatively small frontal lobes, a primitive character, in *Tarsius* that is the main source of resemblance to the early forms (Fig. 7). The relatively broad occipital lobes and voluminous temporal lobes of *Tetonius* and *Necrolemur* are common to all early prosimian brains and therefore do not indicate special phylogenetic relationship to *Tarsius*. Finally, the lack of sulci other than the Sylvian fissure in *Tetonius* and *Necrolemur* may be attributed to their small size and likewise indicates no special affinity to *Tarsius*. Thus, while on other grounds (skull characters), *Tetonius* and *Necrolemur* are classified as tarsioids, and the latter as a tarsiid, their brain morphology does not provide evidence for that classification, since it includes the features one might expect to see in the Eocene ancestors of lemuroids and lorisoids as well as in the ancestors of tarsioids.

The presence of a coronolateral sulcus in *Smilodectes* and *Adapis* supports the suggestion, based on other aspects of cranial anatomy, of phylogenetic relationship to the surviving prosimians, since that sulcus is prominent in living prosimians that are large enough to show it. On the other hand, the absence of a coronolateral sulcus in *Rooneyia*, which has a cerebrum about as large as that of *Smilodectes* and *Adapis* and which is younger in time, suggests possible relationship to the ancestry of the anthropoids, since anthropoid brains lack the coronal sulcus in the region of the primary somatic sensory and motor cortices and instead have between those areas a prominent transverse sulcus, the central sulcus. However, that evidence is far from

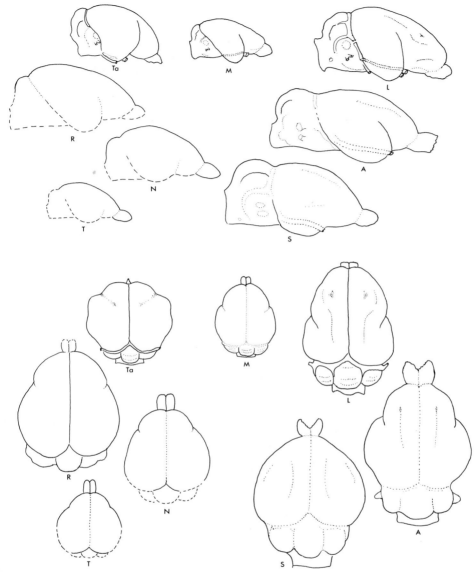

Figure 7. Early Tertiary and Recent prosimian endocranial casts. Abbreviations: A, *Adapis parisiensis*; L, *Lepilemur ruficaudatus*; M, *Microcebus murinus*; N, *Necrolemur antiquus*; R, *Rooneyia viejaensis*; S, *Smilodectes gracilis*; T, *Tetonius homunculus*; Ta, *Tarsius spectrum*. All natural size.

conclusive, since it is conceivable that the ancestors of anthropoids had a shallow coronal sulcus that was obliterated when the central sulcus developed.

The absence of the Sylvian fissure in *Smilodectes*, in contrast to its presence in *Tetonius* and *Adapis*, suggests certain hypotheses on the origin of that cortical fold in primates. *Tetonius*, like *Smilodectes*, has a very small frontal lobe, but it also has prominant orbital impressions. *Adapis*, like *Smilodectes*, lacks orbital impressions but has a more expanded frontal lobe. All three genera have enlarged temporal lobes. This suggests that the primate Sylvian fissure may have resulted from rostrocaudal compression owing to either the development of relatively large orbits or the expansion of the frontal lobes in forms that already had voluminous temporal lobes. The lack of a tightly folded Sylvian fissure in those later primates that lack orbital impressions (*Megaladapis, Palaeopropithecus* and *Daubentonia*) supports the suggestion

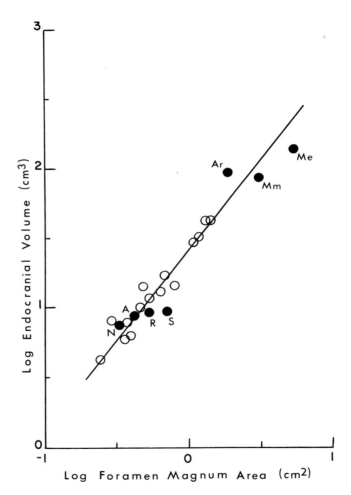

Figure 8. Relative brain size of fossil and recent prosimians. Open circles = representatives of all families of living prosimians; filled circles = fossil prosimians. A, *Adapis parisiensis;* Ar, *Archaeolemur majori;* Me, *Megaladapis edwardsi;* Mm, *Megaladapis madagascariensis;* N, *Necrolemur antiquus;* R, *Rooneyia viejaensis;* S, *Smilodectes gracilis.* Plots based on data from one specimen per species. Line fitted to recent prosimian plots by least squares method.

that restriction of cortical expansion by the wall of the orbit played a role in primate Sylvian fissure formation.

One final point that should be commented on here concerns relative brain size. Hofer (1962, p. 7) and Clark (1962, p. 248) stated that the brain of *Adapis parisiensis* was smaller relative to its body size than is the case in modern prosimians, but neither author gave estimates of body size or other evidence for that conclusion. Jerison (1961, Fig. 1) presented a brain size vs. body size plot for *Smilodectes gracilis* that fell within the lower end of the range for several modern mammals, but the modern species included in the diagram are not identified. I have found the area of the foramen magnum to be highly correlated with body sizes (Radinsky, 1967a and in preparation), and using that to measure relative brain size, I find *Smilodectes* to fall slightly outside of, and *Adapis* within, the range of modern prosimians (Fig. 8).

REFERENCES

Bauchot, R., and H. Stephan. 1967. Encéphales et moulages endocraniens de quelques insectivores et primates actuels. *In* Problèmes actuels de Paléontologie. Coll. Int. Centre Nat. Rech. Sci., No. 163:575-586.

Clark, W. E. Le Gros. 1945. Note on the paleontology of the lemuroid brain. J. Anat., 79:123-126.

———— 1962. The Antecedents of Man, 2nd ed. Edinburgh, University of Edinburgh Press.

———— and D. P. Thomas. 1952. Fossil mammals of Africa, No. 5. The Miocene lemuroids of East Africa. London, British Museum Natural History.

Edinger, T. 1961. Anthropomorphic misconceptions in paleoneurology. Proc. Virchow Med. Soc. N. Y., 19:56-107.

Gazin, C. L. 1965. An endocranial cast of the Bridger Middle Eocene primate, *Smilodectes gracilis*. Smithsonian Misc. Coll., 149(4):1-14. (Publ. 4616).

Hofer, H. O. 1954. Über Gehirn und Schädel von *Megaladapis edwardsi* G. Grandidier (Lemuroidea). Z. Wiss. Zool., 157:220-284.

———— 1962. Über die Interpretation der ältesten fossilen Primatengehirne. Bibl. Primat., 1:1-31.

———— and J. Wilson. 1967. An endocranial cast of an Early Oligocene primate. Folia Primat., 5:148-152.

Hürzeler, J. 1948. Zur Stammesgeschichte der Necrolemuriden. Schweiz. Paläont. Abh., 66:3-46.

Jerison, H. 1961. Quantitative analysis of evolution of the brain in mammals. Science, 133(3457):1012-1014.

Piveteau, J. 1948. Recherches anatomiques sur les lémuriens disparus. Le genre *Archaeolemur*. Ann Paléont., 34:125-172.

———— 1950. Recherches sur l'encéphale de lémuriens disparus. Ann. Paléont. 36:85-103.

———— 1956. L'encéphale d'*Hadropithecus*. Ann Paléont., 42:139-150.

———— 1957. Histoire paléontologique des Primates. *In* Piveteau, J., ed. Traité de Paléontologie, 7. Paris, Masson.

Radinsky, L. B. 1967a. Relative brain size: a new measure. Science, 155(3764):836-838.

———— 1967b. The oldest primate endocast. Amer. J. Phys. Anthrop., 27:385-388.

———— 1968. A new approach to mammalian cranial analysis, illustrated by examples of prosimian primates. J. Morph., 124:167-180.

Russell, D. 1964. Les mammifères Paléocènes d'Europe. Mem. Mus. National d'Hist. Nat., 13:1-324.

Saban, R. 1963. Contribution a l'étude de l'os temporal des primates. Mém. Mus. National d'Hist. Nat., 29:1-378.

Sanides. F., and A. Krishnamurti. 1967. Cytoarchitectonic subdivisions of sensorimotor and prefrontal regions and of bordering insular and limbic fields in slow loris (*Nycticebus coucang coucang*). J. Hirnforsch., 9:225-252.

Simpson, G. G. 1967. The Tertiary lorisiform primates of Africa. Bull. Mus. Comp. Zool., 136(3):39-62.

Smith, G. E. 1902. On the morphology of the brain in the Mammalia, with special reference to that of the lemurs, recent and extinct. Trans. Linnean Soc. London, ser. 2, Zool., 8(10):319-432.

———— 1908. On the form of the brain in the extinct lemurs of Madagascar, with remarks on the affinities of the Indrisinae. Trans. Zool. Soc., 18(2):163-177.

Standing, H. F. 1908. On recently discovered subfossil primates from Madagascar. Trans. Zool. Soc., 18(2):59-162.

Welker, W. I., and G. B. Campos. 1963. Physiological significance of sulci in somatic sensory cerebral cortex in mammals of the family Procyonidae. J. Comp. Neur., 120:19-36.

8

Gross Brain Indices and the Analysis of Fossil Endocasts*

Harry J. Jerison

Antioch College
Yellow Springs, Ohio 45387 †

Brain indices are numbers intended to indicate the relative size of the brain or its parts, taking body size into account. As used today, they permit comparisons among species or higher categories but not among individuals of a single species unless there has been selective breeding of races or subspecies to differ greatly in body size. All of the indices that use data on the weight or volume of the brain or its parts are related to Dubois' "index of cephalization" (1897), which was developed from Snell's analysis (1891 of brain: body relations. These relate brain size to two factors: body size and bodily functions, on the one hand, and, on the other hand, the encephalization of psychic functions. In this discussion of the gross indices, I will analyze the relationships among them and discuss general issues in quantification and its problems. It is possible to use indices based on gross size of the brain (or its parts) because of the statistical orderliness of the geometry of the brain. Though seemingly almost random in small sections, measures of the average neuron density and fiber proliferation are a surprisingly orderly function of brain size independent of species in mammals (Jerison, 1963). The most important conclusion that I have reached, however, is that numerical indices can often be dispensed with, and the analysis of relative brain size can be performed by graphic methods that simply map the relationship quantitatively but not numerically. The method can be applied directly to studies of the evolution of the brain based on the endocranial casts (endocasts) of fossil vertebrates.

We may recognize two types of gross indices, those based on direct measurement of the weight or volume of the brain and body and those that rely on other measures that are related secondarily to either brain size or body size. Anthony's suggested index (1938), the ratio of the cross-sectional area of the corpus callosum to that of the medulla, is an example of an index based on secondary measures because the

* This report was prepared with the support of a grant from The Research Corporation to Antioch College. Some of the work was initiated during my tenure as a Fellow at the Center for Advanced Study in the Behavioral Sciences, Stanford, Calif., and was also supported in part by Fellowship Award No. 1 F3 HD-38, 118-01 from the National Institute of Child Health and Human Development, U.S. Public Health Service.
† *Present address:* The Neuropsychiatric Institute, UCLA Center for the Health Sciences, Los Angeles, California 90024.

former is related to brain size and the latter to body size. The biological problems posed and answered by the proponents of each variant measure are important conceptually, but because of the orderliness of the geometry of the brain and body they may be of minor interest as the basis of an index. If Anthony's index is used, one automatically restricts oneself to placental mammals, but within these mammals one can determine that the relationship between the gross brain size and the cross-sectional area of the corpus callosum is so orderly (cf Bauchot and Stephan, 1961, Fig. 4) that it is appropriate in most instances to use the one to estimate the other, depending on which is easier to measure. Since the gross brain size is usually easiest to measure, it is normally unnecessary to devote oneself to other measurements that give about the same amount of information.

The reason for concern with other measures than body size is the well-known variation in body weight associated with seasonal, ecological, and other factors. In my view, the importance of this variation is overemphasized. The variation would be significant if one were to make judgments about specific specimens. I reject the appropriateness of gross indices for that purpose; Sholl's (1948) criticisms seem particularly valid there. Indices should be used, I believe, only to buttress broad generalizations about relative brain size of the type that may occur in faunal groups isolated from one another either geographically or temporally. On might thus compare the South American fauna of the middle Tertiary with the holarctic fauna of the same period. Another comparison might be among successive fauna, such as a Paleocene-Eocene with an Oligocene fauna (Jerison, 1961). For such comparisons, errors in body size may balance out as one applies an approach like von Bonin's to the description of relative brain size for all of the mammals in one's sample (1937).

Indices based on the parts of the brain offer much promise for the future of comparative neuroanatomy in the quantification of many results. They are usually based on planimetric reconstructions of the type first used by Tilney (1928), though Portmann and his students (see below) developed some approaches involving gross dissection and weighing of the parts of the brain. The development of these indices for the parts of the brain has reached a completely new level of refinement in the work of Stephan and his colleagues (e.g., Stephan, 1966; Stephan and Andy, 1964; Bauchot and Stephan, 1961), who used allometric methods after Portmann's model for the analysis of the planimetric data. It is unfortunate that the analysis of the parts of the brain can be used only in a limited way on paleoneurological data from endocasts, and it is those important data that force us to continue the development of more gross indices (and related approaches, such as mapping) for the analysis of fossil endocasts.

With the recognition of the problem of allometry, the development of brain indices returned to Dubois' approach (while avoiding some of his errors). All workers in comparative anatomy who are concerned with the size of organs recognize a role of a general body size factor because of which large animal species tend to have large livers, hearts, and other organs, including brains. It is natural to want to compare the relative development of brains in animals of different body sizes by eliminating or otherwise controlling the body size factor and to determine, then, whether there is significant residual difference in relative brain development. This is, in effect, what Dubois attempted to do when he created his index of cephalization. Later advances on Dubois' work often consisted of mathematically minor changes in his index that seemed to be easier to rationalize biologically. The work of Portmann (1946, 1947) and his students and colleagues (Wirz, 1950; Stingelin, 1958; Portmann and Stingelin, 1961) is in this category, although they did achieve significant advances by beginning analysis of the relative development of the parts of the brain. Let us now examine the relationships among recent and older approaches.

Gross Brain: Body Indices

All of the methods can yield a gross brain size index, and all do it by relating brain size to body size, although the relation is sometimes hidden in the computations. As originally developed by Dubois (1897), the index began by accepting an allometric function for brain:body relations (Snell, 1891) of the form

$$E = k \; P^\alpha \qquad (1)$$

in which E and P are brain and body weights or volumes measured in the same units, and k and α are constants. By more or less *ad hoc* methods, Dubois estimated $\alpha = 0.56$ and could thus calculate k for any particular specimen (or species-average) in which E and P were known. He called k the index of cephalization for the specimen.

To appreciate the meaning of the index, we should note that in logarithmic transformation Equation (1) becomes:

$$\log E = \log k + \alpha \log P \qquad (2)$$

This is a linear equation in log E and log P with a slope α. Log k is the intercept and has the value log E at log P = 0. The index of cephalization as defined by Dubois was, therefore, the value of k_i for a particular individual (i) with brain and body sizes, E_i and P_i in Equation (2) and with $\alpha = 0.56$. If Dubois sought the index of cephalization for a cat with a 25 g brain and a 3,000 g body, he could graph the point (25, 3,000) on log-log paper, draw a line of slope 0.56 through the point, and read the intercept at P = 1 (i.e., at log P = 0) on the ordinate. He would find it to be 0.28. A lion with a 225 g brain and a 150 kg body would also have an index of caphalization of 0.28. (Dubois actually defined his value of α to produce such an equality because he believed cat and lion to be equally "cephalized.") In short, lion and cat lie on the same line.

Recognizing that Dubois' approach to evaluating α was *ad hoc*, von Bonin (1937) undertook the more objective approach of fitting a single straight line to the logarithms of brain and body weights of a relatively large, though haphazard, sample of mammals, following a regression analysis. A graphic presentation of data on over 100 mammals did look like a scatter-plot and served to justify the procedure. With this procedure he found that $\alpha = \frac{2}{3}$ approximately, which agreed with Snell's theoretically determined value (1891). (This results in an index of cephalization of 0.14 for the cat and 0.08 for the lion.) I was able to confirm this slope (Jerison, 1955, 1961) on other data, using a least squares curve-fitting method somewhat more suitable to such data, by performing a functional analysis (rather than regression analysis) in which errors of measurement are assumed in both brain and body measures.

My work with the index began with the question of its reliability, and I ask
first whether k_i was really independent of body weight. To my surprise (Jeris
1955) I found that the von Bonin index when applied to primates was negativ
correlated with body weight and although the relationship was curvilinear, it v
extremely orderly. What I found I now realize could have been predicted from d
then in the literature. Sholl (1948) had reported a much flatter slope for data amc
macaque species ($a=0.18$) than either the Dubois or the von Bonin a. From otl
reports, e.g., Lapique (1907), it was well known that closely related species with
a genus had flatter slopes than those resulting from fits to more disparate grou
My situation was effectively as diagrammed in Figure 1, in which a series of brai
body "points" or "data" aligned along a line with a flat slope such as $a=\frac{1}{3}$ a
fitted by equations such as Equation (2) with $a=\frac{2}{3}$. The result is that points fro
lighter species will have higher values of k_i than points of heavier species, and t
relationship between k_i and P will necessarily be orderly and negative.

These details are instructive because they indicate the effects of apparently min
differences of assumptions on the indices. Since brain:body data present arrays

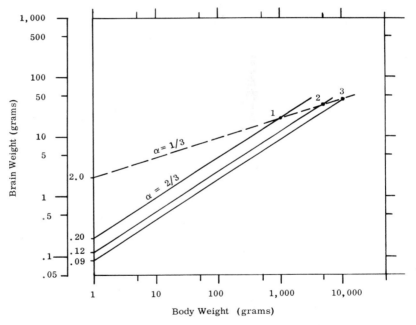

Figure 1. Effect of choice of slope of the basic allometric brain:body function on tl
measure of the index of cephalization, k. Three hypothetic animals related by a "true
$a=\frac{1}{3}$ are placed on mammalian allometric functions with $a=\frac{2}{3}$. The smaller anima
have higher values of k (at $P=1$ kg, $k=0.20$; at $P=5$ kg, $k=0.12$; at $P=10$ kg, $k=0.09$
which is also seen to be the parameter of the functions. An assumption that the inde
should be based on a "natural" relationship for these particular points would lead to
a slope (a) of $\frac{1}{3}$ and the same index ($k=2.0$) for the three species. The meaning of k
as the intercept of the brain weight axis at $P=1$ gram (log $P=0$) is illustrated by the
inner ordinate on which the several numerical values of k are indicated.

.ttered points, it is obviously an uncertain business to choose among possible func-
ns that could fit subgroups of the points. But contrary to some critics such as
oll (1948), there is an obvious orderliness to brain:body data that cannot be
10red. Although the computation of indices for individual specimens may be ques-
nable, the orderliness of the relationship in overall data may be useful in other
ys. In my judgment, indices may be used properly to discriminate among very
oadly defined groups of animals as Wirz (1950) has done for living families of
1mmals and as I have done for an evolutionary succession (Jerison, 1961).

I have lately been limiting my inferences more and more to differences among
rays of points contained in nonoverlapping maps, regions defined by minimum
nvex polygons, a procedure that requires no assumptions about parameters of a
atistically determined equation. That procedure, which is described on page 234
es the orderliness of brain:body data directly to reach decisions about which set
particular specimen belongs to. In the case of one use (Jerison, 1968), I was able
conclude that the earliest known bird, *Archaeopteryx lithographica* was intermediate
relative brain size between a basal level represented by living and fossil reptiles and
e level attained by living birds. On page 236, I will present a supplement to an
rlier report (Jerison, 1961) in which I will describe a basal mammalian level to
tend the proposition of Stephan and his co-workers that certain insectivores represent
e basal level for the evolution of the mammalian brain.

ndices Based on a "Primitive" Base Line

Working with birds at about the same time that von Bonin was revising the
sage of a in mammals, Portmann (1946, 1947) followed by Stingelin (1958) devel-
ɔed an approach that was parallel to Dubois' in its basis but more direct in applying
ubois' assumptions. In order to determine the fraction of the brain weight devoted
ɩ bodily functions, Portmann and Stingelin (1961) divided bird brains into forebrain,
ɔtic lobes, cerebellum, and the *Stammreste* ("brain stem rest," including diencephalon
1d some mesencephalon), which they associated with autonomic or general bodily
ɩnction. Portmann (1946) had determined a relationship between this fraction of
.e bird brain and the body weight for gallinaceous birds as the most primitive of
ving birds, and the relationship served as a primitive base line. He then estimated
ɩe amount of encephalization beyond the requirement for primitive autonomic control
ɩ any bird by dividing its total brain weight by the weight of the *Stammreste* of a
allinaceous bird of the same body size. (The procedure was also applied to the
eights of the parts of the brain relative to the same primitive base line.)

The procedure is formally identical with that involved in the use of Equation
2) because as actually applied, Portmann (1946) had developed the allometric func-
on for *Stammreste* size as a function of body size, finding the value of $a = 0.52$. A
otalindex for a particular bird was then defined as its brain weight divided by the
computed *Stammreste* weight at its body weight. Portmann, therefore, presented the
same kind of results as in a Dubois index when he analyzed the total brain size. The
analysis differed only in the exponent. Effectively he computed a value of k_s for the
Stammreste and calculated $k_i = E/P^{0.52}$. His *Totalindex* was k_i/k_s.

Since the same kind of analysis was performed by Portmann's student, Wirz (1950), in her work with mammals, our more detailed comparison of this method with that of Equation (2) will be based on Wirz's results. She found an allometric function for the most primitive placentals, the insectivores, for the *Stammreste* weight as function of body weight. Working backward from her data it can be shown that the constants were $k_s = 0.03$ and $a = 0.48$, and the allometric function was therefore:

$$Stammreste = 0.03 \ P^{0.48} \tag{3}$$

She then apparently defined a *Totalindex*, to assess gross brain size in many living families of mammals, as the average brain weight of the group divided by the primitive *Stammreste* size for the corresponding average body weight as given by Equation (3). We can note, therefore, that the *Totalindex* and an *index of cephalization* defined as k in Equation (1) or (2) for a specified brain and body are very simply related. By definition, we have:

$$Totalindex = \frac{E}{Stammreste}$$

Since E in Equation (1) and *Stammreste* in Equation (3) are both defined in terms of the body weight, P, we have:

$$Totalindex = \frac{k_i P^\alpha}{.03 P^{0.48}}$$
$$Totalindex = 33.3 k_i P^{\alpha - 0.48} \tag{4}$$

In short, the *Totalindex* is the same as the index of cephalization, k_i, multiplied by a constant and by a body weight factor. It may be noted that for the Dubois index the body weight factor is $P^{0.08}$ and for the von Bonin index it is $P^{0.18}$. Her *Totalindex* is easily computed by taking an index of cephalization, k_i, with $a = 0.48$ and divided that by $k_s = 0.03$.

The procedure followed by Stephan and his colleagues (e.g., Stephan and Andy, 1964) is a development of Wirz's and an improvement, because it does not require *ad hoc* assumptions about the *Stammreste*. Effectively, they used the data on total brain and body size of certain insectivores, characterized as "basal" because of their relatively small neocortical development, to derive the basic relationship between brain and body. This resulted in an equation like Equation (1), with $a = 0.64$ or 0.63 (different values appear in different papers), and they related the brain size of other mammals to the brain size of insectivores. (When they looked at parts of the brain they related these to corresponding parts, instead of only the *Stammreste*, of basal insectivores, accounting for body size by using Equation (1).) Because of the value of a that they used, their gross indices are formally almost identical with those used by von Bonin. Their indices, presented as percentages, are indices with $a = 0.64$ divided by a basal index, $k = 0.033$.

All of the approaches reviewed thus far are based on a multiplicative hypothesis, which appears graphically as the assumption that steps in cephalization among mammals occur by displacements of a basic brain:body line upward as a series of parallel lines. This is multiplicative because it signifies a multiplication of the brain weight by some constant. In alternative terms, one might state this by giving brain size as a percentage (greater than 100) of some basal brain size or a percentage of the size of the *Stammreste*. To my knowledge, I am the only one who has proposed an additive hypothesis in which the concern is with an amount of tissue added to a basal brain size (Jerison, 1955) or, alternatively, a conversion of the measure of amount of tissue into a measure of the number of neural elements or extra neurons contained in that tissue (Jerison, 1963). Some of the implications of additive versus multiplicative hypotheses will be considered later in passing, but not in depth.

The multiplicative hypothesis advanced by Brummelkamp (1940) (stepwise increments of the Dubois version of Equation (2) with $a = 0.56$ by displacements of k in units of $\sqrt{2}$) was analyzed statistically by Sholl (1948), who showed that the hypothesis was untenable. Sholl also showed that Dubois' value of $a = 0.56$ was not a demonstrable constant for related species of mammals, and he presented evidence that $a = 0.26$ for individuals within a species with considerable variation in body size as proposed by Lapique (1907) was not demonstrable in squirrels and Rhesus monkeys. Sholl extended his criticisms beyond the data that he had evaluated to make a sweeping condemnation of the whole process of deriving indices. This has had unfortunate effects in deflecting interest (1) from the obviously orderly brain:body relations that exist and are easily demonstrated and (2) from the possibility of interpreting and using those relationships for comparative analysis. One of my purposes here is to correct that effect by showing where indices and related quantifications are clearly appropriate.

Encephalization, Brain Function, and Gross Indices

The process of encephalization according to all of the gross indices just reviewed is defined relative to a reference regression line, which implicitly or explicitly is a line defining a basal level of cephalization. In Dubois' or von Bonin's analysis, the implicit basal level would be a line with slope 0.56 or 0.66 below which no brain: body points of living mammals lie. This also happens to be the case for Stephan's group because of the explicit placement of the brain:body line for basal insectivores at a near minimum for living mammals. Only the opossum (*Didelphis marsupialis*) is below Stephan's line. In Wirz's case the explicit line is Equation (3), which is also a line that falls considerably below any brain:body coordinate of a living mammal.

The basal measure of the brain is a weight, and the exact assumption involved in a computation of an index as, e.g., a 200 percent increment, is that the more cephalized animal has a brain that weighs so many times (e.g., twice) as much as the basal weight independently of body size. The biological implication is that this relative amount of shift produces an equal effect in any mammal regardless of the absolute difference in weights. One of the implicit assumptions is that the gross weight of the brain is a kind of natural statistic that is related to other properties. I have examined this possibility in some detail (Jerison, 1963, and unpublished data), and it seems to be surprisingly tenable. Specifically, the gross brain weight for a reasonably broad sample of progressive living mammals, including primates, ungulates, and carnivores (Harman, 1957) can be used to estimate both the volume of the cortex and the total number of neurons in the brain, and may also be related to the degree of dendritic proliferation.

It may, therefore, be appropriate to calculate indices from gross brain size, because gross brain size should be related to a gross physiological process such as total information transmission and storage capacity. This concept of capacity can be a source of difficulty and should be discussed a bit more carefully.

If the gross brain size is related to the number of elements in the information processing system of the brain and the degree to which the elements can affect one another, the amount of information processed (which must also be determined by these elements in the formal information-theory sense) may be a relatively simple function of the size of the brain. In considering this view nothing is suggested about the kind of information that is processed or the locus of the processing. There may be auditory information stored or processed at a brain stem, collicular, geniculate, or neocortical level, and olfactory information processed via a system that is essentially paleocortical. There may be information associated with short-term memory processed by neocortical sensory systems and hippocampal paleocortical systems, and there may be attention systems that are largely subcortical and paleocortical in their more accessible (for study) portions. But the total information processing capacity may be the sum of the capacities of these and other part-systems and their interactions.

One's model for brain-behavior relations may affect the kind of index considered relevant. If the model is punctiform, with independent physiological functions associated rather specifically with specific structures, indices suggesting an overall information processing capacity may be of little interest. On the other hand, recent evidence points to the waking brain as being a complex interactive system in which truly isolated functional systems probably never occur (Magoun, 1963). The isolation of systems is, in a sense, an artifact of experimental methods which artificially isolate parts of the system in order to study them more easily. The historically interesting view which was skeptical of localization of function (Flourens, 1824) was made more modern and precise by Lashley (1950), who could recognize some localization while emphasizing the importance of action of the mass of neural tissue in the brain. We are, perhaps, ready for further refinement in which the interacting subsystems, localized anatomically or physiologically, can be recognized as elements of a total system for which total capacity for information handling may be defined. And that total capacity may be associated with gross brain size.

In many instances a definition of total capacity would be of great interest, even where the basic concern is properly with the mechanism of a single system or part of a system in the processing of a particular kind of information (e.g., color in the visual system). By understanding the total system we can better evaluate the role of the part-system as contributing to the whole. For evolutionary analysis, it is particularly important to consider broad advances in grade as well as specific advances or adaptations for niches. Orderly changes in total information processing capacity implicit in changes in average brain size of faunal groups from different geological strata (Jerison, 1961) raise issues for this kind of evolution (anagenesis) that can resolve conflicting interpretations of selection pressures and the brain.

The problem of deriving and using indices to measure broad faunal changes is different from their use to suggest a precise ordering of closely related living species with respect to brain development. It is apparent from graphical analyses of the type presented earlier in Figure 1 that the numerical values of computed indices are very much influenced by and sensitive to mathematically minor differences in certain constants. Since those constants (e.g., a) are of uncertain biological significance and are really empirical constants derived from possibly biased data and uncertain curve-fitting procedures, the indices that are derived are inevitably *ad hoc* to some extent. Only when a rationale can be presented for specific values for the constants and for the computations can we judge the utility of indices as ways to make sense of data. It is, nevertheless, true that when broad arrays of data are used, representing, for example, whole families of mammals or even several orders of mammals, the basic data may be in an array of points on a graph, and the indices applied to arrays may simply indicate the displacement of groups of points from one another.

The difficulty with indices arises from the fact that they are numbers and we are accustomed to think of numbers as precise. It is only in recent years that students of the life sciences have become aware of the possibility of numbers varying in their precision. Most of us are now sensitive to the fact that some numbers are little more than labels for categories and imply no ordering with respect to an ordered dimension, whereas other numbers can be used in the usual sense of physical weights and measures (Stevens, 1946). Indices should be and are usually expected to be numbers of the latter type in which an index of 4 is twice as great as 2 and 2 units away from it, both numbers being referable to a zero point on the index scale or dimension. But the *ad hoc* nature of actual indices limits the inferences possible, and in many cases the scale of measurement is not an appropriate one. For example, if there is a doubling of brain size relative to a basal line, we may be properly hesitant about equating a doubling from a basal size of 3 g to an enlarged size of 6 g as being the same as a doubling from a basal size of 50 g to an enlarged size of 100 g. Many more elements are added in an extra 50 g than are added in an extra 3 g, and presumably there would be a shift in information processing capacity proportional to the absolute rather than the relative number of elements added. It was this consideration that led me to try an additive rather than a multiplicative index (Jerison, 1955, 1963) for analyzing relative brain development in the order Primates.

This argument leads to the conclusion that the numerical methods associated with the development of indices always need careful analysis. It would be useful, for example, if we could work from a theoretical model of the growth and development of the brain and its nuclei, within and between species; this model should be in the form of precise equations relating gross brain size to body size and the size of the parts of the brain to both brain and body size. We would then have a rational basal equation against which deviation in particular species could be projected and analyzed. It is likely that several such equations would have to be developed, and that the basic equation would contain parameters associated with orders of mammals. In any case, until such procedures are developed (and the work of Stephan and his associates seems to be bringing the quantitative data to a point at which this kind of development may become an easy exercise in quantitative morphology), particular indices can be quite misleading if presented simply as an array of numbers. It is much more useful to present, along with the indices, a representation of the data on which they are based. For example, an array of the brain and body weights presented graphically along with the basal equation to which the points are to be related provides an excellent device to eliminate undue reliance on numerical representation sometimes limited to the indices alone. In the case of Figure 1, it would be immediately apparent that there exists a natural relationship among the points that is overlooked in the computation of the indices.

Nonnumerical Analysis with Convex Polygons

It may be helpful to devote a few pages to a kind of analysis that I have been using lately in which many of the assumptions involved in the writing and computations of indices are avoided and which has the useful property of showing variation as well as averages. The method still takes advantage of the orderliness of brain:body data and uses these data in ways similar to those possible by the development of numerical indices. In many analyses one seeks only a decision about the level of brain development of a particular specimen compared to that of more broadly defined groups. For that purpose it may be sufficient to map the brain:body relations of broadly defined groups and simply plot a point for the specimen of concern.

To illustrate the nature of the regularities available in this apparently gross analysis I have regraphed data collected on various expeditions by Crile and Quiring (1940) on brains and bodies of 198 species of vertebrates: 94 mammals (including 18 primates), 52 birds, 20 reptiles, and 32 fish. Each species is represented by the heaviest individual of that species in their sample. (The rationale was that a wild species represented by only a few more or less haphazardly obtained specimens would more rarely be represented by full-grown healthy specimens than by less adequate specimens. Hence the largest specimen would represent a kind of optimum estimate of the adult phenotype.) These are shown in Figure 2. The regularities and orderliness are impressive. They have not been noted in previous reports on these data. Quiring (1941) apparently used the entire sample of several thousand individual specimens described by Crile and Quiring (1940) to produce a set of best-fitting lines on log-log coordinates by an unspecified procedure. His results are shown in Figure 3, in order to indicate how information may be lost by an undue reliance on curve-fitting procedures. There is no indication of variability in Quiring's curves nor of the degree of overlap between mammals and birds on the one hand and between reptiles and fish on the other. It is apparent that much information from Figure 2 is simply lost in Figure 3 and that a true situation is represented much more adequately by Figure 2.

In mathematical terms, the situation is even more serious for curve-fitting approaches. The philosophy of curve-fitting as practiced by most biologists is really that the points of the scatter-plot are random deviates from a particular line. Continued sampling from the population from which the points were drawn should show a true mean of the points lying exactly on the line, and the frequency distribution of points for a particular body weight should be a bell-shaped curve. Each point then represents a random deviation from the line, and the deviation should be attributable to error of measurement. This is, of course, not the case for brain:body data. Each point in Figure 2 represents a kind of best estimate of the location of future samples from a particular species, in particular of healthy nonemaciated adults of the species.

A curve-fitting procedure applied to Figure 2 might properly assume that there exists a region within which the set of brain:body data from living species is located,

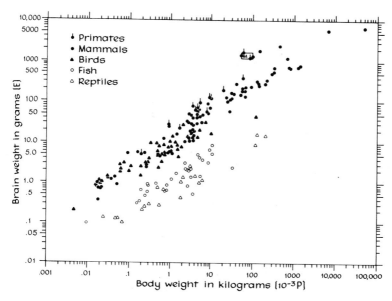

Figure 2. Brain and body weights of the largest specimens of 198 vertebrate species collected by Crile and Quiring (1940. *Ohio J. Sci.*, 40:219-259). Data on man represented by four points on rectangle labeled "M" show the extreme measures of their sample of 50 men (heaviest and lightest brains and bodies). Note that fish and reptiles jointly form an array of points that does not overlap with mammals and birds and that despite the range of the human measures (from 45 to 95 kg bodies and from 1,130 to 1,570 g brains) the entire human distribution occupies only a small area when graphed on log-log coordinates. (From H. J. Jerison, 1969, *Amer. Nat.* 103: 575-588.)

and any point in that region is equally likely to be occupied by a living species. In short, rather than assume a normal distribution of errors in order to find a regression line we would do better to find a principal-axis for the set of points distributed rectangularly (equiprobably) in the area within which they lie. We should use the equation of that principal-axis if we need a best-fitting line for the points. (A principal-axis has as its physical model an axis around which a form cut out of metal or wood, shaped like the area, would rotate most freely, minimizing the moment of inertia. Its computation by hand is overwhelming, but it is a relatively simple problem for computer analysis by the use of the methods described by Knoll and Stenson, 1968.)

In Figure 4 the sets of points for mammals, birds, fish, and reptiles are enclosed in minimum convex polygons (which map the areas of the sets) and illustrate the relationships among them. It is clear that the orientation of the polygons is approximately the same, that their shapes are similar, and, most importantly, that two and only two groups of vertebrates are completely distinct with respect to relative brain size. The mammals and birds form one natural grouping, with overlapping polygons, and the fish and reptiles form a second grouping with overlapping polygons. But these two groupings are completely nonoverlapping. An unassigned specimen such as *Archaeopteryx* can be represented as a point in the space of Figure 4, and it is on that basis that the decision that it was intermediate between its reptilian ancestors and

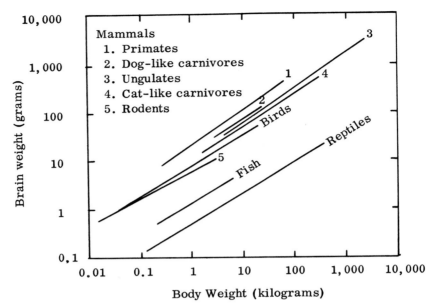

Figure 3. Curves fitted by Quiring (1941. Growth, 5:301-327.) to data of the more than 3,000 specimens from which sample of Figure 2 was drawn. Although representing different species by unequal numbers of individuals and including many juveniles, full data population results in lines similar to those that could be fitted to the more properly determined sample of Figure 2. Note loss of information about range and overlap and inappropriate implication of differentiation by the lines. If the several groups in this figure were treated as random samples from their respective populations, it would be possible to differentiate only two groups statistically, the lower vertebrates (fish and reptiles) and the higher vertebrates (birds and mammals). The analysis may be contrasted with that of Figure 4.

its avian descendants was made (Jerison, 1968). Similarly, it can be shown that other fossil reptiles with known endocasts, such as pterosaurs, dinosaurs, and the mammal-like reptiles, all fall within the reptilian polygon or a natural elongated extension of that polygon (Fig. 5) to include larger reptiles rather than at a position either below or above that polygon (Jerison. In press).

Convex Polygons and Archaic Tertiary Mammal Endocasts

The analysis applied to the earliest mammals is instructive, especially in connection with Stephan's work and his association of the basal insectivores with the most primitive level of mammalian brain evolution. Since the mammals are descended from early Mesozoic therapsid reptiles, it is appropriate to examine their relative brain size in relation to that of living mammals and reptiles. For this analysis it is even more appropriate to analyze the reptilian level by including fossil data. In Figure 5, I have presented the two convex polygons for the mammals and reptiles of Figure 2 and have extended the reptilian polygon by including data on Mesozoic reptiles: 10

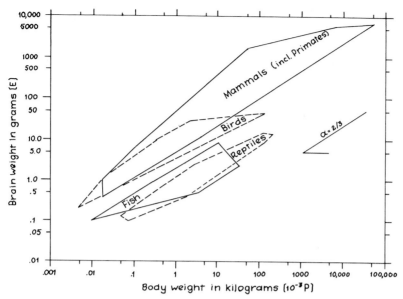

Figure 4. Minimum convex polygons enclosing the vertebrate classes of Figure 2. The polygons can be described by their principal-axes (see text) to suggest best-fitting slopes, and these are 0.69 for mammals, 0.56 for birds, 0.50 for fish, and 0.62 for reptiles. It is also clear, however, that each polygon can be oriented reasonably well about a line with a slope of ⅔.

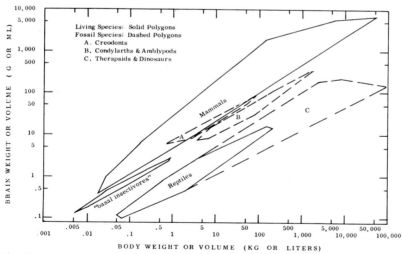

Figure 5. Minimum convex polygons for living and fossil mammals and reptiles as devices for the analysis of brain evolution. Living and fossil reptiles form a single natural lower group. Fossil archaic Tertiary mammals (A and B) are similar to living basal insectivores, above the reptilian level but below or at the lower range of the typical level of living mammals. Living species polygons from Figure 2 and from Bauchot and Stephan (1966. Mammalia, 30:160-196.) for basal insectivores. (Fossil data discussed in text.)

dinosaur species, 5 pterosaur (flying reptiles) species, and 4 mammal-like (therapsid) reptile species. Only the dinosaurs are beyond the range of living reptiles because of their huge body sizes, but the earlier assertion that they fall within the same general grouping as living reptiles is clear from Figure 5, (see Jerison, in press.)

The analysis of brain size in the early Tertiary mammals presented in Figure 5 is restricted to archaic species of Paleocene, Eocene, and in one instance (the creodont, *Hyaenodon horridus*) an early Oligocene species. Thus, the fossil mammals are from between about 60 and 35 million years ago, and the particular species are from the orders, Condylartha, Amblypoda, and Creodonta, which are archaic in that they were replaced as orders by living ungulates and carnivores in their adaptive niches. The analysis in Figure 5 includes one additional living group of mammals, the living basal insectivores as defined by Stephan (1966), with their data provided by Bauchot and Stephan (1966). The data on the fossil mammals are from some of my own work in progress, and the species representing the corner points of the fossil mammal polygons are indicated in Table 1.

The most impressive feature of Figure 5 is that the polygons are oriented in more or less the same way, a slope of $2/3$ for a best fitting line is really quite easy to visualize for all of them. It suggests, therefore, that the users of indices are fundamentally correct in assuming that encephalization occurred by an upward displacement of a function such as Equation (2). That is, one may interpret Figure 5 as showing that a basal level of vertebrate brain size is common to living and fossil reptiles and that living and fossil mammals evolved from that basal vertebrate level.

Examining the polygons of the basal insectivores and of the condylarth-amblypod data suggests a second and especially useful observation. Apparently the evolution from the basal vertebrate level was by an upward displacement of the reptilian function to a basal mammalian level. (Fossil insectivores such as the lower Oligocene *Neuro-*

TABLE 1.

Endocast and Body Volumes of Selected Archaic Tertiary Mammals *

Order	Genus and Species	Endocast Volume (ml)	Body Volume (liters)
Condylartha	*Arctocyonides arenae*	8.3	11
	Meniscotherium robustum	15	6
	Phenacodus primaevus	31	56
	Pleuraspidotherium aumonieri	6.0	4
Amblypoda	*Uintatherium anceps*	300	1400
	Tetheopsis ingens	345	2500
Creodonta	*Thinocyon velox*	5.7	0.8
	Cynohyaenodon cayluxi	8.3	3.0
	Pterodon dasyuroides	62	42
	Hyaenodon horridus	85	56

* These measures given to two significant figures are the corner points in the polygons of Figure 5, Creodonta for Polygon A and Condylartha and Amblypoda combined for Polygon B. Measures of volume were by water displacement of specimens or scale models, by the use of numerical double integration (Jerison, 1968. Nature, 219: 1381-1382.), or by the use of weight: length equations. This is part of a larger sample of archaic mammals, the remainder of which fall within the polygons. Additional information on these specimens is available in Piveteau (1961. Traité de Paleontologie.), Russell and Sigogneau (1965. Mem. Mus. National d'Hist. Nat., 14 (Ser. C) : 1-36.), and Gazin (1965. Smithsonian Misc. Coll., 149 (No. 2) : 1-98.).

gymnurus [Dechaseaux, 1964] can be shown to fall within the basal insectivore polygon, or slightly above it.) That mammalian level is represented by living basal insectivores, as discussed by Stephan (1966). In his discussion and use of data on the basal insectivores, Stephan assumes that the brain:body function for these generally small animals can be extended to mammals of much larger body size. The results of Figure 5 support his assumption. A line through the basal insectivore polygon and the condylarth-amblypod polygon is readily drawn, and it can have a slope of 0.63 as required by Stephan's analysis.

It is of secondary interest for my present expository purpose that the archaic Tertiary fossil mammals are readily divided into two groups, the condylarths and amblypods, on the one hand, which are encephalized to the extent expected for a basal mammalian level (if Stephan's views are accepted), and, on the other hand, the creodonts which were about 50 percent more cephalized. That is, the centroid of the creodont polygon lies at a point indicating a 50 percent increase in brain size above the level of the insectivore-condylarth-amblypod line. Such a result may have some utility in the analysis of the systematics of the Creodonta, especially in view of recent work which would place a few of the basal insectivores used by Stephan and the order Creodonta into a single new order, Deltatheridea (Van Valen, 1966, 1967). The problem involved is that the new order would include relatively highly cephalized fossil forms from one long-extinct branch (the creodonts) and less cephalized forms in a living branch (the tenrecs and others). This is not a crucial criticism. A similar situation is known in many orders of mammals, including primates which include relatively uncephalized living lemurs and highly cephalized fossil hominids.

This is an interesting result, nevertheless, for the appreciation of broad trends in cephalization. The creodonts were the highly specialized carnivorous mammals of their time, and the amblypods were the comparably specialized herbivores. Condylarths were a less specialized group reflecting a broad range of adaptations almost certainly including carnivorous, omnivorous, and herbivorous species (see Romer, 1966). There is some suggestive material for speculation in Figure 5 with regard to the role of brain evolution in the success of the species. This is especially relevant in view of the fact that from the Oligocene onward the ungulates (Perissodactyla, Artiodactyla, Proboscidea) typically had relatively larger brains (as revealed in an analysis of the type shown in Figure 5) than the Carnivora, and the Carnivora in turn had larger brains than the Creodonta. It is appropriate to speculate that a kind of leapfrogging occurred in which the evolution of the larger creodonts exerted selection pressures in favor of the larger-brained ungulates and against the smaller-brained archaic ungulates. This eventually may have led to a selection pressure in favor of the larger-brained Carnivora to replace the smaller-brained Creodonta as the large predators of their ecological system, when the amblypods and condylarths became extinct.

Other Indices

A brief comment on other indices is now in order. We may, first, consider indices analyzing the relative sizes of parts of the brain. As indicated earlier, such an analysis was initiated by Portmann and his students and colleagues, Wirz and Stingelin. The major criticism of that work is that the reference axis or level is the *Stammreste,* and it implies that the volume of that part of the brain is always the relevant one for reference. I prefer Stephan's analysis in which a basal group of animals is selected and relative development of the brain in other species is thought of as incremental for either the whole brain or for corresponding parts of the brains of the comparative species and the basal group. My additive index (Jerison, 1963) was relative to a basal function for fossil archaic mammals, and the basal function was conceptually equivalent and mathematically almost the same as Stephan's.

Stephan's approach is conventionally punctiform in its implicit assumptions about brain-behavior relations—e.g., the reference for an index of the relative development of the paleocortex of any species is the relative amount of paleocortex in the brains of basal insectivores. These assumptions are nevertheless superior to Portmann's and Wirz's which would in the previous example relate paleocortex to the *Stammreste.* In my view, the partitioning of functions to localize them within regions, even in generally accepted ways (e.g., to acknowledge differentiation between brain stem and cortex), begs the question. It may be that for a truly comparative analysis in which direction of adaptation is taken into account, the relatively large paleocortex should be thought of as a specific insectivore adaptation for the kind of information processed in their brains. From the point of view of efficiency at information processing, it may make little difference if a particular network involves brain stem and cortex, another involves paleocortex, and a third involves corticocortical connections. The critical question may be the amount of tissue in the system. However, most neurologists do not, at this time, accept such a view and are not accustomed to thinking in terms of total information-processing capacity of a brain. One can scarcely criticize Stephan's approach to the analysis of partial systems for being consistent with current views.

It is difficult to exaggerate the importance of part-indices and the quantitative analysis of the nuclei of the brain for the comparative neuroanatomy of living animals. Such an analysis can lay the foundations for a genuine quantitative morphology of the brain from which many theorems about function could be developed. At the present time we may rely on the many and important, but still too few, studies by Stephan and his colleagues and on an analysis of the results reported by Wirz (1950).

There is insufficient space here to present full documentation of the following assertion, but it seems likely from those studies that there is a surprising fixity in relative size of the parts of the brain as a function of body size and that in most instances allometric functions of the type of Equation (2) would fit the data of the parts as well as the whole brain with $a = \frac{2}{3}$. Curve-fitting by the method of least squares results in a variety of values of a, but my point is that reasonably adequate fits would be possible with a slope of $\frac{2}{3}$. Minimum convex polygons drawn about measures of the parts of the brain as a function of body size are similar to, though displaced downward from, the polygons of Figure 4 or 5. This kind of association explains Andy and Stephan's results (1966) when they correlated one part of the brain with another. In most instances (save only the olfactory bulbs) the regression line that associated two parts of the brain had a slope of 1.0, indicating a linear relationship among the volumes of the parts.

The implication of this argument is that it is, in principle, likely that given the total brain size one may predict with accuracy the size of any of the parts of the brain, and that, furthermore, the allometric functions for the total brain size and for the size of the parts as a function of body size may be considered to have equal slopes. The functions are, therefore, additive (Reeve and Huxley, 1945) and may be combined to yield an allometric function for the brain as a whole.

The data on the analysis of the parts do not, therefore, alter the picture obtained from analysis of whole-brain:body relations. Wirz's results (1950) agree with Stephan's. I have performed additional analysis of parts of fossil endocasts, the results of which I will not present here but can describe briefly. In archaic Tertiary mammals the endocasts are characteristically unflexured, and one can estimate the volumes of olfactory bulbs, forebrain, and hindbrain separately. (The latter, which includes cerebellum, pons, and medulla, cannot be further separated very easily.) The allometric analyses of relative size of the forebrain and hindbrain are essentially the same and produce essentially the same results as that of the whole endocast shown in Figure 5, differing only in that the polygons are displaced downward. The olfactory bulbs, on the other hand, do not follow an allometric function and were actually smaller in the archaic mammals than in their living replacements in their niches.

An important new analysis recently suggested by Radinsky (1967) would relate the total volume of the mammalian endocast to the cross-sectional area of the foramen magnum. The suggestion is analogous to those discussed earlier in which brain:body relations are examined indirectly by replacing them with other bodily measures closely related to either brain or body. Radinsky's measure of the cross-section of the foramen magnum is related fairly directly to body size, as noted by Anthony (1938), and can readily replace body size measures in the allometric function. It is important, however, to determine the limits of the equivalence. In the amblypods, and probably in other orders of mammals, it is likely that the foramen magnum was incompletely filled by the medulla and thus the foramen magnum of these animals probably overestimates body size. The special utility of Radinsky's work lies in the availability of an additional estimate of body size and in the possibility of estimating a body size factor with nothing available except the back of the skull. It will be useful to obtain other data, however, on the degree to which the region of the endocast of the foramen magnum and the medulla are alike.

Conclusions

In this discussion of indices I have limited myself to those that are useful for the analysis of endocasts of fossil animals. Indices based on the microstructure of the brain are therefore not part of this discussion, although they are relevant for the general problem of the evolution of the brain as it is approached with comparative data on living animals. In the analysis of the evolution of the brain as an information-processing system it is also not necessary to consider morphological details such as the positions of cranial nerves and blood vessels or the detailed anatomy of the otic region, despite their importance for other purposes. They may provide important details on lines of descent, of course, but the primary evolutionary problem with which I am concerned is the identification of selection pressures and their ultimate effect on the evolution of grades or levels of brain and behavior. For this purpose it may be sufficient to establish general trends while recognizing that specific lines of descent are not being explored. Instead, our topic is the ultimate effect of an evolutionary process on the general characteristics of a fauna. Indices may actually be misleading for such an approach in their implication of numerical exactness in specifying a brain's development. It may be better to map brain:body relations, as I have done in Figures 4 and 5 with convex polygons, and to determine the effect of selection pressures by examining displacements of the various polygons as if we were dealing with changing mappings of sets.

Some specification of trends may be possible within narrower lines of descent by a careful examination of the polygons or maps. One clear result, manifest in Figure 5, is the common trend or orientation of all the polygons, indicating a general vertebrate brain:body pattern. We can also confirm at least one of the sometimes questioned laws of Marsh about the brains of Tertiary mammals (see Edinger, 1960) : the earliest of Tertiary mammals did have smaller brains than those that replaced them in their niches. To be more precise, the relative increases in size may be read from Figure 5 as a 50 percent increase for creodonts and about a 400 percent average increase for progressive living mammals beyond the level of the most primitive fossils living. The basal forms are genuinely primitive from the perspective of this analysis; they are indistinguishable from the earliest mammals with known brain:body data. Finally, the data on reptiles presented here are an example of how the mapping technique is sensitive enough to force rejection of hypotheses. The map can and does disprove another of Marsh's laws in which he asserted that there was an increase in brain size in reptiles in their evolution (Marsh, 1886, p. 59). Living and fossil reptiles are comprehended by a single brain:body map or polygon. These results can be stated unequivocally from the maps without computing a single index.

REFERENCES

Andy, O. J., and H. Stephan. 1966. Phylogeny of the primate *septum telencephali*. *In* Hassler, R., and H. Stephan, eds. Evolution of the Forebrain. Stuttgart, Georg Thieme Verlag, pp. 389-399.

Anthony, R. 1938. Essai de recherche d'une expression anatomique approximative du degré d'organisation cérébrale autre que le poids de l'encéphale comparé au poids du corps. Bull. Soc. Anthropol. (Paris), 9 (ser. 8) :17-67.

Bauchot, R., and H. Stephan. 1961. Étude quantitative de quelques structures commisurales du cerveau des insectivores. Mammalia, 25:314-341.

———— and H. Stephan. 1966. Données nouvelles sur l'encéphalisation des insectivores et des prosimiens. Mammalia, 30:160-196.

Bonin, G. von. 1937. Brain weight and body weight in mammals. J. Gen. Psychol., 16:379-389.

Brummelkamp, R. 1940. Brain weight and body size: a study of the cephalization problem. Proc. Kon. Nederl. Akad. Wet., 39:1-57.

Crile, G., and D. P. Quiring. 1940. A record of the body weight and certain organ and gland weights of 3690 animals. Ohio J. Sci., 40:219-259.

Dechaseaux, C. 1964. L'encéphale de *Neurogymnurus cayluxi* insectivore des phosphorites du Quercy. Ann. Paleontol., 50:83-100.

Dubois, E. 1897. Sur le rapport du poids de l'encéphale avec la grandeur du corps chez les mammifères. Bull. Soc. Anthropol. (Paris), 8 (Ser. 4) :337-376.

Edinger, T. 1960. Anthropocentric misconceptions in paleoneurology. Proc. Rudolf Virchow Soc., 19:56-107.

Flourens, P. 1824. Recherches Expérimentales sur les Propriétés et les Fonctions du Système Nerveux dans les Animaux Vertébrés. Paris, Crevot.

Gazin, C. I. 1965. A study of the early Tertiary condylarthan mammal *Meniscotherium*. Smithsonian Misc. Coll., 149 [No. 2]: 1-98.

Harman, P. J. 1957. Paleoneurologic, neoneurologic and ontogenetic aspects of brain phylogeny. The James Arthur Lecture. New York, American Museum of Natural History.

Jerison, H. J. 1955. Brain to body ratios and the evolution of intelligence. Science, 121:447-449.

———— 1961. Quantitative analysis of evolution of the brain in mammals. Science, 133:1012-1014.

———— 1963. Interpreting the evolution of the brain. Hum. Biol., 35:263-291.

———— 1968. Brain evolution and *Archaeopteryx*. Nature, 219:1381-1382.

———— 1969. Brain evolution and dinosaur brains. Amer. Naturalist. 103:575-588.

Knoll, R. L., and H. H. Stenson. 1968. A computer program to generate and measure random forms. Percept. Psychophys., 3:311-316.

Lapique, L. 1907. Tableau générale des poids somatique et encéphalique dans les espèces animales. Bull. Soc. Anthropol. (Paris), 8 (Ser. 5) :248-262.

Lashley, K. S. 1950. In search of the engram. *In* Sympos. Soc. Exp. Biol. No. 4:454-482. Cambridge, England, Cambridge University Press.

Magoun, H. W. 1963. The Waking Brain, 2nd Ed. Springfield, Ill., Charles C Thomas.

Marsh, O. C. 1886. Dinocerata. Monogr. U. S. Geol. Survey, 10, 243 p.

Piveteau, J. 1961. Traité de Paléontologie. Tome VI, Vol. 1. Mammifères: origine reptilienne; évolution.

Portmann, A. 1946. Études sur la cérébralisation chez les oiseaux. I. Alauda, 14:2-20.

———— 1947. Études sur la cérébralisation chez les oiseaux. II. Alauda, 15:1-15.

———— and W. Stingelin. 1961. The central nervous system. *In* Marshall, A. J., ed. Biology and Comparative Physiology of Birds. New York, Academic Press, Inc. 2:1-36.

Quiring, D. P. 1941. The scale of being according to the power formula. Growth, 5:301-327.

Radinsky, L. 1967. Relative brain size: a new measure. Science, 155:836-838.

Reeve, E. C. R., and J. S. Huxley. 1945. Some problems in the study of allometric growth. *In* Clark, W. E. Le Gros, and P. B. Medawar, eds. Essays on Growth and Form. Oxford, Clarendon Press.

Romer, A. S. 1966. Vertebrate Paleontology, 3rd Ed. Chicago, University of Chicago Press.

Russell, D. E., and D. Sigogneau. 1965. Étude de moulages endocraniens de mammifères Paléocenes. Mem. Mus. National d'Hist. Nat., 14 (Ser. C) :1-36.

Sholl, D. A. 1948. The quantitative investigation of the vertebrate brain and the applicability of allometric formulae to its study. Proc. Roy. Soc. Biol., 135:243-258.

Snell, O. 1891. Die Abhängigkeit des Hirngewichtes von dem Körpergewicht und den geistigen Fähigkeiten. Arch. Psychiat. Nervenkr., 23:436-446.

Stephan, H. 1966. Grössenänderungen im olfaktorischen und limbischen System während der phylogenetischen Entwicklung der Primaten. *In* Hassler, R., and H. Stephan, eds. Evolution of the Forebrain. Stuttgart, Georg Thieme Verlag, pp. 377-388.

———— and O. J. Andy. 1964. Quantitative comparisons of brain structures from Insectivore to Primates. Amer. Zool., 4:59-74.

Stevens, S. S. 1946. On the theory of scales of measurement. Science, 103:677.

Stingelin, W. 1958. Vergleichend morphologische Untersuchungen am Vorderhirn der

Vögel auf cytologischer und cytoarchitektonischer Grundlage. Basel, Verlag Helbing & Lichtenhahn.

Tilney, F.   1928.   The Brain from Ape to Man. (2 Vols.) New York, Paul B. Hoeber, Inc.

Van Valen, L.   1966.   Deltatheridia, a new order of mammals. Bull. Amer. Mus. Nat. Hist., 132:1-126.

——— 1967.   New Paleocene insectivores and insectivore classification. Bull. Amer. Mus. Nat. Hist., 135:217-284.

Wirz, K.   1950.   Zur quantitativen Bestimmung der Rangordnung bei Säugetieren. Acta Anat., 9:134-196.

9

Allometric and Factorial Analysis of Brain Structure in Insectivores and Primates[*]

GEORGE A. SACHER

Division of Biological and Medical Research
Argonne National Laboratory
Argonne, Illinois 60439

Introduction

This chapter surveys some procedures for the quantitative analysis of biological form and applies them to the comparative analysis of insectivore and primate brain structure. It begins with the widely used techniques of bivariate allometry, then introduces the methods of multivariate allometry, and terminates with the methods of multiple factor analysis. Although it might have been desirable to illustrate these methods on a variety of data in order to give an indication of the range of applicability of the procedures, the decision was instead to use just one set of data and to examine it with each of these methods in turn. It is felt that viewing one body of data in these varied perspectives will lead to a better understanding of the nature of multivariate data analysis and of its potential value as a tool for research on brain structure and evolution.

An important recent contribution to the study of the functional morphology of primates by multivariate analysis is the work of Oxnard on the primate shoulder (1967, 1969). In his discussion of function and structure there are points of correspondence to the methods presented here, but he also considers questions of numerical taxonomy which lie outside the scope of this paper. An excellent general review of allometry is given by Gould (1966).

Historical Background: Brain/Body Allometry and Cephalization Indices

The allometric analysis of biological form had its beginnings in the inquiries of Manouvrier (1885), Snell (1892), and Dubois (1897) on the allometric relation of

[*] This work was performed under the auspices of the U.S. Atomic Energy Commission.
Mr. Edward J. Klein wrote the program for the bivariate analysis while at Argonne as a CSUI Undergraduate Honors Research Student. Mr. Anthony J. Strecok, Applied Mathematics Division, modified the UCLA factor analysis program for our use and supervised the computations.

brain weight to body weight in mammals. Their work was the beginning of a major research activity, which continues at a reduced level to the present day, directed toward establishing scales of relationships of brain and body dimensions. The objective of these inquiries was to discover a certain metrical relationship, usually called an *index of cephalization*, expressive of the phyletic advancement of different mammalian groups in regard to their levels of mental development.

This work has an important place in the history of neurobiology, and still influences discussion of the relation of brain to behavior, so it must be put into proper perspective with contemporary research on the dimensionality of brain structure. Unfortunately, the judgment must be rendered that the quest for cephalization indices was on the whole detrimental to the progress of comparative neurobiology. These attempts to construct scales of mental or psychic advancement were made at a time when there were no objective, quantitative assessments of the mental capacities of animals, so each author filled this void by forming his own subjective ranking of the intelligence of different species. The indices that were constructed had no validation other than these subjective rankings, so they were invulnerable to experimental refutation. Even today there is only fragmentary knowledge about the relative mental capacities of animals, including the subhuman primates, so that comparative research on brain organization is still constrained to be for the most part an examination of anatomical interrelations, with only incidental and qualitative references to comparative behavioral data.

The research on cephalization is also vitiated by its reliance on nonstandard, inefficient estimation procedures and on speculative arguments, with the result that there were decades of inconclusive debate about rival laws of cephalization which had little or no objective foundation. The modern period of brain/body allometry dates from the work of von Bonin (1937) and Count (1947), who were the first to use least squares regression to estimate allometric coefficients.

The preoccupation over a period of a half-century with this *naturphilosophisch* approach to the mind-body problem had the consequence that the major development of allometric theory and application took place in other fields of biology. This development owes much to the work of G. Teissier and of Julian Huxley and his school (Huxley, 1932).

Despite the tendency in the past to draw invalid inferences from the data of brain/body allometry, this remains one of the important relationships of neurobiology. Therefore, a recent paper (Holloway, 1966), which is in effect a polemic against the use of brain weight or volume for any kind of inference about the phylogeny of brain/behavior relationships, goes beyond the limits of valid and necessary criticism and becomes a classic instance of throwing out the baby with the bath water. The multivariate analyses described below reveal that there are several independent factors of brain structure at the level of major brain regions but that the general size factor is the largest single factor in the brain structure of insectivores and primates. The accuracy with which the conformation and phyletic relations of a brain can be specified is increased when it can be expressed in terms of several independent factors, but they are still numerical form factors and are a logical continuation of a process that began when only one factor was measurable. The thesis that human behavior is emergent, arising from de novo changes in the nervous systems of man's immediate hominoid ancestors, and not referable to mammalian or primate allometric factors of brain size and conformation (Holloway, 1964), has some interest, but it is methodologically unsound because it does not generate falsifiable hypotheses. It would therefore be premature to abandon the antithetical working hypothesis that there is a discoverable quantitative allometry of the relation of behavior of brain structure, just as there is for every other domain of form/function relationship that has been investigated in mammals. This view has experimental support and is good scientific method because it gives rise to testable hypotheses. It is also good research strategy, for it starts with the evident and accessible relationships and proceeds by the most economical path to the validation of progressively more fine-grained and complex hypotheses about the relation of form and function.

Materials

The materials studied were volumetric measurements on sizes of 12 brain regions in 63 species of anthropoids, prosimians, and insectivores (see Chap. 10). The measurements were done by Drs. H. Stephan and O. Andy and were made available to the author by Dr. Stephan. Table 1 lists the 12 brain regions measured, and Table 2 lists the species studied. Telencephalon, variate 5, is not an independent measurement, for it is equal to the sum of the measurements on the 7 telencephalic subregions, variates 6 through 12.

Because of this dependence, variate 5 is not used in some of the procedures employed here. Two additional measurements, brain weight (variate 13) and body weight (variate 14), were complied by the author, using the values published previously by Bauchot and Stephan (1964, 1966) and Stephan and Bauchot (1965). An additional 16 variates are listed in Table 3, which were constructed (except variate 15) as functions of the first 4. These are described below.

Methods—Computational

The various statistical methods used are described in the sections dealing with them. The treatment of methods is for the most part brief and discursive because there are good, accessible reference works for all the procedures described.

Almost all the procedures to be described entail large amounts of computation, but because they are widely used, they have been repeatedly programmed for electronic computers. A number of these programs are available in packaged form, which means that the program is written for a certain class of computers in a language (such as *FORTRAN*) which these machines can compile, and the program will usually compile and run on any machine of the group without the need for major modifications.

The major multivariate computations used here (eigenvalues and eigenvectors, factor analysis and rotation) are all carried out by a single package program, Program BMDO3M, which is one of a set of programs written at the Health Sciences Computing Facility, University of California, Los Angeles, and distributed by the

TABLE 1

List of variates used in the analyses described here, and their code numbers. Variates 1 to 12 are the set of regional brain volume measurements provided by Stephan (Chap. 10). Variates 13 and 14 are brain and body weights compiled by the author. Variate 15 is a phyletic variate, constructed by putting the various families into rank order, as listed in Table 2. Variate 16 is the total brain volume, found by summing variates 1 through 5. Variates 16 through 28 are relative volumes of the various brain regions. Variates 29, 30, and 31 are three indices of brain/body weight relationship, giving the ratios of brain weight to: body weight (29); body weight to two-thirds power (30); body weight to the one-third power (31).

No.		Name
1		Medulla oblongata
2		Cerebellum
3		Mesencephalon
4		Diencephalon
5		Telencephalon
6		Bulb. olf. + bulb. acc.
7		Paleocortex + amygdala
8		Septum
9		Striatum
10		Schizocortex
11		Hippocampus
12		Neocortex
13		Brain weight
14		Body weight
15		Phyletic Variate
16	Σ (1 to 5)	Sum of variates 1 to 5; total brain volume
17	(1)/(16)	(medulla)/(total brain)
18	(2)/(16)	(cerebellum)/(total brain)
19	(3)/(16)	(mesencephalon)/(total brain)
20	(4)/(16)	(diencephalon)/(total brain)
21	(5)/(16)	(telencephalon)/(total brain)
22	(6)/(5)	(bulb olf. + acc.)/(telencephalon)
23	(7)/(5)	(paleocortex + amygdala)/(telencephalon)
24	(8)/(5)	(septum)/(telencephalon)
25	(9)/(5)	(striatum)/(telencephalon)
26	(10)/(5)	(schizocortex)/(telencephalon)
27	(11)/(5)	(hippocampus)/(telencephalon)
28	(12)/(5)	(neocortex)/(telencephalon)
29	(13)/(14)	(brain weight)/(body weight)
30	$(13)/(14)^{0.667}$	(brain weight)/(body weight)$^{0.667}$
31	$(13)/(14)^{0.333}$	(brain weight)/(body weight)$^{0.333}$

Facility. A manual describing the programs is available (Dixon, 1968). The programs are written in FORTRAN and are more or less readily adaptable to many large or medium-sized modern computers. All the computations described here were performed on an IBM 360/50-75 in the Applied Mathematics Division of Argonne National Laboratory. The modifications required to adapt BMDO3M to Argonne's data processing routine and to carry out some steps not included in the original package are described in an internal document, which is on file in Argonne's computational library (1969).

TABLE 2

List of species used in the multivariate analysis of the phylogeny of brain structure in insectivores and primates. There are 63 species, in each of which 12 brain volumes, brain weight, and body weight were measured. The classification follows Simpson (1945), except for the assignment of the Tupaiidae to the Insectivora. Species names are as given by Stephan. The phyletic variates (variate 15), given on the right, are a ranking of the 63 species in the order of the presumptive advancement of their brain development. The ranking was based on views expressed in the literature, but the author accepts full responsibility for it! The phyletic variate was introduced to see how it related to the actual factors of brain structure.

Species Name and Classification	Phyletic Variate	Species Name and Classification	Phyletic Variate
ORDER INSECTIVORA		I9 Subfamily Tupaiinae	
I1 Family Solenodontidae		*Tupaia glis*	3
Solenodon paradoxus	2	*Urogale everetti*	3
I2a Subfamily Tenrecinae		ORDER PRIMATES	
Echinops telfairi	1	SUBORDER PROSIMII	
Hemicentetes semispinosus	1	INFRAORDER LEMURIFORMES	
Setifer setosus	1	P1 Subfamily Cheirogaleinae	
Tenrec ecaudatus	1	*Microcebus murinus*	4
I2b Subfamily Oryzoryctinae		*Cheirogaleus medius*	4
Nesogale talazaci	2	*Cheirogaleus major*	4
Limnogale mergulus	2	P2 Subfamily Lemurinae	
I3 Family Potamogalidae		*Lepilemur ruficaudatus*	4
Potamogale velox	2	*Hapalemur simus*	4
		Lemur fulvus	4
I4 Family Chrysochloridae		*Lemur variegatus*	4
Chlorotalpa stuhlmanni	2	P3 Family Indridae	
I5 Subfamily Erinaceinae		*Avahi laniger*	4
Erinaceus europaeus	1	*Propithecus verrauxi*	4
Aethechinus sp.	1	*Indri indri*	4
I6 Family Macroscelididae		P4 Family Daubentoniidae	
Elephantulus fuscipes	2	*Daubentonia madagascarensis*	4
Rhynchocyon stuhlmanni	2	INFRAORDER LORISIFORMES	
I7a Subfamily Soricinae		P5 Subfamily Lorisinae	
Sorex minutus	1	*Loris gracilis*	5
Sorex araneus	1	*Perodicticus potto*	5
Neomys fodiens	1	*Nycticebus coucang*	5
I7b Subfamily Crocidurinae		P6 Subfamily Galaginae	
Crocidura russula	1	*Galago demidovii*	5
Crocidura occidentalis	1	*Galago senegalensis*	5
Suncus murinus	1	*Galago crassicaudatus*	5
I8 Family Talpidae		INFRAORDER TARSIIFORMES	
Talpa europaea	2	T1 Family Tarsiidae	
Galemys pyrenaicus	2		
Desmana moschata	2	*Tarsius syrichta*	6

TABLE 2—Continued

Species Name and Classification	Phyletic Variate	Species Name and Classification	Phyletic Variate
SUBORDER ANTHROPOIDAE		A6 Subfamily Cebinae	
A1 Family Callithricidae		*Cebus speciosa*	7
Callithrix jacchus	7	*Cebus albifrons*	7
Leontocebus oedipus	7	*Saimiri sciurea*	7
Tamarin tamarin	7	A7 Family Cercopithecidae	
A2 Subfamily Aotinae		*Colobus badius*	8
Aotes trivirgatus	7	*Macaca mulatta*	8
Callicebus moloch	7	*Cercopithecus ascanius*	8
A3 Subfamily Pitheciinae		*Cercopithecus mitis*	8
Pithecia monacha	7	*Cercopithecus talapoin*	8
		Cercocebus albigena	8
A4 Subfamily Alouattinae		A8 Subfamily Ponginae	
Alouatta seniculus	7	*Pan troglodytes*	9
A5 Subfamily Atelinae		*Gorilla gorilla*	9
Ateles ater	7	A9 Family Hominidae	
Lagothrix lagothricha	7	*Homo sapiens*	9

TABLE 3

Logarithmic and geometric means and standard deviations of 15 brain and body dimensions, measured on 63 primate and insectivore species. Variates 1 to 12 are volumes, expressed in cubic millimeters (mm³), variate 13 is weight in milligrams (mg) and variate 14 is weight in grams (g). Variate 16 is the sum of the volume in variates 1 through 5. Logarithms are to base 10.

Variate Number	Variate Name	Mean LOGA-RITHMIC	Mean GEO-METRIC	Standard Deviation LOGA-RITHMIC	Standard Deviation GEO-METRIC
1	Medulla oblongata	2.628	425.	0.597	3.95
2	Cerebellum	2.972	938.	0.866	7.35
3	Mesencephalon	2.423	265.	0.652	4.49
4	Diencephalon	2.729	536.	0.813	6.50
5	Telencephalon	3.701	5020.	0.919	8.30
6	Bulb. olf. + bulb. acc.	1.909	81.	0.426	2.67
7	Paleocortex + amygdala	2.542	348.	0.527	3.36
8	Septum	1.759	574.	0.609	4.06
9	Corpus striatum	2.548	353.	0.849	7.06
10	Schizocortex	2.131	135.	0.664	4.61
11	Hippocampus	2.500	316.	0.608	4.06
12	Neocortex	3.436	2729.	1.126	13.37
13	Brain weight	3.895	7850.	0.870	7.41
14	Body weight	2.738	547.	0.916	8.24
16	Total brain volume	3.870	7413.	0.874	7.48

It will usually be found that a packaged program can be made to run with a smaller investment of time and money than is required to write the equivalent program from scratch, but operational considerations at a particular computation facility, or the requirement for extensive modifications, may dictate that the program be written anew. The desideratum is for every neuroanatomical laboratory interested in numerical processing to process the computer programs best suited to its own needs, but this may require a long period of research and development. The packaged program approach is one way of getting started in multivariate analysis while this development proceeds.

In this paper it is necessary to introduce a number of technical terms, frequently with no more definition than is given by the context in which they appear. Such terms are given in italics on first appearance.

Bivariate Allometry: Power Functions and Logarithms

One of the basic statements of the allometric relationship is the power function equation,

$$y = k\,x^a \tag{1}$$

where y and x are two body or organ dimensions, and k and a are constants. The power coefficient, a, is usually on the order of unity, i.e., greater than 0.1 and less than 10.

When $a = 1$, the formula reduces to $y = k\,x$. This is the special case of proportional, or *isometric*, relationship. It is not correct to call this a *linear* relationship, for the general linear relation has an additive constant,

$$y = k\,x + a \tag{2}$$

Allometry based on the power function is restricted to sets of variates whose *magnitudes* are greater than zero and in finite ratio to each other. These conditions define a certain scale of measurement known as a *ratio scale* (Stevens, 1951, 1959). Variates that conform to a ratio scale have an absolute zero, so that absolute temperature, length, density, and mass are measured on ratio scales. Equation (1) always holds on a ratio scale, whereas Equation (2) can only hold as an approximation, within circumscribed ranges of the variates.

If the relation between two variates satisfies Equation (1), it is equally valid to state the relationship in terms of the logarithms of the variates as

$$\log y = \log k + a \log x \tag{3}$$

or, if we set $\log y = Y$, $\log x = X$, $\log k = K$,

$$Y = a\,X + K \tag{4}$$

The equivalence between Equations (1) and (3) is fundamental, and there is no sense in which one of these statements is subordinate to the other. However, there are important practical differences between them, for Equations (3) and (4) open the way to the analysis of allometric relationships in terms of the highly developed and powerful mathematics and statistics of linear relationships. Because of this power and convenience, virtually all analysis of allometric relationships is carried out on the logarithmically transformed data.

Despite this consensus, there is a school of thought which asserts that the power function relation is the true one, and that the logarithmic transformation yields invalid results (Sholl, 1947-1948; Zar, 1968). This view must be rejected on two grounds. First, there is no theory which proves that the power function relation is prior or fundamental and the logarithmic relation secondary. In fact, there are theoretical grounds for considering the logarithmic form of the relation to be fundamental, since it can be plausibly related to the concept of the chemical potential or to the formally similar concepts of information theory. The second basis for rejection follows from statistical theory. The interindividual variation in the sizes of structures usually has roughly constant coefficient of variation, independent of the absolute magnitudes. A constant percent variation of the original variate is converted by the logarithmic transformation into a constant dispersion on the logarithmic scale. This means that all the observations have approximately equal statistical weight, which allows the use of the simplest models for estimation of parameters. If this is not taken into account in fitting the power function equation, the estimation is biased. If it is taken into account, the computational difficulty is increased still more.

It must also be pointed out that the multivariate procedures of principal components and factor analysis introduced below are based entirely on linear algebraic relations. These methods are applicable to the logarithmically transformed data, but there is no feasible procedure for carrying out multivariate analysis in terms of the nonlinear power function relationships between the untransformed variables.

Estimation of Bivariate Allometric Coefficients

The discussion noted above established that the statistical estimation problem for interspecies allometry may be reduced to the estimation of the coefficients of linear relationship that subsist among sets of measurements after these have been converted to logarithms. Three procedures for estimating the slope of the linear relationship will be considered: *least squares regression, principal axis, and reduced major axis*.

Least squares regression is so widely used in biology that many biologists are unaware that other bases of estimation exist, or that the assumptions underlying the regression relationship are not appropriate for allometric analysis. The regression model postulates an asymmetric relation between a pair of variates such that one, which we may call Y, is the *dependent* variate, and the other, X, is the *independent* variate. The regression line is fitted on the assumptions that Y is functionally dependent on X and that the scatter in the relation between observed values of Y and X is due to random extrinsic errors that affect only the Y variate. Hence the fitting procedure consists of finding the coefficients of a line such that the sum of the squared vertical deviations of the individual observed Y values from the values predicted by the regression line are minimized. If the same procedure is carried out with X as the dependent variable and Y the independent variable, a different regression line is determined. However, if the assumptions are justified for the regression of Y on X, they cannot be justified for the regression of X on Y, so rigorous application of the reasoning of regression theory forbids the computation of both regressions. Where there is asymmetry between the variates, however, it is usually possible to determine which is the right regression. An exemplary application for the regression model is that of growth as a function of time.

In the case of the relative growth, or relative size, of two organic dimensions, there is no fundamental asymmetry of the two variates. Neither of them is the cause of the other, for the interrelations among organismic dimensions are typically reflexive or closed-loop. There is no intent to use one to predict the other. The intent is rather to say something about a pattern of mutual relationship. Finally, both are internal variates, subject to the same kinds of random disturbances and to the same kinds of measurement errors. Neither of the variates is an external variate, such as clock time, that is measured with much greater precision than the other.

An alternative approach to the estimation of linear relationship is to fit a line subject to the criterion that the squared *perpendicular* distances from the data points to the fitted line are minimized. The line satisfying this condition is known as the *principal axis* of the bivariate distribution, and the estimation procedure is therefore called the principal axis method. The most thorough discussion of the statistical theory of the principal axis is Kermack and Haldane (1950). Jolicoeur (1965) discusses the estimation of confidence intervals for the principal axis slope.

The principal axis procedure operates symmetrically on the two variates, so there is a single principal axis for each pair of variates. The assumptions of the principal axis model are, therefore, appropriate for the analysis of relative size between pairs of variates. This reasoning about relations between pairs of variates continues to hold for the simultaneous relations among numbers of variates, so that the bivariate principal axis procedure has a natural generalization to multivariate principal axis analysis.

The equation for the principal axis slope of a bivariate distribution is

$$\tan 2\theta = \frac{2C_{12}}{C_{11} - C_{22}} \tag{5}$$

where θ is the angle the principal axis makes with axis 1, C_{12} is the covariance between variates 1 and 2, and C_{11} and C_{22} are the variances of variates 1 and 2 respectively. The slope of θ can then be found from the trigonometric half-angle relation

$$\tan \theta = \frac{1 - \cos 2\theta}{\sin 2\theta} \tag{6}$$

The third measure of linear relationship to be considered, the *reduced major axis*, was introduced independently by Teissier and by Haldane (citations given by Kermack and Haldane, 1950). This has the simple form

$$\tan \theta = \left(\frac{C_{22}}{C_{11}}\right)^{1/2} = \frac{\sigma_2}{\sigma_1} \tag{7}$$

where σ is the standard deviation of the variate.

The reduced major axis has a close relationship to the regression slopes. If these are designated b_{12} and b_{21},

$$\tan \theta' = \left(\tan \theta_{21} \cdot \tan \theta_{12} \right)^{1/2} = \frac{b_{21}}{b_{12}} = \frac{\sigma_2}{\sigma_1} \qquad (8)$$

Kermack and Haldane (1950) showed that the reduced major axis has the same sampling distribution as the regression coefficient.

Although the reduced major axis slope is usually in close quantitative correspondence to the principal axis slope for any pair of variates, there is a fundamental difference of the reduced major axis from the regression and the principal axis when multivariate analysis is considered. If there is a set of n variates, then there are $n(n-1)/2$ *linearly independent* regression coefficients or principal axis slopes, but only $n-1$ of the reduced major axis slopes are independent because there are only that number of independent ratios of n standard deviations. The reduced major axis is useful as a quick estimate of the allometric slope when the correlation of the two variates is known to be high.

A comparison of the three estimates of linear relationship is given in Table 4. This compares the slope estimates for four pairings of four variates. The variates examined are telencephalon *(5)*, bulbus olfactorius plus bulbus accessorius *(6)*, paleocortex plus amygdala *(7)*, and neocortex *(12)*. The pairings of these four variates yield correlation coefficients ranging from a low of 0.275 for the pair *6,12* to a high of 0.992 for the pair *5,12*.

TABLE 4

Comparison of the regression, principal axis, and reduced major axis measures of linear relation. Four pairs of variates are compared, chosen to show how the estimates are affected by the degree of correlation between the variates. The variates chosen are: telencephalon (5), bulbus olfactorius + bulbus accessorius (6), paleocortex + amygdala (7), and neocortex (12). The headings of the columns pair the variates with the lower number preceding the higher. The slope coefficients in the body of the table are correspondingly always given for the angle measured from the second variate of the pair as abscissa. Since $\tan(90° - a) = (\tan a)^{-1}$, the slope coefficient estimated with the first variate as abscissa (a_{ji}) is given as the reciprocal, $(a_{ji})^{-1}$, which can be compared with a_{ij}. Note that only in the regression slopes is there any difference between a_{ij} and $(a_{ji})^{-1}$.

| | Variate Pairs | | | |
	6,7	6,12	7,12	5,12
Correlation	0.576	0.275	0.894	0.992
Regression, a''_{ij}	0.466	0.104	0.419	0.810
Regression, $(a''_{ji})^{-1}$	1.403	1.376	0.524	0.824
Principal axis, a_{ij}	0.694	0.120	0.435	0.816
Principal axis, $(a_{ji})^{-1}$	0.694	0.120	0.435	0.816
Reduced major axis, a'_{ij}	0.808	0.378	0.468	0.817
Reduced major axis, $(a'_{ij})^{-1}$	0.808	0.379	0.468	0.817

The symbols for slope coefficients always follow the convention that the second index, e.g., the 2 in b_{12}, is the abscissa from which the angle is measured. Hence, if a principle axis coefficient a_{12} is the slope of angle θ, then a_{21} is the slope of angle $90° - \theta$. The relation of the tangents of θ and $90° - \theta$ is

$$\tan(90° - \theta) = (\tan \theta)^{-1}$$

In the case of the principal axis and the reduced major axis, $a_{ij} = (a_{ji})^{-1}$, as is seen in Table 4. In the case of the regression coefficient, however, $a_{ij} \neq (a_{ji})^{-1}$, and the disparity between the two estimates is the larger as the correlation between the two variates decreases. The reduced major axis is the geometric mean of the two regression slope estimates (Equation 8).

Table 5 gives the complete set of principal axis slopes for the first 14 variates in Table 1. In this table, the columns correspond to the first index and the rows to the second, so that a_{ij} is found in the ith column and j^{th} row. For the reasons given above, these principal axis slopes are the best estimates of the allometric coefficients that can be obtained. They will on the whole be higher than estimates obtained by use of the regression formula.

The species sample being examined here extends over two orders, and the more primitive order, the insectivores, has almost no overlap in body or brain size with even the least advanced primates. All the allometric relationships in this series therefore reflect a considerable degree of confounding between brain size and evolutionary advancement. Moreover, when one examines the bivariate plots of brain variates with one another or with body weight, as in Figure 3, or in the series of plots presented by Stephan and Andy (1964) and Stephan (1967a) for subgroups of the group of species discussed here, one observes a considerable degree of independent variation. This may also be seen in the wide range of correlation coefficients in Table 9.

The slopes of the different variate pairs obviously do not have the same significance over this wide range of correlations. In the case of the visceral organs, such as the liver or heart (Brody, 1945), there is little scatter in the bivariate plots, and the slopes can properly be interpreted as indicative of the dimensional, allometric relationships between the variates because to the extent of 99 percent or more, the measurements are functionally related. Such is not the case for the brain. The slope coefficients are no longer simple expressions of the dimensional relations between the variates, for they depend on the particular sample of species drawn, a circumstance that contradicts the basic conception of allometry. In other words, when we are concerned with a structure such as the brain, which has several independent dimensions of relative and absolute size (as will be shown in more detail below), the fitting of a single relationship, such as the allometric coefficient, is a case of treating a heterogeneous assemblage as if it were homogeneous.

The only possible escape from this impasse of uncertainty is to go beyond the pairwise measurement of allometric coefficients and seek to establish a multivariate mode of analysis more in keeping with what we know about the multiple independent structural units in the brain. The beginning of this approach is given in the following section.

TABLE 5

Bivariate principal axis slopes for 14 brain and body dimensions measured on 63 insectivore and primate species. To find the slope coefficient a_{ij}, giving the dependence of the ith on the jth variates, enter at the ith column and go down to the jth row. For example, the slope of mesencephalon in dependence on cerebellum, a_{32}, is 0.751, and of cerebellum on mesencephalon, a_{32}, is 1.331. Note also that $a_{ij} = a_{ji}^{-1}$, so that $1.331 = 1/0.751$.

	1	2	3	4	5	6	7	8	9	10	11	12	13	14
Medulla oblongata	1	—	1.459	1.095	1.372	1.558	0.490	0.878	1.020	1.437	1.115	1.019	1.938	1.469	1.557
Cerebellum	2	0.685	—	0.751	0.940	1.063	0.241	0.593	0.701	0.982	0.764	0.699	1.306	1.005	1.061
Mesencephalon	3	0.914	1.331	—	1.249	1.418	0.398	0.798	0.932	1.309	1.018	0.931	1.749	1.339	1.432
Diencephalon	4	0.729	1.064	0.800	—	1.131	0.249	0.630	0.744	1.045	0.813	0.743	1.388	1.070	1.134
Telencephalon	5	0.642	0.941	0.705	0.884	—	0.189	0.554	0.657	0.924	0.714	0.654	1.226	0.946	0.996
Bulb. olf. + bulb. acc.	6	2.039	4.156	2.515	4.018	5.300	—	1.440	2.017	4.465	2.274	2.031	8.350	4.656	3.624
Paleocortex + Amygdala	7	1.139	1.687	1.253	1.588	1.804	0.694	—	1.160	1.662	1.275	1.162	2.299	1.698	1.789
Septum	8	0.980	1.428	1.073	1.343	1.523	0.496	0.862	—	1.406	1.092	0.999	1.892	1.437	1.525
Corpus striatum	9	0.696	1.019	0.764	0.957	1.082	0.224	0.602	0.711	—	0.776	0.710	1.328	1.024	1.083
Schizocortex	10	0.897	1.310	0.982	1.230	1.400	0.440	0.784	0.915	1.289	—	0.915	1.734	1.320	1.401
Hippocampus	11	0.981	1.431	1.074	1.345	1.529	0.492	0.860	1.001	1.409	1.093	—	1.897	1.442	1.535
Neocortex	12	0.516	0.766	0.572	0.721	0.816	0.120	0.435	0.528	0.753	0.577	0.527	—	0.771	0.797
Brain weight	13	0.681	0.995	0.747	0.935	1.057	0.214	0.589	0.696	0.977	0.758	0.693	1.297	—	1.056
Body weight	14	0.642	0.942	0.699	0.881	1.004	0.276	0.559	0.656	0.923	0.714	0.651	1.254	0.947	—

Multivariate Allometry: The Multivariate Principal Axis

The first step in the multivariate analysis is the computation of the *covariance matrix*, (Table 6),

$$\text{Cov}(X_i, X_j) = \frac{1}{m-1} \sum_{k=1}^{m} (X_{ik} - M_i)\ (X_{jk} - M_j) \tag{9}$$

where X_{ik}, X_{jk} are measurements of variables i and j respectively on species k, M_i and M_j are the mean values of the ith and j^{th} variates. This matrix is square and symmetric. The off-diagonal covariances, $i \neq j$, are measures of the degree of association between the ith and j^{th} variates, while the diagonal terms are the variances of the variates. The procedure of principal component analysis is to find a transformation of the n given variates into a new set of n variates in terms of which the covariance matrix will be *diagonalized*, i.e., will have all its off-diagonal entries equal to zero. The significance of such a diagonal matrix is that each transformed variate is independent of, or *orthogonal* to, every other. The diagonal entries of the transformed matrix are its *eigenvalues* and are the variances of this set of orthogonal variates.

The second important property of the diagonalized principal component matrix is that the first transformed variate, or *eigenvector*, passes through the longest axis of the n-dimensional cluster of points, so that its eigenvalue (variance) is maximized. The second eigenvector is then the longest axis passing through the cluster of points in the $n-1$ dimensional plane orthogonal to the first eigenvector, the third is the longest axis through the $n-2$ dimensional plane orthogonal to the first two eigenvectors, and so on. The relative sizes of the successive eigenvalues give some information about the number of independent components or factors required to account for the $n \times n$ covariance matrix.

The transformation performed in the diagonalization process is an *orthogonal rotation*, effected by an $n \times n$ matrix, T, of which each column is an eigenvector. If the original covariance matrix is denoted C, and its diagonalized matrix is denoted L, then

$$L = TCT' \tag{10}$$

where T' is the *transpose* of T, formed by the interchange of rows and columns. The n terms making up each column of T are the *direction cosines* defining the coordinates of an eigenvector in terms of the n original axes. Hence, the sum of squares of each column of T is equal to unity. The *inverse* transformation is an orthogonal transformation given by

$$C = T'LT \tag{11}$$

so that a row of T', or column of T, gives the direction cosines of the projection of the corresponding eigenvector on the original axis.

The n direction cosines of the first principal component T_{1i}, $i = 1, \ldots$ n are the cosines of the angles, θ_{1i}, that the axis of the first component makes with the n original variates. Any point on this axis satisfies the relations

$$\frac{X_{11} - M_1}{T_{11}} = \frac{X_{1i} - M_i}{T_{1i}} = \frac{X_{1n} - M_n}{T_{1n}} = \sum_{i=1}^{n} T_{1i}(X_{1i} - M_i) \tag{12}$$

TABLE 6

Matrix of covariances of common logarithms of 14 brain and body dimensions measured on 63 species of insectivores and primates.

	1	2	3	4	5	6	7	8	9	10	11	12	13	14
Medulla oblongata	1	0.356													
Cerebellum	2	0.508	0.749												
Mesencephalon	3	0.383	0.557	0.426											
Diencephalon	4	0.475	0.700	0.526	0.662										
Telencephalon	5	0.534	0.790	0.589	0.744	0.845									
Bulb. olf. + bulb. acc.	6	0.113	0.145	0.115	0.127	0.130	0.181								
Paleocortex + Amygdala	7	0.301	0.430	0.325	0.400	0.454	0.129	0.278							
Septum	8	0.359	0.520	0.390	0.486	0.548	0.124	0.311	0.370						
Corpus striatum	9	0.494	0.730	0.543	0.689	0.778	0.127	0.419	0.506	0.722					
Schizocortex	10	0.387	0.564	0.424	0.528	0.589	0.142	0.332	0.399	0.548	0.441				
Hippocampus	11	0.356	0.518	0.389	0.485	0.543	0.122	0.305	0.365	0.503	0.400	0.370			
Neocortex	12	0.640	0.958	0.715	0.908	1.027	0.132	0.531	0.657	0.948	0.713	0.640	1.267		
Brain weight	13	0.508	0.749	0.559	0.704	0.799	0.130	0.432	0.521	0.736	0.561	0.508	0.969	0.757	
Body weight	14	0.527	0.754	0.564	0.700	0.790	0.196	0.456	0.539	0.728	0.578	0.527	0.937	0.753	0.839

where T_{1i} is the direction cosine for the relation of the first principle axis to the ith variate, X_{1i} is the coordinate of the expected value for the ith logarithmically transformed variate, and M_i is the logarithmic mean of the ith variate. By taking antilogarithms, the relation between any two variates can be converted into the form

$$\left(\frac{x_{1i}}{m_i}\right)^{\frac{1}{T_{1i}}} = \left(\frac{x_{1j}}{m_j}\right)^{\frac{1}{T_{1j}}} \tag{13}$$

where the x_{1i} and m_i are the *antilogarithms* of the logarithmic quantities. This can be rearranged into the standard power function form of the allometry relationship,

$$x_{1i} = m_i \left(\frac{x_{1j}}{m_j}\right)^{\frac{T_{1i}}{T_{1j}}} = m_i \left(\frac{x_{1j}}{m_j}\right)^{\tan\theta} \tag{14}$$

The difference between Equation (14) and the corresponding bivariate allometric relation, Equation (1), must be carefully noted. Equation (1) gives the principal axis allometry coefficient for the *total* relation of variables i and j, whereas Equation (14) gives the allometric relation between variates i and j for only that part of their variance which is *collinear* with the first principal axis.

If the angles, θ_i, of the first axis with the original variates are all equal,

$$\theta_1 = \ldots = \theta_i = \ldots = \theta_n \tag{15}$$

Then $\theta_i = 45°$ for all i and the direction cosines, T_{1i} are equal to $n^{-\frac{1}{2}}$. This is the n-dimensional extension of *isometry*, or simple proportionality between variates, which is represented in the two-dimensional case by $a = 1.0$ in Equation (1). The degree of departure of T_{1i} from $n^{-\frac{1}{2}}$ is then a measure of the allometry of the ith variate *relative to the first principal axis*. This can be made more evident by multiplying each coefficient in T by $n^{\frac{1}{2}}$ so that Equation (12) becomes

$$n^{\frac{1}{2}} \frac{X_{1i} - M_i}{T_{1i}} = \frac{X_{1i} - M_i}{a_{1i}} = \frac{X_{1j} - M_j}{a_{1j}} = \sum_{i=1}^{n} a_{1i} \left(X_{1i} - M_i\right) \tag{16}$$

In this form, positive allometry of the ith variate relative to the first principal axis has $a_{1i} > 1$, and negative allometry has $a_{1i} < 1$, just as in the bivariate case. The coefficient a_{1i} is here the tangent of the angle between the ith variate and the first principal axis. The numbers so obtained have the advantage of being independent of n, the number of variates, and also are comparable with the bivariate principal axis slopes.

The direction cosine of one of the variates can also be used in this way as a reference variate. This could be the body weight, brain weight, or some other appropriate variate. Then, if the reference variate is subscripted h, the others can be normalized to it:

$$\frac{T_{1h}}{T_{1i}}\left(X_{1i} - M_i\right) = \frac{T_{1h}}{T_{1j}}\left(X_{1j} - M_j\right) \tag{17}$$

The coefficient, T_{1h}/T_{1i}, is the tangent of the relation of variate i to variate h, and can be compared with the bivariate principal axis slope, a_{ih}.

The eigenvalues of the 13×13 covariance matrix are given in Table 7. The proportion that each eigenvalue makes of the total variance, and the cumulative proportion, are also given in the table. The variance of the successive components

TABLE 7

Eigenvalues of the 13×13 covariance matrix, variates 1 to 4 and 6 to 14 in Table 6, together with the percent that each eigenvalue makes of the total variance, and the cumulative percent.

Eigenvector number	Eigenvalue	Percent of Total Variance	
		INDIVIDUAL	CUMULATIVE
1	37.4666	95.258	95.258
2	1.2386	3.149	98.408
3	0.2909	0.740	99.147
4	0.1022	0.260	99.407
5	0.0821	0.209	99.616
6	0.0486	0.124	99.739
7	0.0277	0.070	99.809
8	0.0238	0.061	99.870
9	0.0213	0.054	99.924
10	0.0130	0.033	99.957
11	0.0077	0.020	99.977
12	0 0057	0.014	99.992
13	0.0032	0.008	100.000

decreases rapidly at first, and then more slowly. From component 7 through 13 the eigenvalues decrease in approximately linear fashion. This suggests that these are error components, for the number of *degrees of freedom* of the successive components also decreases linearly, and the approximate *equipartitioning* of the variance over these 28 degrees of freedom suggests that this variance arises from randomly distributed error. Although the first 6 of the 13 principal components are nonrandom by this criterion, they need not necessarily be biologically significant, since error components may also be nonrandomly distributed. This equipartitioning criterion is not general. It is presumably applicable in the present case because the 13 variates are homogenous in kind, have about the same magnitude of relative measurement error (coefficient of variation), and are measured independently, i.e., have little or no correlation of errors, and because the eigenvalues are computed for the covariance matrix rather than the correlation matrix, which subjects the variates, and therefore their errors, to changes of scale.

This discussion calls attention to the important point that the efficiency of multivariate analysis can be increased if estimates of the error of measurement are available for each variate. These should include: (1) errors of independent, repeated measurements on the same tissue samples, and (2) the variation, which is not strictly error, between animals of the same species.

The first two eigenvectors are recorded in Table 8, denoted U1, U2. All the individual direction cosines of U1 are positive, and except for the sixth variate (olfactory bulbs) they are of the same magnitude, in the range 0.2 to 0.4. The second eigenvector has both positive and negative signs, as do all subsequent ones.

The tangents of the angle these 13 variates make with the first and second principal axes are estimated by multiplying each direction cosine by $n^{1/2}$, and are recorded in Table 8. By definition the squares of these slopes average to unity. The tangents with the first principal axis range from 0.239 to 1.500. They can be compared

TABLE 8

Direction cosines (eigenvectors) and tangents of the principal components of the 14×14 covariance matrix made by deleting variate 5 from Table 6. A. Direction cosines for the first two principal components. B. Tangents of the angles that the 14 variates make with the first two principal components: obtained from section A by multiplying by $n^{\frac{1}{2}}=3.606$.

Variate number	Direction Cosines		Tangents	
	U_1	U_2	TAN(1)	TAN(2)
1	0.2218	0.0768	0.7997	0.2769
2	0.3246	—0.0470	1.1704	—0.1695
3	0.2432	—0.0004	0.8769	—0.0014
4	0.3048	—0.1065	1.0990	—0.3840
5	—	—	—	—
6	0.0664	0.7653	0.2394	2.7593
7	0.1890	0.2383	0.6814	0.8592
8	0.2273	0.1054	0.8195	0.3800
9	0.3176	—0.1393	1.1451	—0.5023
10	0.2462	0.1288	0.8877	0.4644
11	0.2260	0.0895	0.8149	0.3227
12	0.4161	—0.3978	1.5003	—1.4343
13	0.3259	—0.1247	1.1750	—0.4496
14	0.3312	0.3305	1.1942	1.1916

with the bivariate principal axis slopes in Table 5. The tangents with the first principal axis resemble the bivariate coefficients for variate 4 or 10, which indicates that the first principal axis lies close to these variates.

Anderson (1963) has developed a large-sample test of the hypothesis that the direction cosines are different from $n^{-\frac{1}{2}}$, or from some arbitrary set of specified values.

Jolicoeur (1963a, b, c) proposed that the first principal axis is an appropriate multidimensional generalization of the bivariate allometric relationship. This suggestion opens new possibilities for multivariate allometric analysis, but there are disadvantages to the principal axis which should be considered. The bivariate principal axis is a unique relation, and once it is determined for a pair of variates samples from a particular taxon, it is subject only to minor revision as more extensive or representative data become available. The location of the multivariate principal axis is, on the other hand, a function of the set of variates chosen and of the relative variance of the variates. Hence the multivariate allometric coefficients of a given variate to the principal axis will not be invariant from one battery of data to another.

The development of multivariate neurobiological structure analysis requires that it be possible to establish a system of reference axes that are *invariant* in the way that the directions of physical space are invariant and that can therefore become the means of ordering an ever growing number of measurements of brain structure. The search for these axes will necessarily be difficult, in view of the enormous complexity of the structure being analyzed. A first step toward this determination of the meaningful axes of brain structure is the method of multifactorial analysis, which is discussed in the following section.

Multiple-Factor Analysis

The analysis of multidimensional allometry in the previous section made use of the matrix of covariances of the variates (Equation 9; Table 7). It was shown that the eigenvectors of the covariance matrix are the direction cosines of the principal axes and that the tangents of the variates relative to the first principal axis, given by Equation (16), are equivalent to the bivariate principal axis coefficients. In this section, the analysis of relationships between variates is discussed more extensively, but the allometric, dimensional approach is put aside, and attention turns instead to the use of a dimensionless measure of relationship, the *correlation coefficient*. The correlation coefficient is closely related to the covariance and can be defined as the covariance computed between variates which have been rescaled so that their standard deviations are equal to unity. In Equation (9), if variates X_i and X_j have standard deviations $\sigma(X_i)$ and $\sigma(X_j)$, and if we define $X_{ik}/\sigma(X_i) = W_{ik}$, $X_{jk}/\sigma(X_j) = W_{jk}$, then $\sigma(W_i) = \sigma(W_j) = 1$, and the correlation of X_i and X_j (or covariance of W_i and W_j) is

$$R_{ij} = \text{Cov} \ (X_i, \ X_j) / \sigma(X_i) \sigma(X_j) \tag{18}$$

$$= \text{Cov} \ (W_i, \ W_j) \tag{19}$$

The essential property of the correlation coefficient expressed in Equation (19) is that it gives a measure for the closeness of association between variates that is independent of their magnitudes. This means that a variate with small variance, such as variate 6, is given the same statistical weight in the multivariate analysis of relationship as a variate with large variance, such as variate 12. This is an important property, for there is no necessary relation between the variance of a variate and its importance.

The matrix of intercorrelations of variates 1 to 14 is given in Table 9. Table 10 gives the eigenvalues of the 13×13 correlation matrix made by deleting variate 5 from Table 9, together with the proportion that each eigenvalue makes of the total variance, and also the cumulative proportion. The first eigenvalue extracts 93 percent of the variance and the second about 6 percent. The remaining positive eigenvalues make up 0.9 percent of the total.

The first eigenvalue is large because it represents the general size factor. The 63 species span a 10,000-fold range of brain sizes, from shrew to man, and the first eigenvalue tells us that over this size range 93 percent of the total variance of the correlation matrix can be accounted for by a single vector for the size relationships among the variates. However, much of the information about differential patterns of brain development is contained in the remaining 7 percent of the variance. A considerable part of this remainder is statistically significant, as will be shown in this and later sections.

An eigenvector specifies the *direction* of its axis, and the eigenvalue specifies the *scalar length* of the axis. These can be combined in a single measure. Multiplying each term of the eigenvector by the square root of its eigenvalue yields a vector with the same spatial direction, but with squared length equal to the eigenvalue, i.e., to the variance of the diagonalized variate. These rescaled vectors are the *principal component factors*.

Factorization is carried out on a correlation matrix in which the diagonal entries

TABLE 9

Correlation matrix for the 12 brain volume measurements and 2 supplementary measures. The diagonal entries (in italics) are the squared multiple correlations (SMC), which are entered in the diagonals as estimates of the communalities of the variates when the matrix is factored. There is no SMC estimate for variate 5, because it was excluded from the factor analysis for reasons given in the text.

	1	2	3	4	5	6	7	8	9	10	11	12	13	14
Medulla oblongata	*0.989*													
Cerebellum	0.982	*0.996*												
Mesencephalon	0.984	0.986	*0.995*											
Diencephalon	0.978	0.994	0.990	*0.999*										
Telencephalon	0.973	0.993	0.982	0.994	—									
Bulb. olf. + bulb. acc.	0.444	0.393	0.415	0.368	0.332	*0.870*								
Palecortex + Amygdala	0.957	0.943	0.946	0.934	0.937	0.576	*0.986*							
Septum	0.987	0.988	0.982	0.982	0.979	0.479	0.969	*0.994*						
Corpus striatum	0.973	0.993	0.980	0.996	0.996	0.352	0.934	0.979	*0.998*					
Schizocortex	0.977	0.980	0.977	0.978	0.965	0.500	0.950	0.987	0.970	*0.989*				
Hippocampus	0.980	0.983	0.981	0.980	0.971	0.473	0.951	0.977	0.974	0.990	*0.987*			
Neocortex	0.953	0.984	0.973	0.991	0.992	0.275	0.894	0.959	0.991	0.954	0.957	*0.998*		
Brain weight	0.979	0.996	0.985	0.995	0.999	0.350	0.941	0.984	0.995	0.972	0.977	0.989	*0.998*	
Body weight	0.964	0.951	0.943	0.940	0.938	0.503	0.944	0.966	0.936	0.950	0.952	0.909	0.945	*0.954*

263

TABLE 10

Eigenvalues of the 13×13 correlation matrix for variates 1 to 4 and 6 to 14 from the 14×14 correlation matrix in Table 9, together with the individual and cumulative percentages of the total variance. The correlation matrix as factored has communalities in the diagonal, as given in Table 9. The ninth through thirteenth eigenvalues are negative. This is a consequence of inserting communality estimates in the diagonals of the correlation matrix. The individual and cumulative percentages are based on the eight positive eigenvalues.

Eigenvector Number	Eigenvalue	Percent of Total Variance CUMULATIVE	Percent of Total Variance INDIVIDUAL
1	11.8535	92.901	92.901
2	0.7957	6.236	99.137
3	0.0503	0.394	99.531
4	0.0305	0.239	99.770
5	0.0176	0.138	99.908
6	0.0071	0.056	99.964
7	0.0037	0.029	99.992
8	0.0009	0.007	99.999
9	—0.0004	—	—
10	—0.0021	—	– –
11	—0.0031	—	—
12	—0.0033	—	—
13	—0.0075	—	—

are modified in an important way. This modification comes about because of a fundamental difference of purpose between factor analysis and principal axis analysis. The issue involved is important, but it can be discussed only briefly here. The reader is advised to consult the discussions of the logic of factor analysis by Thurstone (1947) and Harman (1967).

The purpose of the principal axis analysis is to give an exact and unique *canonical representation* of the original data. The purpose of factor analysis, on the other hand, is to account for the interrelations among the n original variates in terms of a number, r, $(r<n)$ of quasi-invariant *structural factors* in the *common factor space*. Hence factor analysis is not a purely statistical procedure in the sense that principal axis analysis is. It is instead part of the heuristic methodology whereby the natural sciences impose a degree of order and invariance, i.e., meaning, on the multiplicity and confusion of the perceived world.

These goals of simplicity and meaning suggested to some that an element of subjective judgment is interposed in the factoring process. Partly for this reason there was opposition to factor analysis in statistical circles during past decades. This has not wholly died out today even though the objection to factor analysis on the ground of subjectivity is now known to be baseless, for the factoring process is carried out by objective matrix operations subject only to content-free structural hypotheses.

There are three distinctive steps in the factorization of a data matrix.

1. *Adjustment of the diagonals* of the correlation matrix. Only a fraction of the

variance of each variate projects into the common factor space. This fraction is known as the *communality* of the variate. The remaining variance is due to *error* and to the *uniqueness*, which is that fraction of the nonerror variance of the variate that has no relation to any other variate in the battery. A correlation matrix with unity in the diagonals has *rank* n, where n is the number of variates. When the communalities are inserted in the diagonals, the rank is reduced to r (r$<$n), where r is the number of common factors. There are several procedures for estimating the communalities, which are discussed by Thurstone (1947) and Harman (1967). The estimate used in the present analysis is the *squared multiple correlation* (SMC). The SMC computation involves taking the *inverse* of the correlation matrix, and this requires the correlation matrix to be *nonsingular*, i.e., to have no columns that are expressible as a linear combination of the remaining ones.

2. *Decision about the number of factors to be extracted.* This cutoff is to some degree arbitrary, but there are criteria that help the analyst to choose the best number of factors for an optimum extraction of relational information.

3. *Rotation of the factor matrix to simple structure.* The beginning of the factoring process is usually the principal component factor solution discussed above, computed for the correlation matrix with communality estimates in the diagonals. Each component minimizes the squared projection of the deviations onto the *normal hyperplane* of the axis in question. This is not a rational criterion for establishing meaningful reference axes, because the location of each principal component is completely determined by the choice of variates making up the battery. Also, because the principal components pass through the *center* of the clusters of data points, all principal components after the first have both positive and negative signs. This makes interpretation difficult, as will be seen below. Rotation to simple structure consists of finding a new set of axes such that the factor loadings are predominantly positive, and the number of near-zero loadings on each factor is as high as possible. The rotation procedure in Program BMDO3M (Dixon, 1968), which was used here, employs an analytical criterion known as *Varimax rotation,* developed by Kaiser (1959).

The Varimax procedure maximizes the variance of the variates over the factors, by seeking a set of coordinates for which the range of loadings is made as large as possible, from near-zero to near-unity. The procedure is iterative, proceeding by successive approximations until a near-stationary condition is achieved, in which the maximum angular shift of the coordinates is less than an assigned value, usually $\frac{1}{2}$ degree.

The basic relation of factor analysis is deducible from Equation (11), and is

$$F'F = R_o \qquad (20)$$

where F is the factor matrix of rank r$<$n, F$'$ is its transpose, and R_o is the correlation matrix with communalities in the diagonals. If F undergoes an orthogonal rotation, Equation (20) holds for the rotated matrix also.

The matrices of the principal components and rotated factors are given in Table 11. Figure 1 gives the factor loadings for the 13 variates, in relation to the principal components (P_1, P_2) and Varimax (I, II) axes. The projections of variate 6 (bulb. olf. plus bulb. acc.) are drawn in to illustrate how the factor loadings relate to the two sets of axes.

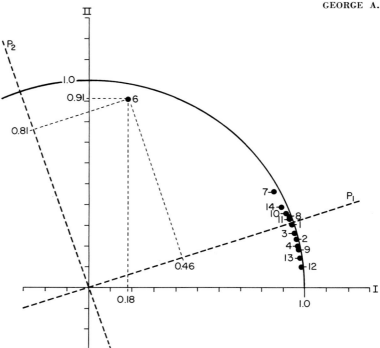

Figure 1. Factor loadings, from Table 11, for the 13 x 13 matrix made by deleting variate 5 from Table 9. The geometrical relations between the 13 points are invariant, so the set of points can be shown in relation to the principal axes (P_1, P_2) and the rotated factor axes (I and II). The numerical projections of variate 6 on the two sets of axes are given for illustration. A section of the unit circle is also drawn in.

When there are only two axes, rotation becomes a trivial process, but the principles involved can therefore be presented more clearly. First, one notes that most of the points, especially the central cluster, lie very close to the unit circle. This means that these two factors together account for a high proportion of the variance of these variates. The amounts range from 83.5 percent for variate 6 to 99.7 percent for variate 12. The first principal axis, P_1, passes through the center of the cluster, as required by the condition that the squared perpendicular deviations from the points to the axis are a minimum. The axis passes between variates 3 and 11, which therefore have the largest projections on this axis and the smallest on P_2. The smallest projections on P_1 are those of olfactory bulbs, variate 6, and neocortex, variate 12. Variates 6 and 12 have the largest projections on P_2, 6 with a high positive, and 12 with a smaller negative projection.

Figure 1 shows how strongly the location of the principal axes depends on the variates analyzed. The loadings on P_1 are, of necessity, a kind of average of all the heterogeneous variates that make up the data matrix. If the factorization had been taken to five factors, the difficulty of assigning any structural or functional significance to the additional factors and the possibilities for equivocal interpretation would be greatly increased.

The two rotated axes found by Varimax rotation could have been located by

TABLE 11

*Principal component and Varimax factors for the 13 variates, 1 to 4
and 5 to 14. Variate 5 omitted because of linear dependence on other
variates.*

Variate	Variate Number	Principal Components Factors		Varimax Factors	
		P_1	P_2	I	II
Medulla oblongata	1	0.990	0.006	0.942	0.304
Cerebellum	2	0.994	0.080	0.969	0.235
Mesencephalon	3	0.990	0.051	0.956	0.262
Diencephalon	4	0.991	0.113	0.977	0.203
Telencephalon	5	—	—	—	—
Bulb. olf. + bulb. acc.	6	0.460	—0.809	0.183	0.912
Paleocortex + amygdala	7	0.965	—0.170	0.864	0.464
Septum	8	0.996	—0.030	0.937	0.340
Corpus striatum	9	0.988	0.129	0.978	0.187
Schizocortex	10	0.990	—0.051	0.924	0.358
Hippocampus	11	0.991	—0.020	0.934	0.330
Neocortex	12	0.971	0.218	0.990	0.097
Brain weight	13	0.991	0.128	0.981	0.188
Body weight	14	0.963	—0.082	0.889	0.380

inspection, for they are an intuitively acceptable resolution of the problem of finding meaningful reference axes. All the loadings are positive, and the two axes have unequivocal interpretations, which agree with the structural categories that are accepted as fundamental factors of brain structure (Stephan and Andy, 1964). Factor I has variate 12, neocortex volume, as its leading variate, and the other variates that are high on I (diencephalon, corpus striatum, cerebellum) are closely associated with neocortex. Variate 6, olfactory bulb plus bulbus accessorius, is the leading variate on factor II, followed by: paleocortex plus amygdala, variate 7; septum, variate 8; schizocortex, variate 10; and hippocampus, variate 11.

It is not desirable to assign precise definitions to these factors on the evidence available, for the data matrix is small, and additional variates can alter the definitions. This will be seen to happen on page 275, where an alternative handling of the data leads to a sharper definition of factor I. With this reservation, it is nevertheless evident that we have to do with a strong factor for neocorticalization and another, almost as strong, related to the paleocortical-olfactory-limbic structures. All of the 11 brain variates are related to one or both of these factors.

Species Factor Scores

After the primary factors are defined, they can be considered to be a new set of variates in terms of which the species can be scored. The species factor scores can then be used, in place of the larger set of scores on the original variates, to characterize the species in the common factor space. The solution to this problem·is given by Thurstone (1947).

The factor scores for each species on the r factors are found as weighted combinations of its measurements on the n variates. If the factor score of the ith species on the pth factor is S_{pi}, it is expressed in terms of the n variates as

$$S_{pi} = \sum_{j=1}^{n} z_{pj} X_{ji} + \epsilon_{pi} \tag{21}$$

where z_{pj} is the regression coefficient giving the statistical weight of variate j the estimation of factor p, and ϵ is the discrepancy of the estimated factor score, S_{pi}, from the true score. The matrix of regression coefficients, z_{pk}, is found from the matrix equation

$$Z_{pk} = R_{pj} R_{jk}^{-1} \tag{22}$$

In this equation, R_{pj} is the matrix of correlations of the variate measurements, X_{ji} with the primary factor scores, S_{pi}, and R_{jk} is the $n \times n$ correlation matrix of the variates with unity in the diagonals.

Equation (22) shows that the inverse of the correlation matrix must be used to obtain the regression coefficients, which means that the correlation matrix must be nonsingular. This condition is satisfied by the 13×13 correlation matrix.

Factor scores were estimated by means of Equation (21) for the two-factor solution given in Table 11 of the 13×13 correlation matrix derived from Table 9. The factor scores are given in Table 12 for the 63 species. The species are grouped by family or subfamily, following the classification of Simpson (1945). The scores on factor II are plotted as ordinate against factor I as abscissa in Figure 2. In this plot, each family group is enclosed by a close-fitting convex curve, and also identified by the alphanumeric code given in Table 12. Each of the orders or suborders is also given a distinctive hatching.

Figure 2 reveals a rather striking pattern in which the three orders or suborders, Insectivora, Prosimii, Anthropoidea, are well separated from each other in elongated clusters with steep positive slopes.

The overall correlation between factors I and II is necessarily zero because of the orthogonality condition, but this orthogonality does not preclude the existence of *nonlinear dependence* between the factors, and that is what we observe here. When the species are identified taxonomically, it turns out that the nonlinear dependence is actually made up of 3 ordinal or subordinal clusters, displaced from one another on the horizontal axis. Within each cluster there is a high degree of correlation (linear dependence) between the two factors. It should be noted that this taxonomic association is not a necessary one. The same nonlinear dependence between factors I and II could theoretically exist purely as a function of the size of the factor scores, without any sorting out by taxonomic groups. A case of this latter kind has in fact been discovered, in the relation of cerebellum weight to cerebrum weight over the whole class Mammalia, but this must be discussed on another occasion.

One conclusion to be drawn from Figure 2 is that there is an allometric association of factor II to factor I within each of the ordinal groups. As neocortex increases, the paleocortex-limbic complex increases also. We cannot estimate allometric coefficients

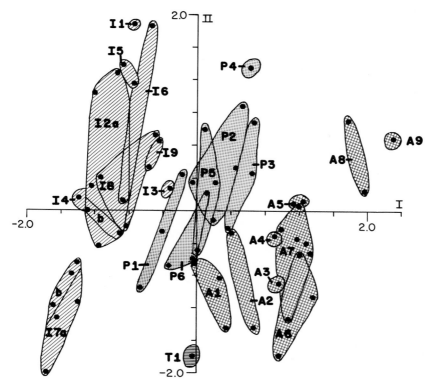

Figure 2. Plot of species factor scores on Varimax factors I and II, for 63 insectivore and primate species, from Table 12. Insectivores (nine groups) are designated by *I* and diagonal hatching; infraorders Lemuriformes and Lorisiformes (six groups) are designated by *P* and stippling; infraorder Tarsiiformes (one species) is designated by *T* and horizontal hatching; suborder Anthropoidea (nine groups) is designated by *A* and cross-hatching. The closed curves enclose all members of the taxa represented; the taxa are of family or subfamily rank. Compare with Figures 3 and 4.

between factors because the factorization of the correlation matrix introduces changes of scale between variates. This problem can be overcome in future versions of the factor analysis program. A way around the difficulty for the time being is to remember that the two factors, the neocortical and the paleocortical, are represented in comparatively pure form by variates 12 (neocortex) and 6 (olfactory bulb plus bulbus accessorius) respectively. When we plot these two variates together in Figure 3, the result is very much like Figure 2, except that the clusters formed by the three ordinal groups have somewhat lower slopes. Within each suborder or order, variate 6 has a highly significant positive correlation with variate 12, and slightly less than unit slope.

Figure 3 shows that the Insectivora, Prosimii, and Anthropoidea form three distinct strata with respect to olfactory lobe-neocortex relationships. The transition from one group to the next may be approximately described as an increase of the ratio of neocortex to olfactory lobe, due primarily to increase in neocortical volume. The fact that this ratio has only two discrete increments suggests that a change in the ratio requires a major reorganization of the brain.

TABLE 12

Species factor scores on Varimax factors I and II, based on variates 1 to 4 and 6 to 14, for 63 species of insectivores and primates. The groupings and the coding are those used in Figures 2, 3, and 4. The classification follows Simpson (1945), except that the Tupaiidae are assigned to the insectivores. Each group containing two or more species is identified by the lowest taxon that includes all its members. Groups containing one species are named at the family level. The species names are as given by Stephan. (Chapter 10)

Classification	Species Factor Scores		Classification	Species Factor Scores	
	I	II		I	II
ORDER INSECTIVORA			ORDER PRIMATES		
I1 Family Solenodontidae			SUBORDER PROSIMII		
Solenodon paradoxus	—0.715	2.184	INFRAORDER LEMURIFORMES		
I2a Subfamily Tenrecinae			P1 Subfamily Cheirogaleinae		
Echinops telfairi	—1.130	—0.424	*Microcebus murinus*	—0.652	—0.945
Hemicentetes semispinosus	—1.242	0.307	*Cheirogaleus medius*	—0.408	—0.244
Setifer setosus	—1.195	1.449	*Cheirogaleus major*	—0.171	0.447
Tenrec ecaudatus	—0.942	1.684	P2 Subfamily Lemurinae		
I2b Subfamily Oryzoryctinae			*Lepilemur ruficaudatus*	—0.064	0.340
Nesogale talazaci	—1.279	0.002	*Hapalemur simus*	0.194	—0.112
Limnogale mergulus	—0.833	—0.256	*Lemur fulvus*	0.463	0.540
I3 Family Potamogalidae			*Lemur variegatus*	0.536	1.291
Potamogale velox	—0.304	0.271	P3 Family Indridae		
I4 Family Chrysochloridae			*Avahi laniger*	0.372	—0.216
Chlorotalpa stuhlmanni	—1.382	0.165	*Propithecus verrauxi*	0.650	0.468
I5 Subfamily Erinaceinae			*Indri indri*	0.655	1.093
Erinaceus europaeus	—0.868	1.777	P4 Family Daubentoniidae		
Aethechinus algirus.	—0.740	1.547	*Daubentonia madagascarensis*	0.617	1.748
I6 Family Macroscelididae			INFRAORDER LORISIFORMES		
Elephantulus fuscipes	—0.869	0.134	P5 Subfamily Lorisinae		
Rhynchocyon stuhlmanni	—0.531	2.273	*Loris gracilis*	0.014	—0.496
I7a Subfamily Soricinae			*Perodicticus potto*	0.091	1.007
Sorex minutus	—1.774	—2.013	*Nycticebus coucang*	0.235	0.361
Sorex araneus	—1.642	—1.316	P6 Subfamily Galaginae		
Neomys fodiens	—1.393	—1.120	*Galago demidovii*	—0.327	—0.674
I7b Subfamily Crocidurinae			*Galago senegalensis*	—0.041	—0.589
Crocidura russula	—1.691	—1.171	*Galago crassicaudatus*	0.110	0.207
Crocidura occidentalis	—1.410	—0.624	INFRAORDER TARSIIFORMES		
Suncus murinus	—1.471	—0.777	T1 Family Tarsiidae		
I8 Family Talpidae			*Tarsius syrichta*	—0.012	—1.783
Talpa europaea	—1.137	0.408	SUBORDER ANTHROPOIDAE		
Galemys pyrendicus	—0.827	—0.220	A1 Family Callithricidae		
Desmana moschata	—0.481	0.884	*Callithrix jacchus*	—0.035	—0.623
I9 Subfamily Tupaiinae			*Leontocebus oedipus*	0.278	—0.826
Tupaia glis	—0.573	0.546	*Tamarin tamarin*	0.351	—1.459
Urogale everetti	—0.461	0.885			

TABLE 12—Continued

Classification	Species Factor Scores		Classification	Species Factor Scores	
	I	II		I	II
A2 Subfamily Aotinae			A7 Family Cercopithecidae		
Aotes trivirgatus	0.381	—0.248			
Callicebus moloch	0.668	—1.451	*Colobus badius*	1.340	—0.516
			Macaca mulatta	1.292	—0.393
A3 Subfamily Pitheciinae			*Cercopithecus ascanius*	1.174	—0.343
Pithecia monacha	0.983	—0.898	*Cercopithecus mitis*	0.980	0.239
			Cercopithecus talapoin	1.081	—1.338
A4 Subfamily Alouattinae			*Cercocebus albigena*	1.205	—0.080
Alouatta seniculus	0.952	—0.313			
			A8 Subfamily Ponginae		
A5 Subfamily Atelinae					
Ateles ater	1.252	0.126	*Pan troglodytes*	1.969	0.243
Lagothrix lagotricha	1.138	0.089	*Gorilla gorilla*	1.767	1.113
A6 Subfamily Cebinae					
Cebus speciosa	1.224	—0.536	A9 Family Hominidae		
Cebus albifrons	1.368	—1.072			
Saimiri sciurea	0.961	—1.801	*Homo sapiens*	2.300	0.889

Although the three groups can be discriminated almost infallibly in terms of the ratio of variates 6 and 12, or of factors II and I, there are nevertheless real variations of the ratio within the groups. There is a tendency for the clusters formed by families and subfamilies to be elongated on the vertical, olfactory axis, meaning that within family, differentiation takes place more through variation of paleocortical-olfactory volumes than through variation of neocortical volume. Between families, the two

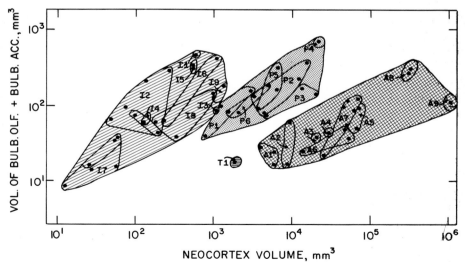

Figure 3. Plot of olfactory bulb plus paleocortex volume, variate 6, against neocortex volume, variate 12, on logarithmic coordinates. The taxonomic groupings and the symbols are as for Figure 2.

variates vary in roughly constant proportion. These relationships are puzzling, and will need much more study before they are properly understood.

    An important consequence of Figures 2 and 3 is that the nature of the factors identified depends on the taxonomic sample drawn. If the order Insectivora alone had been factored, there would still be two factors, because of the broad ellipsoidal shape of the cluster, but because of the orthogonality condition the first factor would be the first principal axis of the cluster, and the second factor would be the second principal axis, orthogonal to the first. A matrix of 16 cortical volume measurements on 21 insectivore species from an earlier report by Stephan (1967b) had been factored previously. The factor scores for this group of species, based on a similar but not identical set of variates, are plotted for the corresponding two factors in Figure 4. It may be seen that the major axis of the insectivore cluster in Figure 2 is now factor I in Figure 4, and the minor axis, considerably expanded, is the new factor II.

    Figures 2, 3, and 4 indicate the value that factorial analysis can have for taxonomy.

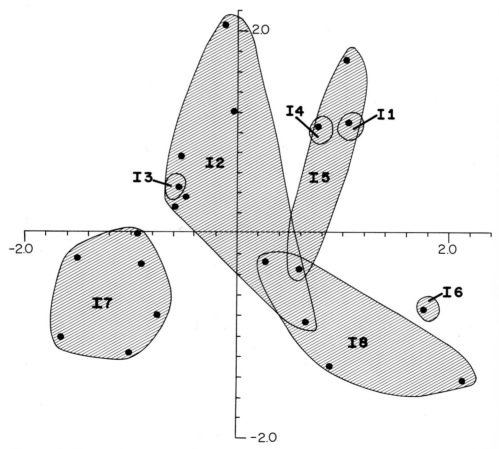

Figure 4. Species factor scores for 21 insectivore species on the factors corresponding to factors I and II in Figure 2. Note that factor I here is the major axis of the insectivore cluster in Figures 2 or 3.

The groupings in these figures were made by prior classification, but it is evident that analysis of the clusters formed by these two factors would establish some significant groupings. The separation at the level of order or suborder is interesting, for it shows that in regard to these factors the Prosimii are as distinct from the Anthropoidea as they are from the Insectivora.

In Figures 2 and 3, *Tarsius* is treated as a distinct suborder, in that it is not brought within the prosimian envelope. This treatment is justified by its isolated position, which is in fact more closely related to the anthropoids than to the prosimians. This aspect of brain structure tends to reject the inclusion of the Tarsioidea in the Prosimii (Simpson, 1945) and to support the view that they should either be made a distinct suborder (Romer, 1968) or be combined with the Anthropoidea to form the Haplorhini (Hill, 1955).

Changes of Variate

Thus far the analysis has dealt with the covariance or correlation matrices for the logarithms of the *absolute* weights and volumes. Due to the large size factor, the intercorrelations are on the whole high (Table 9), and the first eigenvalue is quite large (Tables 7 and 10). It is important to know how much the outcome is affected if the factorial analysis is conducted using combinations, and especially ratios, of the original variates, for neuroanatomical variates are sometimes measured in relative terms, and also theory or experiment may give rise to the hypothesis that a certain behavior is expressible as a function of two or more variates (Stephan and Andy, 1964).

An exploration of this question was undertaken by constructing ratios of the 13 basic variates in Table 1. These functions are given in Table 1 as variates 16 through 31. These fall into three groups.

1. The subregions of the telencephalon (variates 6 to 12) are expressed as ratios to the telencephalon volume (variate 5) to form variates 22 through 28. In the logarithmic transformation, the log of the ratio becomes the difference of logarithms.

2. The five major levels of the brain (variates 1 to 5) are expressed as ratios to brain volume, variate 16, which is the sum of variates 1 to 5. These ratios are variates 17 through 21.

3. Brain weight and body weight are given in three different functional relationships. Brain weight over body weight is variate 29, brain weight over body weight to the two-third power is variate 30, and brain weight over body weight to the one-third power is variate 31. The reason for variates 29 and 30 is that over the class Mammalia (von Bonin, 1937; Sacher, 1959) and over the orders Insectivora and Primates (Sacher, 1966; see also Table 5) brain weight varies as some value between the 0.67 and 1.0 power of body weight. The reason for variate 31 is that in the allometric analysis of the relation of lifespan to brain and body weight (Sacher, 1959) this is found to be the approximate relation of brain weight to body weight for constant lifespan. It is therefore important to know how both these functions relate to the internal structure of the brain.

Variate 13* in Table 13 does not appear elsewhere in this paper. It is the ratio

TABLE 13

Covariance matrix for the transformed variates 16 through 31 of Table 1. The numbering of the variates agrees with that in Table 1.

	17	18	19	20	21	22	23	24	25	26	27	28	13*	14	16
17	0.523														
18	0.039	0.033													
19	0.393	0.029	0.347												
20	0.108	0.013	0.104	—0.054											
21	—0.086	—0.012	—0.065	—0.018	0.016										
22	1.252	0.135	0.993	0.284	—0.208	3.634									
23	0.639	0.038	0.495	0.121	—0.101	1.747	0.923								
24	0.469	0.040	0.363	0.100	—0.078	1.245	0.624	0.465							
25	0.039	0.007	0.030	0.028	—0.005	0.116	0.048	0.038	0.036						
26	0.407	0.056	0.328	0.110	—0.071	1.124	0.525	0.402	0.045	0.413					
27	0.478	0.049	0.383	0.117	—0.080	1.260	0.615	0.462	0.047	0.431	0.509				
28	—0.428	—0.027	—0.304	—0.053	0.071	—1.104	—0.601	—0.404	—0.009	—0.320	—0.392	0.439			
13*	0.008	0.002	0.007	0.002	—0.002	0.020	0.011	0.011	0.001	0.011	0.011	—0.007	0.006		
14	—1.212	—0.011	—1.020	—0.295	0.181	—2.967	—1.591	—1.152	—0.148	—0.943	—1.196	0.958	—0.015	4.447	
16	—1.342	—0.056	—1.070	—0.298	0.208	—3.361	—1.750	—1.275	—0.129	—1.062	—1.299	1.115	—0.022	4.008	4.050

of variate 13, brain weight, as numerator, to variate 16, total brain volume, as denominator. The extremely small covariances of the logarithmic variate in column and row 13* bespeak the high correlation between the reconstructed brain volume and the brain weight. The correlation of variates 13 and 16 is *0.99925*. This indicates that the volume changes arising from fixation introduce very little artifact into the statistical analysis based on these brain volume determinations. Stephan (1966) found a mean volume shrinkage factor of 49.1 percent for the brains of insectivores and primates fixed in Bouin's solution and embedded in paraffin. It is likely that this factor, which varies from species to species (Stephan found factors ranging from 42.7 percent to 54.6 percent) also varies for different brain structures (Welker, 1969). If correction factors are applied, there is no effect of this shrinkage on the measures of regression and correlation unless the shrinkage varies systematically as a function of brain size or taxonomic position. Of the two artifacts, the former need give no concern, for it has no effect on the size of the correlation coefficients for the variates affected. Taxon-dependent shrinkage would give rise to troublesome bias in the numerical analysis, but there is as yet no evidence that this condition exists.

The covariances of the transformed variates, 17 through 31, and of variate 16, are given in Table 13.

The covariances and correlations of the transformed variates need not be recomputed, for they can be expressed in terms of the covariances of the original 14 variates plus variate 16. If we denote the covariance of the logarithmic variates i and j as $Cov(i,j)$, and if k is the index of a normalizing logarithmic variate, then

$$Cov(i\text{-}k, j\text{-}k) = Cov(i,j) - Cov(i,k) - Cov(j,k) + Cov(k,k)$$

For example, the covariance of variates 17 and 18 in Table 13 (i.e., the covariance of relative medulla volume with relative cerebellum volume) is

$$Cov(17,18) = Cov(1,2) - Cov(1,16) - Cov(2,16) + Cov(16,16)$$

$$= 2.69095 - 2.70787 - 3.99376 + 4.04957$$

$$= 0.03889$$

Comparison of Table 13 with Table 6, shows that the change to ratio variates has pronounced effects on the covariance pattern. The eigenvalues are also affected. Table 14 gives the first eight eigenvalues of the correlation matrix derived from the covariance matrix in Table 13, and it may be seen that the first eigenvalue makes up only 77.5 percent of the variance, instead of 92.9 percent for the original variates (Table 10). The succeeding eigenvalues in Table 14 are larger in both absolute and relative value than the corresponding ones in Table 10. This means that the matrix of ratio variates may be expected to have more extractable factors than the matrix of original variates. This is indeed the case, as will be shown below, but first an additional modification of the original matrix will be introduced.

The Augmented Matrix

The factor analytic methods are based on the postulate that the individual measurements on an observed variate may be accounted for as the weighted sum of

TABLE 14

Eigenvalues and their individual and cumulative proportion of the total variance, for the 15×15 matrix of correlations of the transformed variates derived from Table 13. The eigenvalues were computed for the matrix with SMC estimates of the communalities in the diagonals.

Eigenvalue Number	Eigenvalue	Percent of Total Positive Variance	
		INDIVIDUAL	CUMULATIVE
1	11.229	77.510	77.510
2	1.297	8.953	86.463
3	0.999	6.896	93.359
4	0.350	2.416	95.775
5	0.218	1.505	97.280
6	0.174	1.201	98.481
7	0.119	0.821	99.302
8	0.048	0.331	99.633

a small number of independent factors (Thurstone, 1947; Harman, 1967). The procedure for identifying these factors consists of constructing a battery containing a number of related variates, which are presumed to be representable as different weighted combinations of the factors. If the number of variates is larger than the number of factors by a sufficient margin and if the battery is scored for a large enough group of cases, the factor problem can be solved.

In the factor analysis of experimental data, the variates are usually the products of independent acts of measurement. Reasons were given for avoiding the introduction of linear dependence into the data, for this leads to singularity in the correlation matrix, with some awkward consequences for the analysis. This is, however, no more than a technical difficulty, and there is no theoretical objection to the introduction of two or more functions of the same variate into the correlation matrix. In the present context, if we wish to know how the absolute and relative measures of the same brain dimensions are related, we may combine them in a single matrix and factor it in the usual way. This was done by constructing a single correlation matrix containing the entire set of 31 variates in Table 1. This will be called an *augmented matrix*. The augmented correlation matrix is not reproduced here, but its eigenvalues are given in Table 15. The matrix is singular (see legend, Table 15), so the squared multiple correlation (SMC) estimate of the communality was not used, and the diagonals were, instead, set equal to unity.*

The principal axis factors of the first five eigenvectors were rotated to simple structure by the Varimax process, and the factors are tabulated in Table 16. The first two factors are plotted together in Figure 5, and they are readily identifiable as the equivalents to factors I and II of the original correlation matrix (Table 11 and Figure 1). Figure 4 also shows that only the original set of variates has any significant loadings on factor II, the paleocortical factor, while some of the added

* There is a simple way out of the singularity problem, which allows the computation of SMCs and the estimation of species factor scores, but this will be discussed in a subsequent paper.

TABLE 15

The 13 positive eigenvalues of the 31×31 augmented correlation matrix, with their individual and cumulative percent values. The matrix had unity in the diagonals, and the negative eigenvalues after the thirteenth indicate that the matrix has rank 13, in keeping with the fact that only 13 variates are linearly independent and the remaining 18 are functions of these. Note that here, as in Table 14, the eigenvalues decrease more slowly than they do for the original correlation matrix, Table 10.

| Number | Value | Percent of Total Variance | |
		INDIVIDUAL	CUMULATIVE
1	24.146	79.87	79.87
2	3.248	10.74	90.62
3	1.383	4.58	95.19
4	0.550	1.82	97.01
5	0.478	1.58	98.59
6	0.201	0.66	99.26
7	0.106	0.35	99.61
8	0.061	0.20	99.81
9	0.032	0.11	99.91
10	0.013	0.04	99.96
11	0.007	0.02	99.98
12	0.004	0.01	99.99
13	0.001	0.00	99.99

ratio variates become the leading variates on factor I. The leading variate on factor I is variate 28, relative neocortex volume. This indicates that factor I, the tentative factor of neocorticalization, is more closely related to the relative than to the absolute neocortical volume.

The paleocortical factor does not show up at all in the factorization of the 15×15 matrix of ratio variates (this is not reproduced here), and in Figure 5 we see that it is defined exclusively by the absolute value variates, 1 through 14. The probable reason is that in the ratio variates, 22 and 23, formed from variates 6 and 7, the variance of telencephalon is so much larger than the numerator variances that the paleocortical component of the ratio variates is almost completely swamped. This calls our attention to the important conclusion that in the formation of ratio variates either the numerator and denominator variates must have about equal variance, or one of the log variates must be multiplied by a scaling factor to equalize the variances.

The utility of the ratio variates is seen most clearly in factors III, IV, and V. These are important aspects of brain structure, and yet they were not identifiable in the factorization of the absolute value correlation matrix. Factor V has relative diencephalon and striatum volume as its leading variates, with relative schizocortex and mesencephalon volume also showing large loadings. Neocortex is not represented.

Factor IV has one large loading, relative cerebellum volume (18), with relative telencephalon volume (21) second largest, and opposite in sign. Relative schizocortex, striatum, and hippocampus volume (26, 25, and 27) have smaller loadings.

Factor III is almost exclusively concerned with brain/body relationships, with the simple brain/body ratio (variate 29) as the leading variate. The most interesting

TABLE 16

Factor loadings for the five Varimax rotated factors obtained from the 31×31 correlation matrix formed as described in the text and in Table 1. The leading variates on each factor are indicated in bold face. In the right-hand column headed "Sign," the variates that have signs indicated are constructed ratio variates. The minus signs indicate the variates which have predominantly negative correlations with the other variates. In the bifactor plot, Figure 2, these variates have been reflected into the first quadrant by changing the signs of the factor loadings.

Variate Number		Varimax Factors					SIGN
		I	II	III	IV	V	
1	Medulla	0.73	0.58	—0.07	+0.02	+0.30	
2	Cerebellum	0.79	0.52	—0.00	—0.00	+0.32	
3	Mesencephalon	0.77	0.56	—0.00	+0.06	+0.24	
4	Diencephalon	0.82	0.51	—0.01	+0.07	+0.24	
5	Telencephalon	0.80	0.48	0.02	+0.10	+0.06	
6	Bulb. olf.	—0.04	**0.85**	**0.21**	—0.24	—0.06	
7	Paleocortex	0.57	**0.74**	—0.04	+0.10	+0.35	
8	Septum	0.72	**0.61**	—0.05	+0.03	+0.31	
9	Striatum	0.82	0.49	0.02	+0.07	+0.28	
10	Schizocortex	0.74	**0.62**	—0.03	—0.02	+0.22	
11	Hippocampus	0.74	0.60	—0.03	—0.01	+0.25	
12	Neocortex	**0.86**	0.41	0.05	+0.09	+0.27	
13	Brain weight	0.80	0.50	0.01	+0.08	+0.33	
14	Body weight	0.69	0.58	**0.29**	+0.03	+0.33	
15	Phyletic variate	0.91	0.11	0.21	+0.13	+0.14	
16	Total brain volume	0.80	0.50	0.01	+0.08	+0.33	
17	1/16	—0.82	**—0.27**	—0.16	—0.18	—0.37	—
18	2/16	—0.13	0.20	—0.14	**—0.90**	—0.20	—
19	3/16	—0.74	**—0.26**	—0.04	—0.13	**—0.50**	—
20	4/16	—0.29	—0.18	—0.01	—0.12	**—0.94**	—
21	5/16	0.75	—0.16	0.16	**+0.40**	+0.33	
22	6/5	—0.88	—0.05	—0.11	—0.22	—0.39	—
23	7/5	—0.94	—0.12	—0.08	—0.10	—0.27	—
24	8/5	—0.86	—0.20	—0.13	—0.23	—0.35	—
25	9/5	—0.43	—0.21	0.02	**—0.31**	—0.60	
26	10/5	—0.75	—0.09	—0.11	**—0.35**	—0.49	—
27	11/5	—0.79	—0.21	—0.09	**—0.28**	—0.44	—
28	12/5	**0.96**	0.11	0.17	+0.02	—0.03	
29	13/14	0.20	**—0.33**	**0.91**	+0.15	—0.03	
30	13/(14)$^{2/3}$	0.77	0.22	**0.25**	+0.15	+0.26	
31	13/(14)$^{1/3}$	0.82	0.43	0.16	+0.10	+0.32	

relationships of variates 29, 30, and 31 are to be found in their loadings on factors I and II. Figure 2 shows that variate 31, brain weight over body weight to the one-third power, lies very close to variates 5 (telencephalon) and 12 (neocortex) in the I-II plane. This may be quite important, in view of the observation that the brain/body function of variate 31 has a close relationship to longevity in mammals (Sacher, 1959). These interesting, though somewhat enigmatic, results support the view that the brain cannot be studied in isolation. Brain structure must be placed in correct

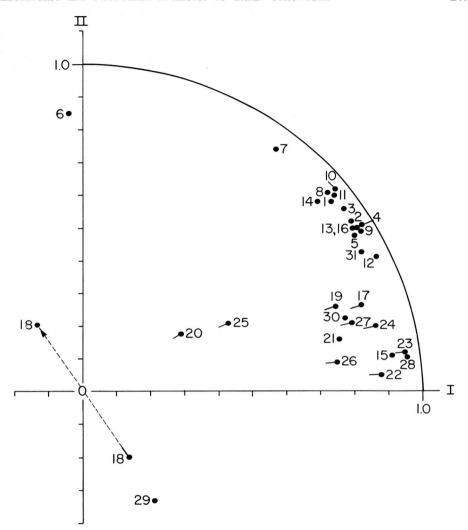

Figure 5. Factors I and II of the augmented factor matrix, Table 13, obtained by Varimax rotation of five factors to simple structure. Variates 17 through 31 are linear combinations of variates 1 to 16, as specified in Table 1. Variates 17 through 20 and 22 through 27 have negative correlation with the other variates, and hence negative loadings on these factors. The positive loadings shown here are obtained by changing the signs of the loadings for these 10 variates (see legend of Table 13). This is equivalent to a reflection through the origin as illustrated by variate 18. The variates with signs changed are designated by the tabs pointing toward the origin. This figure is to be compared with Figure 1. The augmentation of the matrix does not alter the configuration of variates 1 through 14 from the pattern seen in Figure 1, but the improved definition of this factor plane brought about by augmentation has resulted in a shift of the simple structure axes.

relation to body structure as a prelude to the quantitative study of their relationships to physiological and psychological function.

Factors I, II, and V are an important constellation, for all but a few of the 31 variates are represented on one or two of these three factors. This can be seen most clearly in Figure 5, which brings the three factors together in a single diagram, a triangular coordinate plot. If we think of the three axes of a three-dimensional space, and denote them x, y, and z, the plane of the triangular coordinate system has its three apices located at $(1,0,0)$, $(0,1,0)$, and $(0,0,1)$. Points in this plane satisfy the equation

$$x+y+z=1$$

The loadings of all but a few of the variates have most of their variance taken up by factors I, II, and V, and hence the sums of squares of their loadings on these three factors come close to unity. They can be normalized to lie in the surface of the unit sphere by rescaling so that the sums of squares are set equal to unity. These values

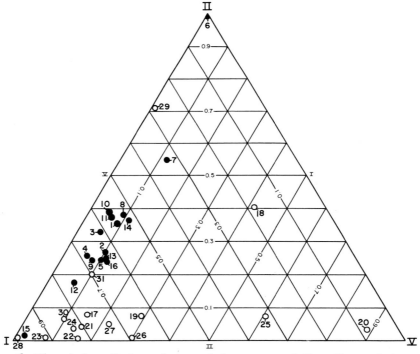

Figure 6. Plot of three Varimax factors of the augmented 31 x 31 correlation matrix. The adjusted factor values are given in Table 14. The plot is on a triangular coordinate grid, which lies in the plane $x+y+z=1$. The points are the squares of the loadings on factors I, II, and V of Table 13, normalized to sum to unity, as described in the text. The filled circles are the 14 original variates, which are logarithms of absolute weights and volumes. The open circles are ratio variates, as defined in Table 1. Variates 18 and 29 have only a small fraction of their variance in this plane, so should be given little weight in this diagram.

are given in Table 17 and are plotted in Figure 6. Variates 18 and 29 should be ignored in this diagram, because their variance on these three factors is small. The remaining 29 variates lie along either the I-II axis or the I-V axis.

In conclusion of this discussion of the Varimax rotated factors, it should be noted that the rotations are carried out without outside guidance, and yet arrive at intuitively acceptable factors. This implies that the human activity of searching for a *primary* set of reference coordinates for the description of a complex system is concordant with the geometrical relationships that subsist among the measurements that can be made on the system. Hence, the *first* stages of discovering these primary coordinate axes can be carried out by seeking a parsimonious geometrical represen-

TABLE 17

Normalized squares of loadings on factors I, II, and V of the augmented factor matrix (Table 13). The right-hand column is the sum of the squares of the loadings on the three factors in Table 13. These values are the divisors used to obtain the normalized squares in the three columns to the left, and the sum of the three values in each row is equal to unity.

Variate Number	Variate Name	Normalized Squares of Factor Loadings			Fraction of Variance in Factors
		I	II	V	I, II, V
1	Medulla	0.555	0.091	0.353	0.965
2	Cerebellum	0.629	0.104	0.268	1.000
3	Mesencephalon	0.611	0.061	0.327	0.977
4	Diencephalon	0.677	0.059	0.263	0.993
5	Telencephalon	0.650	0.115	0.234	0.989
6	Bulb. olf.	0.002	0.004	0.994	0.731
7	Paleocortex	0.329	0.121	0.550	0.986
8	Septum	0.525	0.096	0.379	0.990
9	Striatum	0.675	0.079	0.246	0.991
10	Schizocortex	0.558	0.049	0.393	0.984
11	Hippocampus	0.564	0.065	0.372	0.979
12	Neocortex	0.755	0.072	0.173	0.989
13	Brain weight	0.638	0.112	0.250	0.993
14	Body weight	0.517	0.116	0.367	0.915
15	Phyletic variate	0.963	0.023	0.014	0.862
16	Total brain volume	0.639	0.113	0.248	0.993
17	1/16	0.768	0.152	0.080	0.882
18	2/16	0.184	0.414	0.404	0.099
19	3/16	0.634	0.289	0.078	0.876
20	4/16	0.083	0.886	0.031	0.991
21	5/16	0.810	0.153	0.037	0.704
22	6/5	0.832	0.164	0.003	0.924
23	7/5	0.908	0.078	0.014	0.979
24	8/5	0.817	0.138	0.045	0.905
25	9/5	0.319	0.607	0.075	0.590
26	10/5	0.688	0.302	0.010	0.809
27	11/5	0.729	0.220	0.051	0.863
28	12/5	0.987	0.001	0.012	0.924
29	13/14	0.283	0.007	0.713	0.153
30	$13/(14)^{2/3}$	0.836	0.095	0.069	0.707
31	$13/(14)^{1/3}$	0.696	0.108	0.195	0.962

tation without introducing external considerations of content or meaning. In other words, *there is an order in the measurements themselves which can be brought into correspondence with our human intuition of order.*

Conclusion

The discussion of the augmented matrix and its factorization is the terminus of this first report on the structural or organizational factors that account for the major conformation of primate and insectivore brains. More needs to be said in explanation of the methods, and the results need more detailed presentation and discussion, but this must wait for future occasions.

What has been learned about the factor pattern in Table 16 can be summarized as follows:

1. A neocorticalization factor (I), with relative neocortical volume as its leading variate, and with most other variates represented in greater or lesser degree

2. A paleocortical-rhinencephalic-limbic factor (II), with olfactory bulbs and paleocortex as its leading variates, associated with septum and schizocortex

3. A diencephalon-striatum factor (V), with relative diencephalon and striatum volume as its leading variates, and with important relations to midbrain, hippocampus, and schizocortex

4. A cerebellar factor (IV), on which relative cerebellum volume is the only large loading, and relative telencephalon volume has a smaller loading of opposite sign

5. A factor for brain/body relationships (III)

It is noteworthy that most brain regions participate significantly in two factors. The major exceptions are olfactory bulbs, paleocortex, cerebellum, and neocortex. The lack of evidence for other relations of paleocortex and olfactory bulbs is not conclusive, for reasons given above, but the single-factor relation of neocortex to the remaining 12 variates is interesting. It implies that the neocortex functions as an organizational unit in its relations to the other regions of the brain, despite much good evidence that the neocortex of insectivores and primates contains several independent factors for sensory, motor, and integrative function. It will be interesting to pursue this question, for the resolution of these dissonant findings should contribute to our understanding of brain function at the level of its major systems.

The analysis presented here is not to be regarded as complete or definitive. The species factor scores on three of these five factors remain to be examined, and new questions of taxonomy and phylogeny may then arise.

This paper has been primarily methodological, so there has not been much discussion on the interpretation of these factors. In one sense, such discussion is redundant, for a factor is a perceived fact. The manipulations of factor analysis did not *create* factors. They merely succeeded in *discovering* that certain groups of variates are closely related. This relationship is manifested by a clustering of the coordinates of these variates in the factor space. As was noted above, this clustering is an invariant property of the set of measurements—rotation can move clusters around, but it cannot create or destroy them.

The second sense of factor interpretation consists of relating the newly found grouping to a wider domain of behavioral and anatomical relationships. This cannot be undertaken here, because this process of relating has its own standards, which need to be maintained. In other words, factors established by quantitative, objective procedures must be interpreted, or placed in a larger context, by methods which are themselves quantitative and objective. Some of the ways in which this can be done for the present results are mentioned below.

Without going beyond the present set of anatomical measures, work can begin on the definition and measurement of a battery of ecological, ethological, physiological, and psychological measures which can be put into dimensional relationship with the neuroanatomical species factor scores. The possibility of representing the individual or species scores for a large number of variates in terms of the factor scores on a considerably smaller number of orthogonal factors will make it feasible to carry out brain/behavior correlations on a much wider scale than has been possible heretofore. In view of the global nature of the structural factors defined by the present study, it will be necessary to specify the behavioral categories in equally general terms. The possibility must be faced, however, that the behavioral indices presently available will not have high enough reliability to allow significant relationships to be established. For some time to come, the study of animal behavior will be at a disadvantage relative to our knowledge of structure, chiefly because of conceptual difficulties in defining the higher categories of behavior. There is no reason to doubt that rapid progress can be made in the conceptual analysis of subhuman primate behavior through the instrumentality of factor analysis, for the important contributions of factor analysis to the understanding of human mental abilities are a matter of history and are sufficient warrant for carrying the same general approach into the domain of animal behavior. In fact, the possibilities of structure/function correlation that exist in the comparative domain should make possible a faster and more thorough solution to the problem of animal behavior than can be attained for human behavior and mental abilities.

Another possibility for the immediate future is the linkage of different sets of neuroanatomical measurements made on the same set of species, or on a subset of them. We may cite, in relation to the present data, the extensive measurements by Andy (1966) on septal structures, and by Stephan (1961, 1967b) on cortical systems, in insectivores and primates. There is also the splendid assemblage of measurements by Bauchot (1963) on the thalamic nuclei of insectivores. These measurements were made by a group of collaborating investigators using compatible methods, a virtually identical set of species, and, to a considerable extent, tissue samples taken from the same animals. The full return on this great investment will not be realized until all these measures have been examined for their interrelationships.

The literature of comparative neuroanatomy contains several important data matrices on brain structure in primates, which deserve to be analyzed as a preliminary to any new work undertaken on related structures. The studies of Riley (Tilney and Riley, 1928) on the brain stem of primates are an example.

Measurements of linear brain dimensions are also suitable for multiple factor analysis. Such measurements are taken between reference points on the surface of the brain. The reliability of individual measurements is lower than for volume measurements, but the approach is indispensable for a number of important questions, including the analysis of cortical sulci and the interpretation of brain structure of extinct species from endocranial casts. An important series of linear dimensions of rodent brains has been compiled by Pilleri (1959, 1960a, 1960b).

On the methodological side, several modifications of factoring techniques and theory need to be introduced to adapt the method to the requirements of neuro-anatomical research. Factor analysis was developed originally in application to psycho-metrics, and hence grew up as a method for handling nonmetrical data, such as psycho-logical test scores and rating scales. Neuroanatomical data, on the other hand, are usually metrical quantities which satisfy the axioms of ratio, or magnitude scales. Hence, a way must be found to unite the analysis of relation based on the dimension-less correlation coefficient with an analysis of dimensional relations based on covari-ances and the allometric coefficients. The individual, or species, factor scores as computed above were based on rescaled scores with unit variance, the W_{ij} of Equation (19), and should instead be expressed in terms of the original logarithmic scores, the X_{ij}, so that the dimensional, allometric relations can be preserved and the distortion seen in Figure 2 can be avoided. The use of transformed variates and augmented matrices needs to be put on a rigorous basis, with the goal of maximizing the amount of recoverable relational information. As was noted above, the procedures for esti-mating SMCs and the regression weights for factor scores should be revised so that they will work with singular matrices, such as those produced by the augmentation method.

There is little doubt that continued challenge presented by the problem of geom-etrizing brain structure at all levels, from the global level discussed here to the level of detailed neuronal interrelation, will lead to radical new developments in multi-factorial analysis. As analysis approaches the ultimate structural level, however, the statistical analysis will lose its separate identity, because the whole process, from initial measurement to final result, will be assembled into an integrated methodology. When, at the present level of structural analysis, we observe that a group of volume measurements on brain structures has correlated variation over a taxon, we surmise that these structures participate in some neural process and that the quantitative rela-tionship between them is preserved from species to species because that relation is an optimum one for the process. Future developments will need to be more concerned with putting this surmise to test, by developing measures of the *transfer functions* for the various synaptic junctions in the nervous system. Stark, Semmlow, and Terdiman (1968) discuss a method for calculating the anatomical transfer function through nuclei or relays and give examples for cerebellar neurones. When the appropriate anatomical and dynamical measures of information transfer are available, the methods of comparative multivariate analysis will be useful, together with other methods, for inferring the structure of the functional networks.

The potentialities of the factor analytic method for neurophysiological research are demonstrated in a recent study by Holm and Schaefer (1969), who examined the relationships between the evoked responses measured in six telencephalic, diencephalic, and mesencephalic loci of the cat brain. The interrelations were measured for 30 combinations of stimulus and response sites, leading to a 30×30 correlation matrix. Five factors were found by the principal axis method and rotated by the Varimax procedure. The factorial structure was found to conform to and extend current views about relations between subcortical regions.

What are the prospects for the multifactorial analysis of brain structure? This question will be answered by the research policy decisions of the neuroanatomists of the world. The price that must be paid for the attainment of a stable, meaningful, and constantly expanding geometrization of brain organization is measurable in terms of the effort required for the compatible and coherent measurement of an ever increasing number of brain characteristics on an ever growing set of species. The process need not be carried through blindly or by brute force, but the most efficient and rational plans will still require major efforts. It is hard to evade the conclusion, moreover, that this program must be executed as a cooperative effort. This prospect will not dismay biologists, for they have in their heritage the achievements of the Linnaean, the Darwinian, and the Mendelian-Morganian revolutions, which are among the great monuments to the possibilities of dedicated, corporate human effort.

REFERENCES

Anderson, T. W. 1961. (Unpublished document cited by Jolicoeur, 1963b).

Andy, O. H. 1966. Phylogeny of the primate septum telencephali. *In* Evolution of the Forebrain. Hassler, R., and H. Stephan, eds. Stuttgart, G. Thieme Verlag, 389-399.

Argonne National Laboratory Applied Mathematics Division. 1969. Program 80E 8282 (360 F), Factor Analysis. July 1, 1969.

Bauchot, R. 1963. L'Architectonique comparée, qualitative et quantitative, du diencéphale insectivores. Mammalia, 27:Suppl. 1, 1-400.

———— and H. Stephan. 1964. Le poids encéphalique que chez les insectivores malgaches. Acta Zool., 45:63-75.

———— and H. Stephan. 1966. Donnees nouvelles sur l'encephalisation des insectivores et des prosimiens. Mammalia, 30:160-196.

Bonin, G. von. 1937. Brain weight and body weight of mammals. J. Gen. Psychol., 16:379-389.

Brody, S. 1945. Bioenergetics and Growth. New York, Reinhold.

Count, E. W. 1947. Brain and body weight in man: their antecedents in growth and evolution. Ann. N. Y. Acad. Sci., 46:993-1122.

Dixon, W. J. 1968. Biomedical Computer Programs, 2nd ed. Berkeley and Los Angeles, University of California Press.

Dubois, E. 1897. Sur le rapport du poids de l'encéphale avec la grandeur du corps chez les mammifères. Bull. Soc. Anthropol. Paris (Ser. 4), 8:337-376.

Gould, S. J. 1966. Allometry and size in ontogeny and phylogeny. Biol. Rev., 41:587-640.

Harman, H. H. 1967. Modern Factor Analysis, 2nd ed. Chicago, The University of Chicago Press.

Hill, W. C. O. 1955. Primates, Comparative Anatomy and Taxonomy. 2. Haplorhini: Tarsioidea. Edinburgh University Press.

Holloway, R. L., Jr. 1964. Some Aspects of Quantitative Relations in the Primate Brain. Ph.D. Dissertation, University of California, Berkeley. Ann Arbor, Michigan, University Microfilms, Inc.

———— 1966. Cranial capacity, neural reorganization, and hominid evolution: a search for more suitable parameters. Amer. Anthropol., 68:103-121.

Holm, E., and H. Schaefer. 1969. Eine Faktoranalyse von Schwellen subcorticaler Reizantworten. Exp. Brain Res., 8:79-96.

Huxley, J. 1932. Problems of Relative Growth. New York, The Dial Press.

Jolicoeur, P. 1963a. The degree of generality of robustness in *Martes americana*. Growth, 27:1-27.

———— 1963b. The multivariate generalization of the allometry equation. Biometrics, 19:497-499.

———— 1963c. Bilateral symmetry and asymmetry in limb bones of *Martes americana* and man. Rev. Canad. Biol., 22:409-432.

———— 1965. Calcul d'un intervalle de confiance pour la pente de l'axe majeur de la distribution normale de deux variables. Biometrie-Praximitrie, 6:31-35.

Kaiser, H. F. 1959. Computer program for Varimax rotation in factor analysis. Educational and Psychological Measurement, 19:(3).

Kermack, K. A., and J. B. S. Haldane. 1950. Organic correlation and allometry. Biometrika, 37:30-41.

Manouvrier, L. 1885. Sur l'interpretation de la quantité dans l'encéphale et dans le cerveau en particulier. Bull. Soc. Anthrop. Paris (Ser. 2), 3:137-323.

Oxnard, C. E. 1967. The functional morphology of the primates shoulder as revealed by comparative anatomical, osteometric and discriminant function techniques. Amer. J. Phys. Anthrop., 26:219-240.

———— 1969. Mathematics, shape and function: A study in primate anatomy. Amer. Sci., 57:75-96.

Pilleri, G. 1959. Beiträge zur vergleichenden Morphologie des Nagetiergehirnes, parts 1, 2, 3. Acta Anat., Suppl. 38 (Suppl. 1 to vol. 39):1-124.

———— 1960a. Comparative anatomical investigations on the central nervous system of rodents, and relationships between brain form and taxonomy. Rev. Suisse Zool., 67(29):373-386.

———— 1960b. Beiträge zur vergleichenden Morphologie des Nagetiergehirnes, parts 4, 5, 6. Acta Anat., Suppl. 40 (Suppl. 1 to vol. 42):1-88.

Romer, A. S. 1968. Notes and Comments on Vetebrate Paleontology. Chicago, University of Chicago Press.

Sacher, G. A. 1959. Relation of lifespan to brain weight and body weight in mammals. *In* Wolstenholme, G. E. W., and M. O'Connor, eds. Ciba Foundation Symposium on the Lifespan of Animals. London, Churchill, 115-133.

———— 1966. Dimensional analysis of factor governing longevity in mammals. Paper presented at VIIth Int. Congr. Gerontol. Vienna, 1966. Unpublished.

Sholl, D. A. 1947-1948. The quantitative investigation of the vertebrate brain and the applicability of allometric formulae to its study. Proc. Roy. Soc. (Biol.), 135:243-258.

Simpson, G. G. 1945. The principles of classification and a classification of mammals. Bull. Amer. Mus. Nat. Hist. (New York), 85:xvi, 350.

Snell, O. 1892. Die Abhängigkeit des Hirngewichtes von dem Körpergewicht und den geistigen Fähigkeiten. Arch. Psychiat., 23:436-446.

Stark, L., J. Semmlow, and J. Terdiman. 1968. Anatomical transfer function. Math. Biosci., 2:425-433.

Stephan, H. 1961. Vergleichend-anatomische Untersuchungen an Insektivorengehirne. Acta Anat., 44:12-59.

———— 1966. Grössenänderungen im olfaktorischen und limbischen System während der phylogenetischen Entwicklung der Primaten. *In* Hassler, R., and H. Stephan, eds. Evolution of the Forebrain. Stuttgart, Georg Thieme Verlag, 377-388.

———— 1967a. Zur Entwicklungshöhe der Primaten nach Merkmalen des Gehirns. *In* Starck, D., R. Schneider, and H. J. Kuhn, eds. Progress in Primatology. Stuttgart, Gustav Fischer, 108-119.

———— 1967b. Zur Entwicklungshöhe der Insektivoren nach Merkmalen des Gehirns und die Definition der "Basalen Insektivoren." Zool. Anz., 179:177-199.

———— and O. J. Andy. 1964. Quantitative comparisons of brain structures from insectivores to primates. Amer. Zool., 4:59-74.

———— and R. Bauchot. 1965. Hirn-Körpergenichtsbeziehungen bei den Halbaffen (Prosimii). Acta Zool., 9:134-196.

Stevens, S. S.   1951.   Mathematics, measurement, and psychophysics. *In* Stevens, S. S., ed. Handbook of Experimental Psychology. New York, John Wiley & Sons, Inc.
———— 1959.   Measurement, psychophysics and utility. *In* Churchman, C. W., and P. Ratoosh, eds. Measurement: Definitions and Theories. New York, John Wiley & Sons, Inc.
Thurstone, L. L.   1947.   Multiple-Factor Analysis. Chicago, The University of Chicago Press.
Tilney, F., and H. A. Riley.   1928.   The Brain from Ape to Man. New York, Hoeber.
Welker, W. I.   1969.   Personal communication.
Zar, J. H.   1968.   Calculation and miscalculation in the use of the allometric equation as a model for biological data. Bioscience, 18:1118-1120.

10

Data on Size of the Brain and of Various Brain Parts in Insectivores and Primates

HEINZ STEPHAN,

Max-Planck-Institut für Hirnforschung, Neuroanatomische Abteilung, Frankfurt (Main)-Niederrad, Germany.

ROLAND BAUCHOT

Laboratoire d'Anatomie Comparée, Faculté des Sciences de Paris, Paris, France.

ORLANDO J. ANDY

Department of Neurosurgery, University of Mississippi Medical Center, Jackson, Mississippi 39216

Two papers of this volume are based on data acquired and collected by Stephan, Bauchot, and Andy since 1956 about the size of the brain and of various brain parts. One of these papers (Stephan and Andy, Chapter 5) deals with aspects related to evolution and function of the allocortex; the other (Sacher, Chapter 9) is an extensive factorial analysis of these data.

Their publication, besides presenting the reader with an opportunity to evaluate critically the results of these papers, makes possible the comparison with similar data obtained in other laboratories, allows further analysis with other appropriate mathematical methods, and permits the comparison with behavioral observations.

Since Primates have their phylogenetic origin in insectivore-like ancestors, the data on volume measurements in insectivore brains is also given. We have identified the species with the most primitive cerebral pattern and grouped them together as *Basal Insectivores* (Table 1). These are expected to show the least degree of change since their first appearance (permanent types) and they may still be comparatively similar to the early forerunners of Primates. Thus, they constitute a good base of reference for evaluating evolutionary progress. In contrast, the remainder of the Insectivores reveal distinct marks of higher development, and as such, have been termed *Progressive Insectivores* (Table 2).

The volume data have been determined from serial sections from a total of 63 species in our collection, i.e., from 22 Insectivores, 20 Prosimians and 21 Simians (Tables 1-6). The volumes were estimated from enlarged photographs of serial sections taken at equal intervals (60-80 per brain). The sections were projected

TABLE 1

Data on body and brain weight (in g and mg) and volume of the fundamental brain sections (in mm³) in Insectivores.

	Body Weight * (g)	Brain Weight † (mg)	Total Brain ‡ (net volume)	Medulla oblongata §	Cerebellum ‖	Mesencephalon	Diencephalon	Telencephalon
	1	2	3	4	5	6	7	8
A. *Basal Insectivores*								
1. Sorex minutus	5.3	110	103	17.0	11.0	5.9	8.7	60.7
2. Sorex araneus	10.3	200	188	26.3	18.3	10.6	15.9	117
3. Crocidura russula	11.0	190	178	23.6	21.8	11.7	15.0	106
4. Crocidura occident.	28.0	440	408	59.8	51.3	27.7	28.4	241
5. Suncus murinus	35.0	380	354	50.5	44.8	24.2	26.0	209
6. Echinops telfairi	87.5	620	569	102	56.0	45.5	40.0	326
7. Hemicentetes semisp.	110	830	757	108	117	44.8	48.5	438
8. Setifer setosus	248	1,510	1,404	183	142	75.7	99.7	903
9. Tenrec ecaudatus	832	2,570	2,336	309	339	137	169	1,381
10. Erinaceus europaeus	860	3,350	2,969	289	388	142	229	1,921
11. Aethechinus algirus	700	3,550	3,174	397	407	157	285	1,927
B. *Progressive Insectivores*								
12. Solenodon paradoxus	900	4,670	4,262	493	807	204	272	2,486
13. Nesogale talazaci	50.4	790	741	85.3	92.3	47.2	43.8	472
14. Limnogale mergulus	92.0	1,150	1,046	204	176	67.4	81.0	518
15. Potamogale velox	660	4,100	3,822	746	597	250	294	1,936
16. Neomys fodiens	15.2	320	299	42.2	38.9	17.3	25.2	175
17. Talpa europaea	76.0	1,020	953	95.5	174	49.8	80.2	554
18. Galemys pyrenaicus	57.5	1,330	1,230	147	184	62.2	105	733
19. Desmana moschata	440	4,000	3,620	402	514	219	344	2,140
20. Chorotalpa stuhlmanni	39.8	740	693	68.3	74.7	42.0	51.8	457
21. Elephantulus fuscipes	57.0	1,330	1,233	120	183	117	112	700
22. Rhynchocyon stuhlmanni	490	6,100	5,680	507	798	523	524	3,328

* Body weight from Bauchot and Stephan (1966, 1969) with the exception of the values of *Nycticebus cougang* and *Macaca mulatta*.

† Brain weight from Bauchot and Stephan (1966, 1969) with exception of the value of *Macaca mulatta*.

‡ Total brain (net volume). All volume data are net values, that is they give the volumes of the *pure tissues:* ventricles, meningeal membranes and nerves are excluded.

§ Medulla oblongata. Since it is almost impossible to separate the Substantia reticularis of the Medulla oblongata from that of the Mesencephalon we have included the latter into the Medulla oblongata.

‖ Cerebellum. Included are Brachium and Nuclei pontis.

directly on photographic paper, the borders delineated, and the components of each structure then cut out and weighed. The photographic paper was previously weighed in order to determine the number of square centimeters per gram and care was taken to compensate for changes in paper weight due to varying temperature and humidity. Distances between the histologic sections were calculated, and finally, volumes for each division were derived by applying the formula:

$$V = \frac{AP \times WS \times D}{M^2}.$$

TABLE 2.

Data on body and brain weight (in g and mg) and volume of the fundamental brain sections (in mm³) in Prosimians.

		Body Weight * (g)	Brain Weight † (mg)	Total Brain ‡ (net volume)	Medulla oblongata §	Cerebellum ‖	Mesencephalon	Diencephalon	Telencephalon
		1	2	3	4	5	6	7	8
23.	Tupaia glis	150	3,150	2,959	230	406	261	285	1,778
24.	Urogale everetti	275	4,280	3,997	355	513	307	394	2,428
25.	Microcebus murinus	54.0	1,780	1,663	82.6	226	70.1	127	1,157
26.	Cheirogaleus medius	177	3,140	2,941	206	401	144	245	1,945
27.	Cheirogaleus major	450	6,800	6,323	370	938	224	482	4,309
28.	Lepilemur ruficaud.	915	7,600	7,167	433	1,107	283	614	4,729
29.	Hapalemur simus	1,300	9,530	8,868	485	1,419	313	777	5,875
30.	Lemur fulvus	1,400	23,300	22,053	802	3,411	536	1,580	15,724
31.	Lemur variegatus	3,000	31,500	29,713	1,420	4,286	1,018	2,529	20,461
32.	Avahi laniger	860	9,670	9,075	549	1,423	345	875	5,882
33.	Propithecus verr.	3,480	26,700	25,080	1,199	3,923	741	2,071	17,146
34.	Indri indri	6,250	38,300	36,159	1,376	5,441	972	3,101	25,269
35.	Daubentonia madagasc.	2,800	45,150	42,611	1,517	6,461	897	3,539	30,196
36.	Loris gracilis	322	6,600	6,269	233	728	220	538	4,551
37.	Nycticebus cougang	800	12,500	11,755	528	1,310	345	1,077	8,495
38.	Perodicticus potto	1,150	14,000	13,212	680	1,699	391	1,024	9,418
39.	Galago demidovii	81.0	3,380	3,203	169	413	135	246	2,240
40.	Galago senegalensis	186	4,800	4,512	254	672	205	382	2,997
41.	Galago crassicaudatus	850	10,300	9,602	477	1,361	350	748	6,666
42.	Tarsius syrichta	87.5	3,630	3,416	185	422	171	279	2,359

* Body weight from Bauchot and Stephan (1966, 1969) with the exception of the values of *Nycticebus cougang* and *Macaca mulatta.*
† Brain weight from Bauchot and Stephan (1966, 1969) with exception of the value of *Macaca mulatta.*
‡ Total brain (net volume). All volume data are net values, that is they give the volumes of the *pure tissues:* ventricles, meningeal membranes and nerves are excluded.
§ Medulla oblongata. Since it is almost impossible to separate the Substantia reticularis of the Medulla oblongata from that of the Mesencephalon we have included the latter into the Medulla oblongata.
‖ Cerebellum. Included are Brachium and Nuclei pontis.

V = volume in mm³

AP = average area of the photographic paper in mm² per mg

WS = Weight of the photographic paper of the cut out structure in milligrams

D = distance of measured sections in mm

M^2 = square of linear magnification

The volume of the total brain obtained in this manner is markedly smaller than the volume of the fresh brain. This is due to the shrinkage which results from the fixation and embedding procedures.

The degree of shrinkage is different for each brain, even if these procedures are

HEINZ STEPHAN, ROLAND BAUCHOT, AND ORLANDO J. ANDY

TABLE 3.

Data on body and brain weight (in g and mg) and volume of the fundamental brain sections (in mm³) in Simians.

		Body Weight * (g)	Brain Weight † (mg)	Total Brain ‡ (net volume)	Medulla oblongata §	Cerebellum ‖	Mesencephalon	Diencephalon	Telencephalon
		1	2	3	4	5	6	7	8
43.	Callithrix jacchus	260	7,600	7,248	334	754	295	549	5,316
44.	Saguinus oedipus	405	10,000	10,576	345	958	340	729	7,203
45.	Saguinus tamarin	340	10,300	9,459	434	962	319	706	7,038
46.	Aotes trivirgatus	850	16,000	15,229	641	1,661	427	1,086	11,414
47.	Callicebus moloch	650	15,500	14,434	683	1,287	469	1,101	10,894
48.	Pithecia monacha	1,500	35,000	32,836	1,026	3,961	782	2,167	24,901
49.	Alouatta seniculus	6,400	51,000	47,749	1,840	6,349	1,039	3,217	35,303
50.	Cebus sp.	2,600	73,000	68,672	1,844	8,560	1,153	3,999	53,116
51.	Cebus albifrons	3,000	80,000	75,592	1,896	8,357	1,487	4,623	59,229
52.	Saimiri sciureus	680	22,000	20,691	661	2,071	482	1,311	16,165
53.	Ateles geoffroyi	8,000	108,000	101,034	1,834	12,438	1,482	5,334	79,946
54.	Lagothrix logotricha	5,200	101,000	94,939	1,742	12,016	1,423	5,206	74,553
55.	Macaca mulatta	6,000	93,000	87,896	1,992	8,965	1,380	4,480	71,080
56.	Cercocebus albigena	7,900	104,000	97,603	2,708	10,725	1,770	5,351	77,049
57.	Cercopithecus talapoin	1,000	39,000	36,830	1,139	3,085	767	2,460	29,379
58.	Cercopithecus ascanius	3,600	65,000	61,610	1,583	5,654	1,127	3,498	49,748
59.	Cercopithecus mitis	6,500	76,000	71,505	2,026	6,848	1,372	4,232	57,027
60.	Colobus badius	7,000	78,000	73,818	2,007	8,648	1,333	3,945	57,885
61.	Pan troglodytes	46,000	420,000	396,255	6,032	45,280	3,878	15,962	325,104
62.	Gorilla gorilla	125,000	465,000	437,433	6,983	64,402	4,047	18,014	343,987
63.	Homo sapiens	65,000	1,330,000	1,251,847	9,622	137,421	8,087	33,319	1,063,398

* Body weight from Bauchot and Stephan (1966, 1969) with the exception of the values of *Nycticebus cougang* and *Macaca mulatta*.
† Brain weight from Bauchot and Stephan (1966, 1969) with exception of the value of *Macaca mulatta*.
‡ Total brain (net volume). All volume data are net values, that is they give the volumes of the *pure tissues:* ventricles, meningeal membranes and nerves are excluded.
§ Medulla oblongata. Since it is almost impossible to separate the Substantia reticularis of the Medulla oblongata from that of the Mesencephalon we have included the latter into the Medulla oblongata.
‖ Cerebellum. Included are Brachium and Nuclei pontis.

the same. In order to obtain comparable values it is necessary to correct the figures to the volume of the *fresh* brain. The latter can be found by dividing the weight of the fresh brain by the specific brain weight.

The specific gravity of fresh brains were found to be close to 1.036 grams/cm³ (Stephan, 1960). Thus:

$$\text{Volume of fresh brain} = \frac{\text{weight of fresh brain}}{1.036}.$$

To obtain the factor of correction (FC) this volume must be divided by the serial section volume:

$$FC = \frac{\text{volume of fresh brain}}{\text{serial section volume}}$$

TABLE 4.

Volume of the various components of the telencephalon in Insectivores (in mm³).

	Bulbus ol-factorius 9	Paleocortex + NA * 10	Septum † 11	Striatum ‡ 12	Schizocortex § 13	Hippocampus 14	Neocortex ‖ 15
A. Basal Insectivores							
1. Sorex minutus	8.7	17.2	2.0	6.0	3.6	10.5	12.7
2. Sorex araneus	14.2	32.7	3.8	10.1	7.2	20.6	28.1
3. Crocidura russula	16.4	30.2	3.6	8.2	6.1	15.9	25.5
4. Crocidura occident.	37.8	68.4	6.9	16.8	13.3	38.5	59.1
5. Suncus murinus	34.4	56.2	5.5	14.8	12.6	31.2	54.1
6. Echinops telfairi	65.7	118	11.0	24.1	9.6	49.6	48.5
7. Hemicentetes semisp.	93.8	148	12.8	29.8	17.4	63.7	73.4
8. Setifer setosus	210	338	26.0	55.6	41.9	97.7	134
9. Tenrec ecaudatus	293	452	37.9	101	71.3	146	280
10. Erinaceus europaeus	350	507	46.2	134	120	220	543
11. Aethechinus algirus	297	504	41.6	163	113	268	541
B. Progressive Insectivores							
12. Solonodon paradoxus	478	683	68.1	235	140	299	583
13. Nesogale talazaci	74.6	139	11.2	31.2	20.7	98.9	96.2
14. Limnogale mergulus	43.2	87.4	19.5	57.9	36.4	78.2	196
15. Potamogale velox	87.0	191	50.7	132	142	294	1,039
16. Neomys fodiens	15.9	36.0	6.4	18.7	9.0	32.9	56.6
17. Talpa europaea	60.0	112	14.9	60.2	39.6	86.7	181
18. Galemys pyrenaicus	39.2	107	20.1	74.4	44.9	109	339
19. Desmana moschata	142	320	42.6	222	163	267	983
20. Chorotalpa stuhlmanni	60.8	131	11.3	43.5	21.4	59.1	129
21. Elephantulus fuscipes	63.9	121	16.8	44.5	46.8	171	236
22. Rhynchocyon stuhlmanni	427	705	81.5	222	220	582	1,089

* Paleocortex + NA. The Corpus amygdaloideum (Nucleus amygdalae, NA) has so far not been separated from the Palaeocortex since it is difficult to delineate the periamygdaloid cortex from the subcortical nuclei. A more detailed study is in progress.

† Septum. Included is the Diagonal band of Broca in its whole extend.

‡ Striatum. Included is the internal capsule since it is strongly dispersed in the low insectivores and therefore difficult to separate from striatum.

§ Schizocortex. It is made up of the Regio entorhinalis, Regio perirhinalis and Regiones prae- and parasubicularis, and characterized by the presence of one or several, almost cell-free zones between the various layers (Rose, 1927).

‖ Neocortex. Includes the underlying white substance.

The size of this factor of correction is clearly distinct in different types of fixation. The following means were found:

FIXATION FLUID	N	Factor of correction		Volume loss in % of fresh brain	
		MEAN	RANGE	MEAN	RANGE
Bouin's fluid	45	1.97 ± 0.16	1.72 — 2.23	49.2	41.9 — 55.2
Formol-alcohol	2	1.47 ± 0.11	1.37 — 1.58	32.2	27.0 — 36.7
Formol 10%	8	2.43 ± 0.17	2.26 — 2.74	58.8	55.8 — 63.5

TABLE 5.

Volume of the various components of the telencephalon in Prosimians (in mm³).

	Bulbus olfactorius	Paleocortex + NA *	Septum †	Striatum ‡	Schizocortex §	Hippocampus	Neocortex ‖
	9	10	11	12	13	14	15
23. Tupaia glis	128	256	32.1	133	84.2	138	1,007
24. Urogale everetti	186	362	45.1	199	124	173	1,338
25. Microcebus murinus	40.3	94.5	15.5	94.3	39.4	100	773
26. Cheirogaleus medius	99.3	181	31.5	146	59.5	175	1,252
27. Cheirogaleus major	155	315	64.1	336	144	332	2,963
28. Lepilemur ruficaud.	131	287	57.1	388	199	380	3,287
29. Hapalemur simus	79.4	223	62.1	441	214	525	4,331
30. Lemur fulvus	229	638	121	1,152	433	709	12,442
31. Lemur variegatus	374	985	206	1,591	608	1,404	15,293
32. Avahi laniger	80.6	256	78.1	444	206	476	4,341
33. Propithecus verr.	168	565	160	1,425	395	1,044	13,389
34. Indri indri	142	830	223	1,755	808	1,535	19,976
35. Daubentonia madagasc.	693	1,538	254	2,765	1,044	1,776	22,127
36. Loris gracilis	88.1	256	41.1	351	99.7	191	3,524
37. Nycticebus cougang	164	510	92.0	760	212	566	6,192
38. Perodicticus potto	312	661	114	712	328	607	6,683
39. Galago demidovii	84.4	181	25.7	169	59.9	152	1,568
40. Galago senegalensis	81.8	163	35.7	210	107	261	2,139
41. Galago crassicaudatus	180	405	70.6	504	178	412	4,919
42. Tarsius syrichta	18.1	95.0	20.9	133	64.3	138	1,890

* Paleocortex + NA. The Corpus amygdaloideum (Nucleus amygdalae, NA) has so far not been separated from the Palaeocortex since it is difficult to delineate the periamygdaloid cortex from the subcortical nuclei. A more detailed study is in progress.
† Septum. Included is the Diagonal band of Broca in its whole extend.
‡ Striatum. Included is the internal capsule since it is strongly dispersed in the low insectivores and therefore difficult to separate from striatum.
§ Schizocortex. It is made up of the Regio entorhinalis, Regio perirhinalis and Regiones prae- and parasubicularis, and characterized by the presence of one or several, almost cell-free zones between the various layers (Rose, 1927).
‖ Neocortex. Includes the underlying white substance.

Because of these large differences it is impossible to compare uncorrected figures from material with unknown or different types of fixation. Even if the same fixation and embedding procedures are applied to a series of brains, corrections remain appropriate because of the wide range of volume loss to be expected as indicated in the last column of the above table.

This factor of correction calculated for the *total* brain is then used to correct all the *various parts*. This may not be quite correct, since various parts of the brain may have somewhat different degrees of shrinkage. However, such differences are difficult to ascertain and since they are expected to be small, they were not taken into account.

We have endeavored to include representatives from as many species as possible. But the majority of the species here investigated are rare and/or valuable; and the

TABLE 6.

Volume of the various components of the telencephalon in Simians (in mm³).

	Bulbus ol-factorius	Paleocortex + NA *	Septum †	Striatum ‡	Schizocortex §	Hippocampus	Neocortex ‖
	9	10	11	12	13	14	15
43. Callithrix jacchus	28.4	224	49.7	332	85.2	238	4,357
44. Saguinus oedipus	24.6	282	68.6	420	99.6	259	6,050
45. Saguinus tamarin	16.8	203	43.6	415	113	278	5,969
46. Aotes trivirgatus	60.3	394	92.9	779	255	479	9,354
47. Callicebus moloch	16.8	425	64.7	721	212	481	8,973
48. Pithecia monacha	38.2	699	123	1,642	283	850	21,266
49. Alouatta seniculus	45.2	943	154	2,566	428	1,325	29,843
50. Cebus sp.	49.6	1,186	212	3,295	436	892	47,045
51. Cebus albifrons	37.2	892	161	3,635	401	1,029	53,073
52. Saimiri sciureus	25.4	411	83.0	929	154	316	14,246
53. Ateles geoffroyi	92.6	1,625	324	4,950	732	1,366	70,856
54. Lagothrix logotricha	83.0	1,502	241	4,662	597	1,381	66,087
55. Macaca mulatta	84.3	1,220	271	4,032	639	1,353	63,481
56. Cercocebus albigena	121	1,639	294	4,146	630	1,485	68,733
57. Cercopithecus talapoin	22.3	732	121	1,835	237	684	25,747
58. Cercopithecus ascanius	96.5	1,136	243	2,627	673	1,154	43,818
59. Cercopithecus mitis	118	1,282	249	2,769	625	1,385	50,599
60. Colobus badius	51.3	998	288	3,156	814	1,671	50,906
61. Pan troglodytes	267	2,852	882	12,700	2,093	3,919	302,392
62. Gorilla gorilla	294	4,530	1,090	13,547	2,537	4,446	317,542
63. Homo sapiens	114	9,161	2,610	28,559	6,142	10,287	1,006,525

* Paleocortex + NA. The Corpus amygdaloideum (Nucleus amygdalae, NA) has so far not been separated from the Palaeocortex since it is difficult to delineate the periamygdaloid cortex from the subcortical nuclei. A more detailed study is in progress.
† Septum. Included is the Diagonal band of Broca in its whole extend.
‡ Striatum. Included is the internal capsule since it is strongly dispersed in the low insectivores and therefore difficult to separate from striatum.
§ Schizocortex. It is made up of the Regio entorhinalis, Regio perirhinalis and Regiones prae- and parasubicularis, and characterized by the presence of one or several, almost cell-free zones between the various layers (Rose, 1927).
‖ Neocortex. Includes the underlying white substance.

type of quantitative investigation presented here is extremely time consuming. It was therefore necessary to restrict ourselves to a very limited number of specimens.

Nevertheless, to obtain volumes which are as representative as possible we have performed a second correction. This was accomplished by taking into account the difference between the individual weight of the brain treated here and the standard brain weight of each species as given by Bauchot and Stephan (1966, 1969) from more comprehensive material. Such differences are due to intraspecific variations in brain weights.

$$C = \frac{\text{weight of standard fresh brain}}{\text{weight of individual fresh brain}}$$

This second correction (C) once again was determined by comparing *total* brains, and utilized to correct all the various parts of the brain. This is possible, since according to our experience, extremely small or extremely large brains within one species have generally the same composition. There is no indication of directed changes in composition related to the size of the brain, only a normal range of variation.

In most species, only one brain was investigated. However, in order to get some indication of the degree of intraspecific variation, we investigated two brains of 18 species (table numbers 2, 3, 4, 8, 10, 15, 16, 17, 18, 20, 21, 22, 23, 37, 38, 39, 57, 60). The *mean* of the two individual values for each structure is given in the tables and the percentage deviation of the individual values from these means has been calculated. The average of the total of 216 values (12 structures from 18 species, respectively) is 3.7 ranging from 0 to ±21.3. Eighty per cent of all values fall below 6 and 95% below 10. Thus we expect, that in future investigations of a more extensive material the values given here will not vary more than 10%. Similar results were reported also for Chiroptera (Stephan and Pirlot, 1970). More than 10% deviation of the individual values from the mean were found in the striatum of *Erinaceus europaeus* (11.5), mesencephalon and olfactory bulb of *Neomys fodiens* (10.5 and 13.1), neocortex of *Talpa europaea* (21.3), schizocortex of *Chlorotalpa stuhlmanni* (15.1), olfactory bulb and palaeocortex of *Perodicticus potto* (11.3 and 15.1), schizocortex by *Nycticebus cougang* (12.4) and medulla oblongata and olfactory bulb of *Cercopithecus talapoin* (12.9 and 18.0).

These high deviations of individual values from the mean are obviously due to true intraspecific variation and not to difficulties in delineation, since the means for each of the various structures (except for total telencephalon and neocortex) are similar. These means, taken from all 18 species, vary from 3.2 to 5.0 as compared to the overall mean of 3.7 already mentioned, independent of difficulties in delineation.

Structures difficult to delineate (e.g. medulla oblongata, mesencephalon, diencephalon), have the same or even a lower average deviation than structures easy to delineate (e.g. cerebellum, hippocampus, olfactory bulb). The olfactory bulb, as a structure which can be delineated very easily and clearly, is represented 3 times in the figures higher than 10, thus pointing to a great variability. Less variability is found in the telencephalon as a whole and in the neocortex. The means are 1.4 and 2.8 respectively, thus lying below the above mentioned range (3.2-5.0). In general, the variation of the neocortex is very similar to that of the total telencephalon. The figure 2.8 is influenced by the very high value of *Talpa europaea* (21.3), which is the highest of all values under consideration. If we exclude this value, the average for the neocortex is 1.7. The more than 10 times higher deviation of *Talpa* seems to be due to an error and requires reconsideration.

All volume data smaller than 100 are indicated with one decimal fraction to the right of the unit figure, all data larger than 100 only in unit figures. In cases of very large figures, the last places to the left of the unit figure are of course fairly unimportant since a variability of up to 10% may be expected as above indicated.

REFERENCES

Bauchot, R. and H. Stephan. 1966. Données nouvelles sur l'encéphalisation des Insectivores et des Prosimiens. Mammalia 30:160-196.

Bauchot, R. and Stephan, H.   1969.   Encéphalisation et niveau évolutif chez les simiens. Mammalia 33:225-275.

Rose, M.   1927.   Der Allocortex bei Tier und Mensch. J. Psychol. Neurol. 34:1-111.

Sacher, G. A.   1970.   Allometric and factorial analysis of brain structure in Insectivores and Primates. *In* Noback, C., and Montagna, W., eds. Advances in Primitalogy, Vol. 1:245-287 New York, Appleton-Century-Crofts.

Stephan, H. and O. J. Andy.   1970.   The allocortex in primates. *In* Noback, C., and Montagna, W., eds. Advances in Primatology, Vol. 1. New York, Appleton-Century-Crofts.

Stephan, H.   1960.   Methodische Studien über den quantitativen Vergleich architektonischer Struktureinheiten des Gehirns. Z. wiss. Zool., 164:143-172.

Stephan, H. and P. Pirlot.   1970.   Volumetric comparisons of brain structures in bats. Z. Zool. Syst. Eval. Forsch. (in print).

11

Neural Parameters, Hunting, and the Evolution of the Human Brain

RALPH L. HOLLOWAY, JR.

Department of Anthropology, Columbia University, New York, N.Y. 10027

Introduction

Comprehensive quantitative studies of many parameters of the primate brain have been reviewed by Holloway (1966, 1968a) and Blinkov and Glezer (1968). This paper will concentrate on the uses and limitations of such quantitative studies in trying to understand the general and specific problems of human brain evolution. A tentative framework will be offered which might serve to synthesize multiple levels of neural organization with behavioral attributes that had their major basis in the evolution of human hunting during the last two million years. Human hunting has been selected because of the current focus on the evolutionary aspects of this topic, and its suitability for breakdown into behavioral activities more closely related to neurological processes. Where possible, quantitative neuroanatomical data will be used to illustrate my thesis that natural selection pressures on human behavior resulted in evolutionary changes of *neural systems*, rather than singular gross parameters such as weights, volumes, or cross-sectional areas of particular neural structures. Finally, I will summarize the major conclusions from this approach and their application to the problems of (1) human mosaic evolution, and (2) the interpretation of the fossil record and evolutionary dynamics.

Problems of Specificity and Generality

In a recent symposium on anthropology and war, I argued the point that a fuller understanding of human aggression required a framework that viewed this behavior in species-specific terms (Fried et al., 1968, pp. 29-48). Carpenter's remarks (1968, pp. 49-58) on this indicated, at least to me, a misunderstanding of my position. Wider frameworks (i.e., comparative) are of value. My basic point was that the understanding of human aggression requires a concentrated study of neural structures

299

and their organization and of the psychosocial developments that are specific to man as well as those processes shared with other primates and other mammals. Both frameworks are complementary and necessary.

The evolution of the brain presents a similar epistemological problem. Each primate species has its own unique assemblage and interdependent organization of anatomical structures and behavioral patterns derived through processes of evolutionary modification. Limb proportions, muscle masses, sensorimotor capacities, and social behavior vary between and within major taxa, reflecting numerous strategies of evolutionary adaptation to different and similar ecological settings. Obversely, in spite of the stamp of specificity on each species (indeed, individual), there is still an underlying core of adaptive commonalities gained through millions of years of adaptation and evolution within an arboreal existence, involving locomotion, prehensility, dependence on visual information, gregariousness, need for stimulation, curiosity, and plasticity of behavior. Similarly there is an underlying neural "core" which is common to almost all primates, particularly the higher ones.

Truly comparative studies of primate behavior, combining both natural and laboratory studies are just beginning. At the present time, comparative primate neurochemical studies are lacking, and comparative neurophysiological studies relating to behavioral specifics are scant (Welt, 1962; Kitsikis, 1968; Gfeller, 1968; MacLean, 1962; Robinson and Mishkin, 1968). Even neuroanatomical data, while more extensive, leave vast hiatuses, particularly with regard to subcortical organization. This is not a problem unique to primates. One reason is that brain morphology, cast in such terms as brain weight (absolute or relative), cortex size and differentiation, neuron number, density, dendritic branching, glial/neural ratios, cross-sectional areas or volumes of nuclei and fiber tracts, may not be the most appropriate neural levels to make meaningful syntheses between bodily structures and behavioral patterns integrated in a taxon's adaptations. Nevertheless, these are reasonable, if not essential, starting points and necessary for future analyses aimed at systems of neural structures.

For example, what are the essential neural levels or substrates responsible for the behavioral differences between chimpanzee and gorilla, macaque and langur monkey, Siamese and alley cat, cocker spaniel and basenji hound, or the well-studied familiar grey Norway and black rats? Two huge problems present themselves in attempting to relate structural variations of the brain to behavioral patterns distinct at the species or lower and higher levels: (1) What units of behavior does one choose? (2) What units of neural structure are appropriate for the synthesis?

It should be obvious that these problems cannot be answered without intense laboratory and field studies both of a comparative nature and those limited to one species. We can measure our sophistication of knowledge in both enterprises by doing either of the following: (1) predicting behavioral qualities and quantities from a description of the nervous system and remaining anatomy; (2) predicting brain morphology from descriptive behavior. Obviously, we have an enormously long way to go.

Problems of Evidence

The limits of evidence that constrain our study and understanding of the evolution of primate brains are detailed elsewhere (Holloway, 1966, 1968b, in press). These can be summarized as follows. (1) In the strict sense, it is impossible to study the evolution of any primate brain, human or otherwise. (2) Endocasts of fossil forms are inadequate, since they do not show internal organizational changes. (3) Comparative extant series are end products of their own evolutionary lines, not stages in human or other primate evolutionary lines.

Man's behavioral specificities or differences cannot be reduced to any single variable, whether it be mass, neuron numbers, infraparietal lobules, base ratios of different RNA's in neurons and glia, or volumes of particular nuclei and fiber tracts. Behavior, whether of discrete sensory or motor actions, aggression or submission, or thinking, abstracting, symbolizing, involves the interactions of many neural components (nuclei, fiber tracts, cortical fields) acting simultaneously or in short intervals of milliseconds. Behavior is the resultant of both an environmental set of gestalten or cue stimuli and systems of neural tissue and other bodily components interacting through time, based on past interactions. This does not at all suggest foregoing analytic study of the brain, meaning its singular components, since each contributes to observable and unobservable behavior.

We must hope that by combining the studies of comparative series and fossil records with our ongoing study of the neural basis of categories of behavior and the interdependent variations between behavioral and neural variables, one can arrive at both specific and general formulations that can be applied to the indirect evidence from the fossil record. In this way, one can work toward a meaningful synthesis of what man is and how he came to be.

Quantification and Parameters

By now, the message should be clear: in addition to studies of the brain and behavior, we also need to do a great deal of thinking. While a fuller discussion of these matters appears elsewhere (Holloway, 1968a; 1969), a general summary is useful here. In essence, one determines quantities to compare the size of structures between forms and with organizations of structures. In general, what is big is also important, and differences in sizes of structures between related organisms gives a crude indication of natural selection acting on behavioral units mediated by the structures. Increases in size must eventually relate to more molecular processes, such as duration and/or rates of mitotic division, in turn relating to codes of amino acid sequences in DNA, and turn-on-turn-off interactions between these codons.

Quantification indicates something about both the magnitude and direction of reorganization of multiple neural components in different primate brains. From the reviews I made of this literature, I conclude that these data show that monkey, ape, and human brains are not simply enlarged or smaller versions of each other, and we must stop theorizing as if units of mass were truly commensurable. Through their evolutionary developments, each brain bears a stamp of specificity. Much of the current and past anthropological literature ignores this simple and obvious point.

A parameter is a number characterizing a population, a measure of some attribute or relationship of structure or structures. Obviously, the *amount* of functioning nervous tissue an animal utilizes is a *variable* related to its behavior. Absolute and relative brain weights or volumes are *parameters* of such a variable. Other examples of parameters are neuron numbers, amounts of particular kinds of cortex, number, size, and density of neurons, fiber numbers, nuclei volumes, and glial/neural ratios.

The important question is what parameters are useful in understanding the relationship between structure and behavior in evolutionary context? Will these morphological parameters suffice, or should we move to more neurophysiological or neurochemical ones? The answer, ironically enough, is what question do you want to ask? My own bias is that quantitative morphological parameters are too crude for showing anything beyond the most molar or trivial relationships, particularly at the species level. These are useful in showing that reorganizational changes have occurred at all neural levels and that both brain volumes and brain weights are practically useless, except in describing general trends. Nor is it likely that either neurochemical or neurophysiological parameters will suffice taken alone. Rather, these will correlate with the neuroanatomical parameters.

In short, brain morphology, either purely descriptive or quantitative, is probably not the appropriate level at which to make more than simple correlational relationships to species-specific behavior patterns, e.g., cortical hand area and manual dexterity, or mass and intelligence, or plasticity of behavior. For example, electrode stimulation of many areas of the limbic system and cortex in squirrel monkeys will result in a penile display (MacLean, 1962). Stimulation of most of the same sites in Rhesus monkeys will also result in penile erection but no display behavior (Robinson and Mishkin, 1968). In the latter species, stimulation of posterior hypothalamic sites does not result in penile erection, while it does in squirrel monkeys. This region is known to be associated with aggressive behavior, and penile erection and thrusting is a dominance display in squirrel monkeys. Think about it. What magic level of neural structure or structures does one use to explain this item of species-specific behavior? Does one measure the size of the posterior hypothalamic areas involved? the surrounding nuclei? afferent and efferent fibers? Or must one move to questions of thresholds, neurochemical and humoral transmitters, or summations of facilitative and inhibitive *systems* operating among hypothalamus, limbic nuclei, septal nuclei, thalamus, and varieties of cortex? Is the problem insoluble? Hopefully, this example might serve to make a very obvious point: quantitative relationships, at the morphological level, are not sufficient to explain species-specific behavior. They are only starting points, and we need new ways of attacking these problems.

Toward A Framework—Hunting Behavior and the Evolution of the Brain

There is no difficulty in making hypotheses about the evolution of the human brain. The difficulty is to propose a set of hypotheses which can utilize the indirect evidence from the fossil record and comparative neurological sciences to an extent where testable questions can be framed. In addition, there has to be a means of synthesizing behavioral attributes with brain structures within an evolutionary framework, as well as demonstrate the interrelatedness of behavioral processes, such as cooperation, memory, foresight, and abstraction, with man's capacity for symbolization.

To move this problem from the level of hypothesis to the level of theory, minimal information relating to the following questions must be obtained. (1) In terms of behavior—ability to symbol, think abstractly, concentrate on complex tasks, learn, organize experience, and socioemotional perception—how does man differ and yet remain similar to other primates? (2) How can the significant differences—stone tools, living sites, hunting techniques—be abstracted from the study of fossil man and his "fossilized behavior"? (3) What are the functions of neural structures and their integrated systems operations in behavioral streams? (4) What are the relationships between variations in neural structures and systems and variations in behavior? Obviously, we are a long way from realizing any of these requirements, and we cannot even be certain that we have yet begun to ask the meaningful questions.

Most of the existing hypotheses are either trivial or reductionistic in that they propose single factor relationships between brain size increase and single behavioral attributes. For example, is there any point in suggesting that natural selection for behavior resulted in larger brains, or that man's brain evolved to provide him with a more successful adaptive base? Or that man's brain evolved to enable him to hunt more effectively, or make better stone tools, or communicate by means of language? Do we really need to be told that language evolved because it was adaptive, since communicating about environments would likely confer a selective advantage (Lancaster, 1968)? Or that a larger brain meant more memory (Krantz, 1968)? Or that stone tools resulted in better brains? If it is the study of primate behavior in natural settings that brings us to these banal conclusions, we are in greater trouble than we realize. Such simplistic reductions to tautologies were long ago overcome in the analyses of Count (1958), Etkin (1954, 1963), and Hallowell (1956).

It is now fashionable to view the "hunting way of life" as the most appropriate framework for analyzing human behavior and its evolution. However, as far as I am aware, there are few if any hunting frameworks broad and significant enough to assemble the variables of neural structures and behavior into a synthesizable problem. The rubric of "hunting" requires a systematic treatment like that provided by Hockett's "design features" and communication (1960). A recent article by Laughlin (1968) represents a commendable move in such a direction, for he provides five elements of the total hunting pattern which can eventually serve as a basis for synthesis between behavior, structure, and evolution, and in units more molecular and meaningful than such currently used, units as cranial capacity, language, and toolmaking.

The five elements Laughlin suggested, based on his studies of Eskimo hunting, are (1) programming of the child; (2) scanning or collection of information; (3) stalking and pursuit of game; (4) immobilization of game; (5) retrieval of game.

A schema based on these elements follows. It is meant to be suggestive and thus purposely speculative.

1. Development of motor and perceptual skills, involving visual, auditory, olfactory, and touch (warmth, texture) factors as well as musculoskeletal apparatuses utilized in making tools and weapons, stalking, actual wounding, following, and butchering of game. These behavioral patterns would require considerable degrees of selective perception of ever-changing stimuli, regulation of figure-ground relationships in defining cues from animal, vegetation, and meteorological conditions. The ana-

tomical linkages would be musculoskeletal, exteroceptors and afferent pathways to and through the brain, and cortically directed components which gate perception.

2. Development of motivational factors beyond factors of simple hunger, e.g., prestige, pride, familial and male-bonding, aggression and fear, egoism.

3. Social interaction relationships which help structure the motivational aspects, and selective perception, or the setting of figure-ground relationships. Selection pressures for cooperative behavior, affectual ties, sexual dimorphism and division of labor, domestication of male, inhibition of intraspecific and personal egoistic impulses.

4. Associated communicative skills, verbal and nonverbal. Development of symbolically based behavior, related not only to communication about environments and perceptual cues but also to role behavior and socioemotional sets associated with social control and social learning.

5. Organization of experience, coded through symbols and classification, abstraction dependent on (3), (4), (5), here and above.

6. Memory, concentration, and attention. Memory as a complex of the following factors: impressionability, permanence or span, ease of recall (dependent on how experience is organized), and the amount or complexity of memory. Related are factors such as ability to concentrate on a task, to maintain attention to await future stimuli, to inhibit extraneous movements or premature acts, and to accept discomfort, cramping, immobility and boredom. Memory of ecological contexts i.e., possible appearance of other predators or other dangers inherent in hunting behavior.

If the above factors were involved in the evolution of hunting and human behavior, it is clear that numerous matrices of structures at all levels of the brain may respond to the pressures of natural selection.

Clearly, transitions in such complexity during evolution are almost impossible to learn from the fossil record or comparative neurology, at least in its present state. However, the following lines of evidence might be utilized as indicators of selection for these aspects of hunting behavioral effectiveness: (1) range of species utilized; (2) size and speed of game; (3) aggressiveness of game; (4) ecological expansions; (5) numbers killed; (6) varieties of methods associated with tool-making, use, and complexity, including entrapment techniques; (7) butchering and transportation methods.

The following tentative organizational complexes are presented as a basis for synthesizing structural and behavioral data within an evolutionary framework.

I. *SENSORY AND MOTOR ORGANIZATION AND REFINEMENT*

    A. Basic components (anatomical directness, e.g., cephalization of function.

        Anatomical Units (examples)
1. Lemniscal enlargement and directness *
2. Pyramids *
3. Agranular cortex, e.g., Betz cells *
4. Areas or volumes of cortex associated with hand, etc.*

---

* Anatomical data exist showing reorganization (see Holloway 1966, 1968a).

    B. Secondary or modulatory components (proprioceptive utilization, smoothness, development of skill through learning and practice)
Anatomical Units
        1. Cerebellum, cortex, and nuclei *
        2. Extrapyramidal system *
        3. Brain stem (sensory and motor nuclei) *

    C. Tertiary or setting components (set, attention, concentration, incorporation of memory, coding sequences of motor patterns, inventiveness and capability for new and sudden motor patterns; plasticity)
Anatomical Units
        1. Cortex *
        2. Thalamus *
        3. Caudate nucleus
        4. Limbic system
        5. Ascending and descending reticular systems

II. INTELLECTIVE, PROBLEM-SOLVING, SYMBOLIZATION

    A. Basic components (number of units, switching points, capacity, complexity of information)
Anatomical Units
        1. Neuron number in cortex *
        2. Cell size, cell density, dendritic branching, dendritic spines, glial/neural ratios *
        3. Intracortical and intercortical fibers
        4. Frontal, parietal, temporal, occipital, cortical differentiation and expansion *

    B. Secondary components (learning, storage, span, recall, potency, permanence, scanning strategies)
Anatomical Units
        1. Glial/neural interaction
        2. Corticothalamic integration
        3. Caudate, limbic, hippocampal, cortical integration

    C. Tertiary components (motivation, set, arousal, concentration, efferent or corticopetal priming of exteroceptor and motor pathways)
Anatomical Units
        1. Ascending and descending reticular systems
        2. Reticular, thalamic, septal, hypothalamic, and cortical integration

III. SOCIAL-BEHAVIORAL (SOCIALITY, AFFECT-ORIENTATION, MOTIVA-TIONAL, HEDONISM-EGOISM, SENTIMENT, FEAR, AGGRESSIVITY, TEMPERAMENT)

It is tempting to try a similar breakdown into suggested components with concomitant anatomical units, but this area is so complex as to preclude any such attempt. The behavioral units are totally undefined (hence the selection of terms with only connotative power) and involve complex integrations of almost all neural elements in the brain.

IV. PERIPHERAL OR EXTRANEURAL CHANGES

A. Basic components (musculoskeletal changes related to bipedalism, tool-making, object-throwing, aiming, features related to sexual selection, e.g., dimorphism)
   Anatomical Units
   1. Muscle masses
   2. Joint effectiveness, muscle attachments, leverage, stability
   3. Peripheral nerves to level of end plates and receptors.
   4. Sexual dimorphism (height, weight, deposition of fat, and its distribution, hair distribution, teeth)
B. Secondary components (physiological organization involving endocrines, target tissues, autonomic nervous system, changes in growth and maturation, sexual development and reproductive physiology, placentation, gestation, nursing)
C. Tertiary components (immunochemical, disease resistance, tolerance, immunity, water and ionic balance, incorporation of proteins, vitamins from diet)
   Anatomical and Physiological Levels
   1. Blood—biochemical, excretions, secretions (sweat)
   2. Endocrine—thyroid, parathyroid, adrenals
   3. Internal organs

This framework is in no way suggested as anything more than tentative, incomplete, and arbitrarily segmented. The choice of terms, such as basic, secondary, and tertiary, should not be taken literally. They are more the constructs of my organization than the realities of structure, behavior, and evolution. My major objective is to show that our categories of behavior, whether sufficient or not, involve the interactions of many systems, at least in the brain, and that hunting behavior, in its evolutionary development, cannot be conceived as a series of single items strung out in concatenated fashion through time.

I have also avoided a major task—that of synthesis with our knowledge of neuroanatomical variation in the primates. For one thing, this is a task beyond the capacities of one person, and I believe my other publications on quantitative parameters have at least suggested that many of the neural components mentioned without bibliographic reference do show quantitative changes in comparative perspective. Nor have I attempted to integrate the behavioral processes with the fossil record as I have tried elsewhere (1966, 1967a and b, 1968a, b, and c).

Human Mosaic Evolution

Mosaic evolution simply means that different organs or systems of organs evolved at different rates (Mayr, 1963). Human evolutionary change, once considered to be a series of discrete leaps, is now viewed as gradual changes in one sector (e.g., bipedal structures) and then another (e.g., skull, brain, etc.). This concept has had a necessary corrective effect on views of evolutionary development in many taxa, including Hominidae. Most views seem to relegate a terminal role to the brain in human evolution, based, of course, on the obvious fact that cranial capacities in hominids show an increase after changes in other areas, such as the pelvis, dentition, and hand.

The concept of mosaic evolution has a useful function when applied at gross, or molar, anatomical levels, but I would argue that a strict application of this concept to detailed analyses of hominid evolution is both trivial and misleading. In the first place, any concept other than mosaic evolution requires that the total genome change simultaneously, an obvious impossibility. On the other hand, the unfolding of the genome and its epigenetic processes are complicated affairs, involving pleiotropic and multiple gene interactions affecting different systems at the same time. One may divorce cranial capacity from the pelvis, but one can hardly divorce the evolution of bipedalism from the evolution of the brain, particularly the interdependent neural systems operating. Mosaic evolution is a truism at gross levels of description, but invocation of the principle can obfuscate evolutionary dynamics at more molecular levels. The view that the brain was the last organ to evolve in hominid evolution is one such obfuscation.

An associated view of Washburn and Hamberg (1965) and Washburn and Shirrek (1967) states that behavior precedes structure in evolution. Rather than cast the complexity of evolution into such a chicken/egg model, it is more appropriate to say that behavior mediates structure and evolution since natural selection confers advantages upon those structure/behavior interactions that are more adaptive. Obviously, for any behavioral change to have evolutionary significance, it must have an organic basis, underlain by a genetic change of a mutational or recombinatorial nature. These two views, mosaic evolution and behavior preceding structure have led to the current views of the brain evolving last. A bone, or piece of it, is not an isolated piece of matter, associated only with surrounding muscles. While imbedded in muscle, it was also supplied with blood and nerves, as was the muscle, and was thus an extension and integral part of behaviors. Any item of locomotory action, (e.g., bipedalism) is behavior with an underlying neural basis, related to and involving other behavioral processes, such as proprioception, perception, cognition, and motor sequences under cortical command.* We separate these points because of our language.

The frameworks offered earlier have suggested a complex array of different components involved in a hunting adaptation and neural correlates of behavior. If one finds, in the fossil record, evidence for different anatomical patterns (e.g., tool-making, bipedalism, incipient or persistence hunting as suggested by Krantz, 1968), there must also have been different behavioral patterns, and one can logically assume that the brain of such an animal was *differently* organized than those of pongids, *regardless* of the cranial capacity. (See Holloway, in press b, for a fuller discussion.) In sum, the brain was not the final adjustment in human mosaic evolution but an essential component from the beginning.

---

* This more holistic viewpoint was discussed in Chapter III of G. E. Smith's 1927 edition of *The Evolution of Man*, London, Oxford University Press. Apparently, his message has been forgotten.

Evolutionary Dynamics and the Fossil Record

Washburn and Hamberg (1965, p. 613) have suggested that the adaptive function of an extended growth period is to provide an animal more time to learn. In the case of man and hominid evolution, an inversion of this statement is suggested: the function of prolonged youth or growth was to provide a better brain to accomplish the learning. During early hominid evolution, a number of evolutionary changes took place in social behavior, involving emotive and cognitive components (e.g., permanent receptivity of the female, prolonged growth of offspring and the brain, reduction in certain sexual dimorphic features with increases in others, and these integrated to favor increased brain growth (Etkin, 1954, 1963; Holloway, 1968b). Neural parameters, such as neuron size, neuron density, dendritic branching, and glial/neural ratios, relate to cortical expansion and underlie changes in cranial capacity, as well as increases in neuron number, (Holloway, 1966, 1967a, 1968a, b).

The term "complexity-management" (Holloway, 1967a) refers to behavioral attributes related to efficiency, fineness of discrimination, and adaptive problem-solving ability, processes continuous within the primate order. The great expansion of the brain from Australopithecines on involved evolution in complexity-management through a complex synthesis between factors of individual variation and social complexity, deviation-amplification or positive feedback (Maruyama, 1963), environmental complexity, neural complexity, and selection for redundancy in neural structure and behavioral organization. Early hominid evolutionary dynamics, such as symbolization, cooperative sharing and hunting, decreased and increased sexual dimorphism, are changes that were present during Australopithecine or early *erectus* times, not dependent on cranial capacity but rather on neural reorganization. These changes together make up what might be called the "initial kick" (Maruyama, 1963), which, once in progress, structured an interdependent interaction of structures and processes elaborated by the above factors involved in "complexity-management." Exactly what such neural changes were that led to those social behavioral changes and associated capacity for symbolization are unknown. I would strongly argue that these were more than cortical, involving interactions between limbic, cortical, thalamic, and reticular systems of neural tissues, changes which may have had no, or little, relationship to cranial capacity. Furthermore, any reductionistic attempts to relate the major behavioral differences between apes and man to isolated portions of the cortex, e.g., frontal or inferior parietal lobes, are erroneus. Focusing on these single items of cortical change is likely to have the same effect as a literal adherence to the concept of mosaic evolution—a masking of evolutionary dynamics, which must, in the long run, be gained from the analyses of the archaeological and fossil records.

In short, I regard the social-behavioral changes which took place in early hominid evolution the keys to our understanding of the evolution of the brain. That is one reason, at least, that our conceptions of hunting behavior must advance to a point where we better understand the design features or attributes of what a hunting existence means in terms of social behavior, cognitive programming, selective perception, and sensorimotor refinement and organization. We should no longer use the term as a rough rubric to cover a complex interdependent organization of behavioral and anatomical attributes, without first understanding what it involves in a multiplicity of ways. The growth or expansion of cranial capacity is not our primary problem in understanding brain and behavioral evolution. Comparative, ontogenetic, and experimental evidence abounds to indicate its meaning and what contributes to such expansion. Rather, our problem is to understand the roles of neural systems in behavior and integrate this knowledge with the fossil record and evolutionary theory to produce a synthetic theory of human evolution beyond the level of platitudes. The judicious application of quantitative parameters of brain organization is only a beginning step in such a direction. We must also try to understand what tool-making means in cognitive psychological terms, whether the structure of this operation is similar to that of language (Holloway, 1970), what these processes mean in terms of social behavior, and how they interact.

REFERENCES

Blinkov, S. M., and I. I. Glezer. 1968. The Human Brain in Figures and Tables. New York, Plenum Press.

Carpenter, C. R. 1968. The contribution of primate studies to the understanding of war. *In* Fried, M., et al., eds. War: The Anthropology of Armed Conflict and Aggression, 49-58. New York, Natural History Press.

Count, E. W. 1958. The biological basis of human sociality. Amer. Anthropol., 60: 1049-1085.

Etkin, W. 1954. Social behavior and the evolution of man's mental faculties. Amer. Naturalist, 88:129-143.

——— 1963. Social behavioral factors in the emergence of man. Hum. Biol., 35:299-310.

Fried, M., M. Harris, and R. Murphy, eds. 1968. War: The Anthropology of Armed Conflict and Aggression. New York, Natural History Press.

Hallowell, A. I. 1956. Structural and functional dimensions of a human existence. Quart. Rev. Biol., 31:88-101.

Hockett, C. F. 1960. Logical considerations in the study of animal communication. *In* Lanyon, W., and W. Tavogla, eds. Animal Sounds and Communication, 393-430. Washington, D.C., American Institute of Biological Sciences.

Holloway, R. L., Jr. 1966. Cranial capacity, neural reorganization, and hominid evolution: a search for more suitable parameters. Amer. Anthropol., 68:103-121.

——— 1967a. The evolution of the human brain: some notes toward a synthesis between neural structure and the evolution of complex behavior. General Systems, 12:3-19.

——— 1967b. Tools and teeth: some speculations regarding canine reduction. Amer. Anthropol., 69:63-67; see also, 70:101-106.

——— 1968a. The evolution of the primate brain: some aspects of quantitative relations. Brain Res., 7:121-172.

——— 1968b. Cranial capacity and the evolution of the human brain. *In* Montagu, M. F. A., ed. Culture: Man's Adaptive Dimension, 170-196. New York, Oxford University Press.

——— 1968c. Human aggression: the need for a species-specific framework. *In* Fried, M., et al., eds. War: The Anthropology of Armed Conflict and Aggression, 29-48. New York, Natural History Press.

——— 1969a. Some questions on parameters of neural evolution in primates. *In* Petras, J. and C. Noback, eds. Comparative and Evolutionary Aspects of the Vertebrate Central Nervous System. Annals New York Academy of Sciences, 167:332-341.

——— 1969b. Culture: A human domain. Current Anthropology, 10:395-412.

——— 1970. The role of the brain in human mosaic evolution. To be published under the proceedings of the VIIIth International Congress of Anthropological and Ethnological Sciences, Toyoko and Kyoto, Japan.

Kitsikis, A. 1968. Suppression of arm movement in monkeys: threshold variation in caudate nucleus stimulation. Brain Res., 10:460-462.

Krantz, G. 1968. Brain size and hunting ability in earliest man. Current Anthrop., 9: 450-451.

Lancaster, J. 1968. Primate communication systems and the emergence of human language. *In* Jay, P., ed. Primates, 439-457. New York, Holt, Rinehart and Winston.

Laughlin, W. S. 1968. Hunting: an integrating biobehavior system and its evolutionary importance. *In* Lee, R. B., and I. DeVore, eds. Man the Hunter, 304-320. Chicago, Aldine Publishing Co.

MacLean, P. D. 1962. New findings relevant to the evolution of psychosexual functions of the brain. J. Nerv. Ment. Dis., 135:289-301.

Maruyama, M. 1963. The second cybernetics: deviation-amplifying mutual-causal processes. Amer. Sci., 51:164-179.

Mayr, E. 1963. Animal Species and Evolution. Cambridge, Harvard University Press.

Robinson, B. W., and M. Mishkin. 1968. Penile erection evoked from forebrain structures in Macac mulatta. Arch. Neurol., 19:184-198.

Washburn, S. L. 1967. Perspectives and prospects. Amer. J. Phys. Anthrop., 27:367-374.

———— and Hamberg, D. 1965. The study of primate behavior. *In* DeVore, I., ed. Primate Behavior, 1-15. New York, Holt, Rinehart and Winston.

———— and Shirrek, J. 1967. Human evolution. *In* Hirsch, J., ed. Behavior-Genetic Analysis. Chap. 2. New York, McGraw-Hill Book Company.

Welt, C. 1962. Cortical Somatic Sensory and Motor Areas of Primates. Doctoral Dissertation, University of Chicago.

INDEX OF SPECIES

Page numbers in italic type refer to figures and tables.

311

INDEX OF SUBJECTS

Page numbers in italic type refer to figures and tables.

315